Fundamentals of Modern Chemistry

R.T. SANDERSON
Arizona State University

Scott, Foresman and Company
Glenview, Illinois   London

PREFACE

We live in a time when, especially in the sciences, new information is being accumulated far more rapidly than we know how to assimilate it. Chemistry is in a state of expansion so rapid that it is leading to more and more fragmentation into highly specialized subjects. No longer can all of these subjects be neatly classified as inorganic, physical, organic, and analytical. Instead they overlap in all directions, not only with each other but with all other sciences and mathematics as well. The resulting educational problems are vast and formidable. What indeed is the appropriate educational background for the omniscience which tomorrow's citizen would seem to require?

Substantial improvements in the teaching of high-school chemistry have occurred in recent years, largely because of the heroic efforts of dedicated teachers at both secondary and college levels. Unfortunately, however, many students still enter the college general chemistry program inadequately prepared for the rigorous presentation of physical chemical principles now in vogue at many colleges and universities. In part, this may be due to the atmosphere at many public high schools, where even the most talented teachers find it difficult to maintain standards appropriate for college preparation. In part, it may be the result of the practice of taking high-school chemistry during the junior year, which allows a whole year for memory leakage before college entrance. Whatever the cause, many students need help in the form of college-level preparation for the usual general chemistry course. It is the purpose of this book to provide such help.

Today's chemistry teacher, viewing the increasingly chaotic condition of chemical science, is perhaps more aware than ever before that we must cling to the fundamentals or all is lost. Immediately we are confronted by the problem that *fundamental chemistry is not simple*. Our sense of logic tells us that before we try to erect a comprehensive structure of chemistry, we should build a firm foundation of fundamental principles. Our experience tells us that no real understanding of such principles is possible until a substantial part of the structure of chemistry is available to make the principles meaningful. Our problem is that a completely logical development of chemistry would be incomprehensible to beginners. It is not easy to teach a subject in which the most difficult topics come first.

So, like all reasonable approaches to the learning of chemical science, this book represents a compromise. I have tried to introduce the material as logically as seems practical. Recognizing, however, the inherent sterility of concepts unrelated to practical experience, I have tried constantly to show the relationships between fundamental principles and practical applications. No student, it seems to me, should be expected to acquire a truly useful understanding of a science by a once-through coverage even if in considerable depth. I have tried to implement this conviction by explaining all new material and by repeatedly referring back to the principles studied earlier. If this book has any central guiding principle or motivation, it is my fervent desire that all serious students should acquire from it a sense of appreciation of chemistry as a science and as a human activity—an appreciation based on *genuine understanding*.

My sole concern in the writing of this book has been for the student, for whom I have tried to make every figure and illustration meaningful and instructive. To this end, many of the figures are accompanied by unusually detailed explanations that give the student a fresh and independent view of concepts and principles already detailed in the text. Both the laboratory manual and instructor's manual, written by Raymond F. O'Connor, are designed to complement and enhance the basic text while providing both student and instructor with the necessary tools for a fundamental approach to the study of chemistry.

Despite the difficulties, mainly mathematical, which bar the way to highly sophisticated modern chemical theory, I am convinced that there is much that can be presented to beginning students in terms which, although simple enough for comprehension, still contribute significantly to the student's genuine appreciation of the science. I sincerely believe that much more can be accomplished in this direction than has previously been achieved. Throughout my own professional career my principal research has been directed toward explaining chemistry simply yet honestly. This book reflects, I trust, my conviction that understanding is the heart of true learning.

Paradise Valley, Arizona R. T. Sanderson

CONTENTS

INTRODUCTION

WHAT IS CHEMISTRY?

This is the story of chemistry. It begins with man's earliest struggle with Nature, long before the dawn of history. It leads through the mysterious arts of ancient and medieval alchemy and into the awakening intellects of the first scientific chemists three hundred years ago. With ever-accelerating progress it brings us to the modern world of fantastic theoretical understanding and incredible materialistic achievement. The story never ends. Wherever chemical scientists are working, still more fascinating chapters are being written. As long as man has curiosity and brains to seek the answers, the study of chemistry will go on and on forever.

To each of you, if you choose, comes the opportunity to add your own individual paragraph to this unending story. More remains to be discovered than has been learned since the very beginning of time. And whether you choose to add to this story or write another, you will need some knowledge of chemistry to become an educated person, one who knows how to put the most into life.

The story of chemistry is a story of all that is gaseous, liquid, or solid. Chemistry is the science of matter. It seeks to answer three basic questions about matter: What is matter? Why does matter have the properties it has? How can changes from one form of matter to another be controlled?

When we ask what matter is, we are really asking what it is made of: What are its components? When we observe different properties, we ask why some materials are gases, others liquids, and still others solids. Why are some materials colorless, some red, some green, and some purple? Why are some hard, some soft, some weak, and some strong? Why are some materials harmless, some nutritious, and some poisonous? When we ask how chemical and physical changes can be controlled, we are essentially implying that we are familiar with the remarkable changes that matter may undergo. Iron rusts;

wood burns; food is digested. Thousands of different substances can be made from the familiar materials at hand. Rocks and minerals, water, air, vegetation—all serve the chemist in his quest to create new kinds of matter which will hopefully improve the quality of man's life.

If the new substances are more useful than those from which they are produced, we wish to learn how to *bring about* the change. If the new substances are less useful, we need to learn how to *prevent* the change. The very essence of practical chemistry is the *control of chemical change*. One of the purposes of this book is to explore the various ways of effecting such control. Consider these three questions together. What is matter, why does it have the properties it has, and how can we control its changes from one form to another? The answer to the last question must depend on the answer to the second, which, in turn, must depend on the answer to the first. Chapter 1 therefore begins by trying to answer the question, What is matter?

First, however, it is important to know something about how chemists work. For modern chemistry is living proof of the remarkable effectiveness of the methods of science.

THE METHODS OF SCIENCE

Much has been said about the scientific method. People generally agree that use of this "method" has been the primary cause of today's tremendous acceleration in the acquisition of new information. It has been estimated that the total quantity of information on chemistry is now doubling every dozen years. Acceleration in other areas of science is comparably rapid. If this is the result of application of the scientific method, then we had better learn something about what this method is.

Strangely, there is no general agreement on exactly what the scientific method is. This is not, however, as strange as it may seem. The scientific method is actually a combination of methods by which scientists work. Since scientists are only individual people, their methods may vary according to their individual qualities and talents. Certain fundamental principles do, however, underlie the work of all scientists. These we can profitably examine. In the process, perhaps some of the confusion commonly existing concerning the meaning of the word "scientific" can be dispelled. Commercial advertisers, anxious to capitalize on the successes of science, have been major contributors to this confusion. A more fundamental source of this confusion is the gulf between the imagined ideals of scientific discovery and the truth about how such discoveries are made.

The Method of Experiment

Deliberate scientific experimentation is so common these days that it is difficult to realize how scarce it was three centuries ago. Then, anyone who had the time and an inclination to wonder about the mysteries of nature could observe naturally occurring events only if he were lucky enough to be present when the events happened. He could think about these occurrences, too, and speculate about the magic that caused them. But seldom, if ever, did it occur to him that he might avoid waiting by himself manipulating nature. Seldom did he recognize that a simple experiment might tell him whether his speculations were correct. Little did he realize the importance of identifying all the factors that might have influenced what he observed. Consequently, the discovery of new knowledge was erratic and extremely slow.

Gradually, beginning about three hundred years ago, man began to realize that he himself could *initiate* natural phenomena. At his own convenience he could bring together the ingredients and control the conditions under which he wished to observe their reactions. Furthermore, he could create experimental conditions rare or nonexistent in nature. As he learned to conduct his own experiments, he found he could study nature over a much wider range of conditions and make much more accurate observations. He could repeat experiments exactly, as often as he wished, to see whether his observations could be reproduced. Equally important, he learned to record his experiments in such a way that other investigators could duplicate them and make the same observations anywhere else in the world at any later date. To borrow a phrase from the TV commercials, this development was the original "scientific breakthrough." It was the dawn of a new era in civilization. From this time on, our knowledge of the physical world has increased at an ever-accelerating rate.

Experimental design is largely a technical matter. A scientist chooses conditions, designs equipment or apparatus, and plans experiments that will produce maximum information at the least cost in money and time. He tries to produce results that can be observed with ease and accuracy. Ideally, they should be results whose meaning is completely clear. Often such experiments require a combination of mechanical ingenuity and manipulative skill. Their planning requires originality, logical thinking, and most of all, a sound knowledge of the subject under investigation. Every scientist, therefore, must keep continuously up to date in his reading of the work of other scientists. This not only gives him knowledge of the field in which he wishes to experiment, but also tells him what others have already done. Without this knowledge he might waste months duplicating what someone else has already accomplished.

The information obtained from experiments is of course their very reason for being. Careful, complete, and totally honest observations are, therefore, absolutely essential. No informed person can avoid having opinions or expectations concerning the probable nature of the results of the experiments he undertakes. But a scientist must school himself to keep his observations of fact entirely separate from his opinions or preconceived notions of what the facts "ought to be." His opinions *must not* influence the accuracy of his observations. The truth of this statement is emphasized by the fact that many, if not most, truly great scientific discoveries have been unexpected. A scientist, or anyone else, would be ill prepared to recognize the unexpected if he were too sure in advance that it would not happen.

Seldom is it possible to observe experimentally the precise information really wanted. Practically always, one needs to interpret the observations in terms of the information he seeks. For instance, a dye called litmus turns pink or red when placed in a water solution containing acid. A water solution containing acid looks exactly like plain water. No one can see the acid. If one wishes to learn whether a water solution contains acid, he must perform some experiment. A simple experiment is to dip a piece of litmus paper (paper containing the blue dye litmus) into the solution. If the water does contain acid, the paper will turn pink or red. This fact we know from thousands of experiments with solutions which were known to contain acid because the acid was deliberately added to the water. But the point is, even in this very simple and seemingly direct experiment of dipping litmus paper into the water, one only *infers* from a pink color that acid is present. The paper does not come out of the water with a big ACID written on it. No bells ring or lights flash while a huge "acid" sign drops from the ceiling. Nevertheless, on the indirect evidence of the pink color, we confidently conclude that acid is present. If the paper remains blue, we conclude that no acid is present.

In this particular example, we are fairly safe. Although complications could confuse the interpretation of our observation, they are relatively unlikely. But in practically all experimental work, the scientist must interpret the observations he makes in terms of the information he seeks. The information is thus obtained *indirectly,* and there is always the possibility of faulty interpretation. There is the well-known example of the man who sought to discover the intoxicating ingredient of liquor. He drank whiskey and water and became intoxicated. He drank rum and water and became intoxicated. He drank gin and water and became intoxicated. Becoming sober once more, he studied his observations carefully and noted that all three drinks had similar effects. It was obvious to him what must be the intoxicating ingredient. What was common to all three was *water*.

It is in the interpretation of their experimental observations that scientists are most fallible. Usually, this is the most difficult part of the investigation. Unfortunately, it is also the least objective part. It is the part most susceptible to the influence of the scientist's previous experience—his training, his personality, his prejudices, his flaws and human weaknesses. Here the ideals of scientific methods encounter the non-ideal fact that all scientists are human beings. To the extent that scientists are widely informed, open-minded, objective, and clever, their interpretations can be enlightening and stimulating, and contribute usefully to understanding. To the extent that they are narrow, opinionated, or dull, their interpretations can be misleading or even nonexistent. Many scientific workers enjoy experimentation and are very good at it, but do not concern themselves much with wondering about the meaning of the measurements so carefully made. Although such people are essential in science and perform invaluable service, they should be recognized as technicians rather than scientists. The true scientist, fallible though he must be, has an active interest in understanding the significance of his observations. The methods of science have proven extremely effective because most scientists are able, most of the time, to interpret their experimental results in a way that is useful to the further development of their science.

The Role of Intuition and Luck

The unsung heroes of scientific research are *intuition* and *luck*. These factors seem so "unscientific" that their role is often minimized. One hardly expects the Nobel prize winner to say, "I just dreamed up the experiment and was plain lucky it came out the way it did." But understanding the importance of these uncontrollable factors is necessary to appreciate the full nature of science.

Intuition is a function of the human intelligence that seems to combine imagination and subconscious wisdom into a sometimes effective guide for guessing. In other words, intuition provides the "education" in an "educated guess." A good creative scientist rarely can say with assurance, "I will now carry out this experiment which will reveal this hitherto unknown result." He seldom knows for certain what new experiment to do or what it will reveal, but he thinks hard about all the possibilities he can imagine. In itself, this activity may be unproductive. Yet conscious thinking can set in motion certain thought processes that sometimes work more effectively while his conscious attention is directed elsewhere. These subconscious thoughts seem less inhibited than conscious thoughts. They may fit together facts seemingly so unrelated that his conscious mind would be embarrassed to consider them. But in this process of relating all stored knowledge to the problem at hand, the "subconscious" sometimes produces creative and original ideas. Later, while the scientist is shaving or weeding the garden, one of these ideas may pop suddenly into his consciousness; he has a "hunch." His intuition "tells" him that he should test the idea in the laboratory to see what happens.

The chances are good that the idea will not lead anywhere. The way to successful research is strewn with the remains of magnificent ideas that just did not work. But there is also a reasonable chance that his hunch may produce an important discovery. The scientist may never understand exactly what led him to the idea, but he will say with obvious satisfaction, "I finally figured out how to do it." The implication that he consciously organized and directed all the thought processes leading to the idea is quite misleading.

A scientist needs intuition. To develop it, he must absorb information, not merely within his specialty, but in all areas of knowledge. Man has arbitrarily divided up his knowledge to help organize his facts in a useful way. Knowledge cannot really be organized in neat categories. Such artificial boundaries may hinder the free wanderings of the imagination, both conscious and subconscious, that facilitate effective intuition.

A scientist also needs information. He also needs practice in using it. This means practice in reasoning, practice in solving problems. He needs practice in using past experience as a guide to (but never a dictator of) future actions. This is why such practice is so important in the training of scientists, as well as in the education of people for any useful pursuit. A wise man has said that the mind of man is not a pot to be stuffed but a lamp to be kindled. True, but let us be sure that the fuel supply is ample. To be a good scientist, to possess useful intuition, one needs both information *and* the ability to think. Neither one comes without effort.

Now, what of the role of luck? This too must not be underestimated. We are tempted to judge the quality of a scientist by the fame he acquires. Were not fame, fortune, and fate so fickle, this might be a fair judgment. But we must remember that for every famous scientist there are many who may be equally skillful and hard-working, but who have had less luck. Even though the great scientist is usually exceptionally able and has a highly developed intuition, the final ingredient essential to his fame is *luck*.

Perhaps a simple illustration will emphasize the importance of luck. No one knows exactly what, if any, kind of compound will cure cancer without harming the patient. Imagine two equally competent and worthy chemists each engaged in synthesizing new compounds to be tested against cancer. Each makes a new compound. One proves to be of no value. The other one cures cancer. Which chemist do you think will receive the fame?

Luck probably comes more often to those making an effective effort to accomplish something, but it is luck nonetheless. Surely the *unpredictability of research results* that makes luck so important is one of the most significant characteristics of science.

In summary, the methods of science as actually practiced involve deliberate control of conditions wherever possible. Scientific methods require careful recognition and measurement of uncontrollable factors. They require experiments thoughtfully designed to reveal as much information as possible, as economically as possible. They involve impartial, objective observations and accurate records. They are based on the conviction that seeing or measuring what happens can be far more reliable than merely reasoning out what *should* happen. Also, they involve deep and careful thought directed toward understanding the results and building them into a firm structure of knowledge. Both the planning of new experiments and the interpretation of results require not only sound information and skillful reasoning but also effective intuition. All of this is of little avail without occasional good luck.

Despite human weaknesses and limitations and despite many failures, the practice of scientific methods has yielded more knowledge of the material universe and greater material progress within the past three centuries than all previous history had produced without scientific methods.

APPLICATIONS OF SCIENTIFIC METHODS TO OTHER AREAS

Physical scientists ordinarily have a great advantage over others in quest of understanding, because the systems they work with are *relatively* easy to isolate, control, and observe exactly. Hence they are much more vulnerable to attack by scientific methods. Physical scientists can usually be very methodical, systematic, precise, rigorous, quantitative, and reproducible in their work. The results of their experiments are therefore *relatively* more believable, reliable, and easily interpreted than the work of people in other fields. Scientific results can be checked by other independent experimenters much more easily. In general, they bring greater intellectual satisfaction to the simple, compartmentalized mind of scientific man.

On the other hand, scholars who study such things as the development of civilizations, the formation of personality, the emotional impact of art and music, economics, or the art and practice of politics have a much more difficult task. The systems they study are so complex, so difficult to define, so impossible to isolate, control, or reproduce, that the ideal methods of science are hardly applicable. Perhaps a major reason why man's material progress has so outstripped his social, economic, and cultural progress is that knowledge of material things has been much easier to acquire. It is easier to go to the moon than to eliminate the causes of human suffering.

Nevertheless, whether or not you intend to study chemistry as a profession, you will find that basic aspects of scientific methods can serve you in whatever you undertake. Logical thinking, quantitative experimentation, exact and honest observation, and drawing reasonable conclusions from the observed data are essential in any area of study. The experience you should receive in studying chemistry will help you maintain a broader perspective and a sense of the quality of life, even though you may never be able to control the emotions of a nation of people, place the Civil War inside a liter flask, or work out an exact mathematical equation for an artistic masterpiece.

Part 1

Chemical Composition and Atomic Structure

1

CLASSIFICATION OF MATTER

PROPERTIES OF MATTER

More than two million kinds of matter exist, plus countless mixtures of these individual kinds. What are they made of? What, if anything, have they in common? It is helpful, in approaching a problem of such complexity, to divide it up. Among this enormous number of kinds of matter exist enough similarities to permit classifying them in different groups. Thus, it is easier to examine one group at a time than to tackle two million individual kinds of matter all at once. Probably the most useful basis for the classification of matter is that of properties.

Properties are qualities of matter that identify, characterize, and distinguish one material from others. Properties may be conveniently classified in two main types: physical and chemical. A *physical* property is a quality that can be observed or measured without changing the fundamental composition of the material. At room temperature some materials are solid, some liquid, and some gaseous. This is one way to classify matter, according to physical properties. A *chemical* property is the ability of a material to undergo change or retain its fundamental composition. A *chemical* property cannot be measured without at least trying to change the material into a different kind.

For example, glass is corroded by alkali. This corrosion process changes its composition, and is therefore a chemical property. Glass does not catch fire when a flame is set to it. This too is a chemical property. Neither property could have been discovered without risking a change in composition. We could not know that glass does not burn without first trying to burn it.

On the other hand, glass has a certain density. It is ordinarily colorless and it transmits light. These are physical properties. When they have been observed or measured, the glass is still glass. The brittleness of glass is also a physical property. After a glass object has been broken, it is still glass. A pile of fragments has the same composition as the original bottle.

We usually can recognize two samples of matter as being different from one another because they differ in physical properties. Where the difference is not readily apparent, a physical test may still be preferable to a chemical test. For example, suppose we want to know if the sparkling gem in a ring is a real diamond or only glass. A diamond will burn and glass will not, but we hardly want to risk this change in chemical properties in order to prove which it is. Measuring physical properties is a far better idea.

Is the melting of ice a physical or chemical change? What about the frying of bacon?

If a given sample of matter is examined by observing or measuring some of the physical properties of different portions of the sample, these properties will be either uniform—the same for all portions—or not. If they are not uniform, the sample is described as **heterogeneous,** whereas if they are uniform, it is called **homogeneous.** Materials may be classified according to whether they are homogeneous or heterogeneous. A homogeneous sample has identical properties in all parts—the bottom is exactly like the top and middle

Figure 1.1. States of Matter.

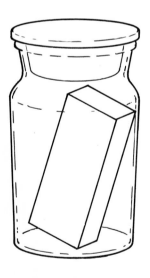  

A **solid** holds its shape against gravity; it has strong cohesive forces.

A **liquid** holds together but flows with gravity, thus assuming the shape of the bottom part of the container; it has fairly strong cohesive forces.

A **gas** defies gravity and spreads out as far as possible, thus occupying the entire container; it has very weak cohesive forces.

portions. In a heterogeneous sample the properties are not constant throughout the material.

The relationship of the physical properties of matter to its composition will be discussed later. For the present, our everyday experience should be enough to assure us of this fact: the different properties of matter are caused by differences in composition. If this is so, we can assume that any sample that is homogeneous with respect to physical properties must also be homogeneous in composition. Therefore, we will define a **pure substance** as one that is homogeneous in both composition and properties, and cannot be separated into heterogeneous parts or fractions by any physical process. An impure substance is a **mixture** of more than one pure substance and therefore must be heterogeneous with respect to both physical properties and composition. A mixture can be separated into heterogeneous parts.

This is a valuable classification because the distinction of materials on the basis of their composition is fundamental. For example, if we take a glass of water and stir in a teaspoonful of sand, what do we have? Sand and water—nothing more. The sand soon settles to the bottom and the water above is clear, revealing that this is a mixture. This visual evidence eliminates the need to resort to physical property measurements to identify the material as a mixture.

Suppose on the other hand we have a mixture of sugar and white sand. If the granules are fine enough and the sand white enough, the mixture will look like a pure substance. However, there are dozens of common white solids, so some additional tests must be made. One commonly measured property of solids is the melting point, the temperature at which a solid changes to a liquid. Since any pure substance will behave throughout in a uniform manner, our mixture, if pure, should melt all at once. By carefully heating the mixture of sand and sugar, we can observe that part of it melts while the rest remains solid, indicating the presence of more than one substance.

Another physical property is solubility in water. If a sample of the sugar and sand mixture is mixed with water, we observe that part of the sample disappears. The rest will remain no matter how long we stir or how much water we add, because sugar dissolves in water but sand does not. Again we have definite evidence—separation by a physical process—that our sample is a mixture, not a pure substance.

Many mixtures, like the sand and water, are obviously heterogeneous. Often we have only to look at them to recognize that they are mixtures. But some mixtures are more difficult to recognize. For instance, when a liquid such as water acts to dissolve a solid such as sugar, the individual molecules of sugar become separated and mix among the water molecules. Such a mixture is called a solution; it appears so homogeneous that by all ordinary examination it can easily be mistaken for a pure substance. A suitable physical process must be employed to separate the components of this type of mixture.

One such physical process is **distillation,** which makes use of the physical property of volatility. A liquid is vaporized by heating, and the vapor conducted to a different location, then condensed back to a liquid by cooling.

Figure 1.2. Homogeneity and Purity.

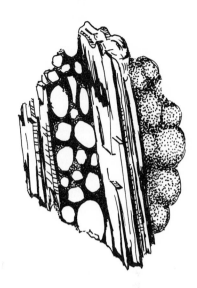

This rock is obviously **heterogeneous** because you can see different kinds of matter in it.

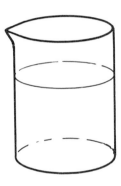

But this salt water is **homogeneous** because the salt is evenly distributed throughout the water.

Both are **mixtures.** We can prove that salt water is a mixture by boiling away the water. The salt remaining behind is homogeneous and a **pure substance.** The water distilled away is also homogeneous and a pure substance.

Both have uniform properties throughout, and neither can be separated into parts having different properties without changing their chemical composition.

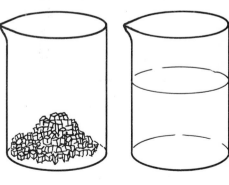

Pure salt   Pure water

This condensed liquid is called the **distillate.** If the liquid being distilled is a pure substance, all portions of the distillate will be identical in properties to that which remains undistilled. If these properties are not identical, then the original liquid could not have been a pure substance (assuming that its composition was not changed by the heat).

One difference between the components of the sugar solution is volatility. Water is much more volatile than sugar. Any attempt to distill the sugar solution will therefore result in vaporization of the water, causing distillation away from the sugar. The distillate will be pure water with a density and other physical properties different from those of the original solution, thus proving that the solution was a mixture.

In summary, we can classify any sample of matter as either a pure substance or a mixture. A pure substance is homogeneous, whereas a mixture is heterogeneous, although not always obviously or visibly so. If a given material seems homogeneous, we can subject it to a physical treatment to separate it

Figure 1.3.   Laboratory Distillation Apparatus.

The flask is heated and the temperature gradually increased until vapors envelop the thermometer bulb, condensing on it and diffusing into the condenser. If the liquid being distilled is a mixture, the most volatile fraction will be collected first and at the lowest temperature. (Boiling chips are inert particles used to prevent superheating and sudden boiling over.)

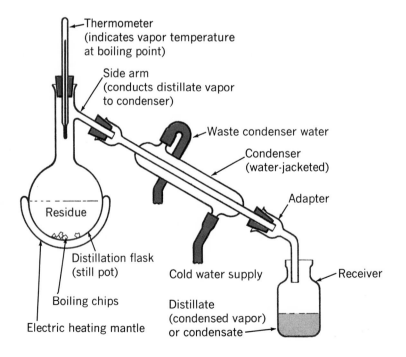

into component parts. For liquids, the most common method of separation is distillation, which takes advantage of differences in volatility. For solids, the most common method of separation is solvent extraction, which is based on differences in solubility. In either case, if the original material was a pure substance, the separated components or fractions will be identical with the original material or the residue. However, if the original material was a mixture, the fractions will differ in properties, clearly distinguishing the material as a mixture.

A few exceptional materials are difficult to classify. A familiar example is glass. Although it could be a pure substance, it usually is not. It appears homogeneous, and being neither volatile nor soluble cannot be fractionated. Yet, we know it is a mixture because its composition can be varied. Fortunately, however, such materials are in the minority. Most materials can be relatively easily identified as either a mixture or a pure substance.

> Should homogenized milk be classified as a mixture or a pure substance? What about ink?

ELEMENTS AND COMPOUNDS

Centuries of experimentation with various materials have led to the recognition of two broad classes of matter within the category of *pure substances*. One class of matter includes all substances that by appropriate chemical treatment can be broken down into simpler substances. Substances which can be broken down in this way are called **chemical compounds.** The other class of pure substances includes all those that cannot be broken down to simpler substances by ordinary chemical means. These include all those substances that result when compounds are broken down as far as possible; they are called the **chemical elements.** To recapitulate, all matter on earth is considered to be either a pure substance or a mixture. Every pure substance is either an element or a compound. Every mixture, consequently, contains two or more elemental substances or compounds.

How is the problem of classifying matter simplified by what we have discussed? The simplification comes from the fact that although millions of kinds of compounds are possible, all of them consist of relatively few elements. In total, the elements number only 90 found in nature to date and at least 14 more which have been made by man in the laboratory. We have now arrived at the greatest simplifying and unifying fact in chemistry: **All matter is composed of one or more chemical elements.**

In the following chapter, we shall consider the history of this concept of chemical elements.

Test Your Memory

1. How many different compounds are known?
2. Define *physical property*. Name several examples.

3. Define *chemical property.*
4. Define *homogeneous* and *heterogeneous.*
5. How does a pure substance differ from a mixture?
6. What is a *chemical element?*

Test Your Understanding

1. Which of the following are chemical properties?
   a) the melting of ice
   b) the combustibility of gasoline
   c) the ability of iron to rust
   d) the reflective property of silver
   e) the softness of chalk
   f) the density of lead
   g) the electrical conductivity of copper
2. Which of the following are probably mixtures?
   a) milk
   b) pure ice and pure water together
   c) soil
   d) air
   e) iron
3. What experiment could determine whether a given sample of colorless liquid is pure water or a solution?
4. What experiment could determine whether a white powder is chalk dust or a mixture of chalk dust and powdered salt?
5. How could you recognize as a mixture a solution of alcohol in water without drinking it?
6. Sugar chars (i.e., forms carbon) when evaporated into a vacuum. What does this tell you about whether sugar is a compound or an element?

2

THE CHEMICAL ELEMENTS

EARLY THEORIES OF MATTER

The early Greek philosophers Thales and Heraclitus believed all matter to be composed of a single fundamental element. Although Thales thought this fundamental element was water, Heraclitus later maintained that it was fire. About 440 B.C., Empedocles suggested that everything was made of one or more of four fundamental elements: earth, water, air, and fire. His ideas were later adopted by the Greek philosopher Aristotle (384–322 B.C.) who amplified them by proposing that all matter combined certain fundamental properties: hotness, coldness, wetness, and dryness. Earth, he claimed, was a combination of coldness and dryness; water a combination of coldness and wetness; air, of hotness and wetness; and fire was a combination of hotness and dryness.

Although Aristotle's simple four-element scheme may seem ridiculous today, it appeared quite reasonable to the learned men of earlier times. So influential were Aristotle's ideas and so slow was the development of experimental knowledge that his theory of four basic elements persisted for nearly two thousand years.

The theories of the early philosophers were generally based on only superficial observations of nature. Because they did not experiment to test the validity of their ideas, they contributed little to practical chemistry. Meanwhile, however, as artisans and builders devoted their talents and skills toward the development of a material civilization, the need to make more extensive use of the environment was recognized. The special qualities of different kinds of materials became apparent, and as the supply of some of these gradually became depleted, substitute materials were needed. Men began to experiment with such materials and with chemical processes by which they might be made more useful. Thus, although the intellectuals were contributing very little toward the development of a science of chemistry, others were building the chemical arts.

WORK OF THE ALCHEMISTS

The chief practitioners of the chemical arts, during the Middle Ages and earlier, were known as **alchemists.** One of their major goals was the conversion into gold of other less costly materials. Although we now recognize that no chemical process can accomplish this goal, the alchemists lacked any fundamental understanding of chemistry. Unlike the earlier philosophers, however, the alchemists did perform experiments. Under the circumstances these were just as reasonable and logical as could be expected. Having observed iron change into a reddish brown powder, and wood into smoke, hot air, and ashes, alchemists reasonably wondered whether mercury or lead could be changed into gold.

Chemical change was mysterious to the alchemists, and their work was consequently a mixture of practical laboratory experimentation and black magic. Often their activities were supported by a wealthy few who sought an opportunity to become even wealthier. To ensure that such support continued despite persistent failure, the alchemists had to create the illusion of great achievement while keeping the details a mystery. Consequently the written records of alchemy are seldom, if ever, the clear, precise descriptions one expects of the modern scientist.

One of the most famous alchemists was Theophrastus Bombastus von Hohenheim (1493–1541), who called himself "Paracelsus." He was influential in shifting some of the emphasis from the search for quick riches to the preparation of chemicals useful in medicine. This broadened the scope of alchemical activity, and in a sense it paved the way for today's intense activity in drug research.

Although the alchemists were not scientific in the modern sense of the word, they did discover useful techniques of experiment and establish a valuable practical knowledge of many familiar chemicals. These discoveries provided a broad background of chemical information upon which development of a real science of chemistry could be based.

CONCEPT OF CHEMICAL ELEMENTS

The concept of chemical elements as we know it did not begin to develop until the latter part of the seventeenth century. Credit for this is given to the Englishman, Robert Boyle (1627–1691), sometimes called the first scientific chemist, who proposed that all matter consisted of relatively few elementary substances that could not be broken down into simpler substances. He called these elementary substances the **chemical elements** and proposed that differences among materials were the result of differences in the relative amounts of the elements present. All complex substances could ultimately be broken down into their individual elements, but no further.

Some substances known to the ancients, such as gold, silver, copper, iron, tin, lead, and mercury, as well as sulfur and carbon, began to be recognized as elements. Other then-familiar substances now known to be elements were arsenic, antimony, and bismuth. As the methods of science were developed, new elements were deliberately sought out and the rate of discovery accelerated with amazing rapidity. In all the centuries of alchemy, only one *new* element, phosphorus, had been discovered. Yet in the century following Boyle, 13 elements were added to the list, followed by 54 more elements discovered in the nineteenth century.

The rapid acceleration in the discovery of the elements during the past three hundred years has undoubtedly been due to the application of the

Table 2.1. Chronological Order of Isolation or Discovery of the Elements

Ancient	Yttrium	Beryllium	Polonium
Carbon	Chromium	Thorium	Radium
Sulfur		Lanthanum	Europium
Iron	19th Century	Uranium	
Copper	Niobium	Erbium	20th Century
Arsenic	Tantalum	Terbium	Actinium
Silver	Rhodium	Ruthenium	Lutetium
Tin	Palladium	Cesium	Radon
Antimony	Osmium	Rubidium	Ytterbium
Gold	Iridium	Thallium	Protactinium
Mercury	Cerium	Indium	Hafnium
Lead	Sodium	Vanadium	Rhenium
Bismuth	Potassium	Gallium	Francium
17th Century	Magnesium	Scandium	Technetium
Phosphorus	Calcium	Holmium	Astatine
	Strontium	Thulium	Neptunium
18th Century	Barium	Samarium	Plutonium
Hydrogen	Boron	Praseodymium	Americium
Cobalt	Chlorine	Neodymium	Curium
Zinc	Iodine	Germanium	Berkelium
Platinum	Lithium	Dysprosium	Californium
Nickel	Cadmium	Gadolinium	Einsteinium
Nitrogen	Selenium	Fluorine	Fermium
Oxygen	Silicon	Argon	Mendelevium
Manganese	Zirconium	Helium	Nobelium
Molybdenum	Aluminum	Neon	Lawrencium
Tellurium	Titanium	Krypton	Element 104
Tungsten	Bromine	Xenon	(not yet named)

methods of science, by which new scientific information leads to the discovery of even more information. The new knowledge of chemistry associated with each discovery is added to the base of scientific knowledge upon which new experimental work can be built.

A listing of the chemical elements in order of their discovery is given in Table 2.1.

OCCURRENCE OF THE ELEMENTS

Only a few chemical elements exist naturally in the pure state; most occur combined with other elements in the form of compounds. Consequently, the relative abundance and occurrence of each element includes its occurrence in compounds.

The earth is believed to consist of three major regions: the core, the mantle, and the crust. The core, at the center, is thought to be composed largely of iron and nickel. The mantle, surrounding the core, is a much less dense layer about 1800 miles thick. It is believed to consist largely of compounds of silicon, oxygen, and some metals called silicates. The outer shell above the mantle is the earth's crust, which extends downward about 22 miles below the surface of the continents and about 6 miles below the ocean beds.

The crust consists of the **lithosphere** (the solid part), the **hydrosphere** (the water part: seas, lakes, and rivers plus the water vapor in the atmosphere), and the **atmosphere** (the blanket of gases that surrounds the crust). Careful analyses of widely selected samples of each portion of the earth's crust have enabled scientists to estimate the total composition.

Figure 2.1.   Representation of the Earth (not to scale).

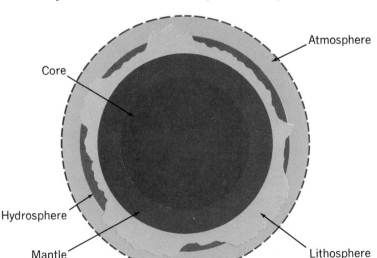

Figure 2.2. Composition of the Earth's Surface, by Weight Per Cent and Atom Per Cent.

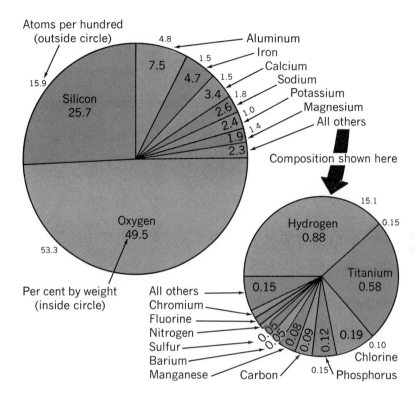

As shown in Figure 2.2, oxygen is by far the most abundant element. About 20 per cent of the atmosphere is oxygen gas. About 89 per cent of the hydrosphere is oxygen combined with hydrogen in the compound water. Oxygen is combined with silicon and metals such as iron and aluminum in the rocks, sand, and soils of the lithosphere. Nearly half the weight of the earth's surface is oxygen. Of every 100 atoms in the crust, 53 are oxygen atoms.

The second most abundant element in the crust is silicon, which constitutes nearly 26 per cent of the total weight—about 16 out of every 100 atoms. On the basis of its weight, aluminum is rated as the third most abundant element, but on the basis of the relative number of atoms, hydrogen is third. Because its atoms are lighter than those of any other element, hydrogen contributes only about 0.9 per cent of the weight of the earth's crust. There are 15 atoms of hydrogen per 100 in contrast to less than 5 of each 100 atoms for aluminum.

On the basis of weight percentage, iron follows aluminum as the fourth most abundant element, calcium is fifth, sodium sixth, potassium seventh, and magnesium eighth. The first eight elements account for 97.7 per cent of the weight of the crust. All other elements together contribute only 2.3 per cent. Of these, hydrogen and titanium each comprise about one third of the 2.3 per cent. The next most abundant elements, in decreasing abundance, are chlorine, phosphorus, carbon, manganese, barium, sulfur, nitrogen, fluorine, and chromium. The more than 70 other elements comprise only 0.15 per cent of the earth's crust.

What is the weight of 0.15 per cent of one ton? If the circumference of the earth is 25,000 miles and the fraction of land surface is 30 per cent and we consider only the top three feet of the land, assuming an average density of 150 lbs per cubic foot, what weight of these 70-odd elements is present?

The origins of these elements have been studied for years and are being actively investigated today. Although numerous theories have been proposed, none seems altogether satisfactory.

As important as origin is distribution of the elements. Certain elements that are very scarce in terms of relative abundance throughout the earth's crust are found in small areas containing high concentrations of them. This is fortunate for man, who finds some of these deposits extremely useful. If these same elements had been dispersed uniformly among all the other elements, isolating them for practical use would be too difficult and expensive. If the reasons that certain elements accumulated in certain areas were known, searches for new sources would be facilitated. Lacking this knowledge we seldom are able to search efficiently. This is especially unfortunate because the consumption of many of our limited natural resources results in distributing them so widely that they can never be recovered. For example, what will we use for lead when all we can find has been blown out the exhausts of millions of automobiles?

What weight of gold would occur in the top three feet of the earth's solid surface if the concentration is about 1.0 mg per ton?

The atmosphere, as previously noted, is about 20 per cent oxygen gas. Most of the remaining 80 per cent is nitrogen gas, plus about 1.0 per cent of argon and smaller quantities of carbon dioxide, water vapor, and other very minor constituents. Most of the hydrosphere is water, a compound in which one oxygen atom and two hydrogen atoms combine chemically to form one molecule. Since water is an excellent solvent for many minerals, the hydrosphere also contains substances leached out of the rocks and soil by rain and carried by the rivers into the oceans. About 3.3 per cent of the ocean is dissolved solids. Practical and economical processes have been developed for extracting sodium chloride (table salt), bromine, and magnesium from the sea. Many other metals are present in compounds dissolved in sea water but in traces too small to justify their extraction for commercial purposes.

All the remaining elements, most of which are metals, make up the lithosphere. Many metals are combined with silicon and oxygen in rocks and minerals, in compounds called **silicates.** The lithosphere also contains large quantities of **carbonates** in which metals are combined with both oxygen and carbon. Calcium carbonate, or limestone, is the most common of these compounds. One crystalline form of calcium carbonate is marble. Many metals occur in the earth's crust as **sulfides,** which contain only sulfur and metal. Also, free sulfur is found in large underground deposits. Most metals occur either combined with oxygen alone, or with oxygen and one or two other elements, or as sulfides. A few metals, such as sodium, occur as **chlorides,** compounds with chlorine.

Practically all of the thousands of different mineral substances are compounds of the metallic elements. The **inorganic** components of the earth, which make up by far its greatest bulk, consist chiefly of metals, oxygen, silicon, a few other elements such as sulfur, chlorine, carbon, and a small amount of nitrogen.

The **organic** components of the earth are compounds containing carbon atoms attached to hydrogen atoms, and other elements as well. They are primarily substances found growing, or giving evidence of once having grown, on the surface of the earth. In some instances, what was once the surface has been submerged or buried beneath mineral matter for millions of years. Fossil remains of the original organic matter are found far below the surface as coal, petroleum, and oil shale. Chemically, the carbon-hydrogen bond that characterizes organic matter may be joined to oxygen, nitrogen, sulfur, and phosphorus as well as other elements. Although inorganic substances vastly exceed organic substances in quantity, organic substances have the added importance of forming the basis for all living systems, including you and me.

Compounds consisting primarily of carbon and hydrogen are found in nature as petroleum and natural gas, and in coal and oil shale. Millions of different compounds that contain only carbon and hydrogen are possible and many of these do exist. Usually they occur in complex mixtures that defy practical separation. When crudely separated, these compounds become natural gas, heavier fuel gases, gasoline, fuel oil, lubricating oil, paraffin wax,

natural gas	asphalt	**Table 2.2. Some Familiar Materials Composed Only of Carbon and Hydrogen**
"bottled" gas	polyethylene	
gasoline	paraffin wax	
lubricating oil	rubber	
	polystyrene	

jet fuel, and asphalt. Each of these materials is a mixture of carbon and hydrogen compounds known as **hydrocarbons.** Materials known as **polyethylenes** and **polypropylenes** also consist only of the elements carbon and hydrogen.

Table 2.3. Some Familiar Materials Composed Only of Carbon, Hydrogen and Oxygen

sugar	alcohol	acetic acid	rayon
starch	Dacron	formaldehyde	fats
cellulose	acetone	ether	Lucite
cotton	Bakelite	oil of wintergreen	cellophane

When oxygen is combined with carbon and hydrogen, the number of possible compounds becomes even greater. Several important classes of compounds contain only these three elements in combination. One class is **alcohols,** related to glycols, glycerin, and sugars, as well as starches and cellulose.

Figure 2.3. Organic and Inorganic Matter.

The sugars and starches are known as **carbohydrates.** Another class of carbon, hydrogen, and oxygen compounds is known as **fats.** Other compounds containing only carbon, hydrogen, and oxygen include synthetic fiber materials such as Dacron, other polyesters, and Bakelite, a plastic.

Many physiologically important compounds including **proteins** are composed of nitrogen along with carbon, hydrogen, and oxygen. Other compounds of these same four elements include nylon, explosives such as TNT, and many dyes and medicines.

Table 2.4. Some Familiar Materials Composed Only of Carbon, Hydrogen, Oxygen, and Nitrogen		
	nylon	aspirin
	TNT	celluloid
	nitroglycerin	cocaine

Figure 2.4. Elemental Composition of Man.

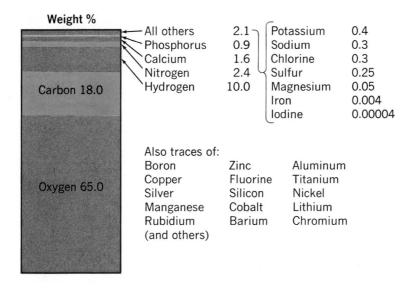

Weight %		
All others	2.1	Potassium 0.4
Phosphorus	0.9	Sodium 0.3
Calcium	1.6	Chlorine 0.3
Nitrogen	2.4	Sulfur 0.25
Hydrogen	10.0	Magnesium 0.05
		Iron 0.004
		Iodine 0.00004

Carbon 18.0

Oxygen 65.0

Also traces of:
Boron   Zinc   Aluminum
Copper   Fluorine   Titanium
Silver   Silicon   Nickel
Manganese   Cobalt   Lithium
Rubidium   Barium   Chromium
(and others)

SUMMARY

Pure substances, which are either elements or compounds, constitute all matter, including the earth's crust. Compounds are chemical combinations of different elements; millions of different compounds can result from the combination of a few elements. Compounds that contain carbon joined to hydrogen are classified as organic, whereas compounds lacking this bond are classified as inorganic. Inorganic compounds make up the bulk of the atmosphere, hydrosphere, and lithosphere; organic compounds, though less abundant, are extremely important because all living things, as well as many valuable synthetic substances, are composed primarily of organic compounds.

The earth is only an infinitesimal speck in the universe of matter. Even though all other matter is far away, some of it which reaches us in the form of meteorites can be analyzed. Other matter in the universe is studied by telescope techniques. Without exception thus far, the very same elements that occur on earth are found to make up the other planets, the sun, and the other stars. So, as we make the effort to learn something about terrestrial chemistry, we can take satisfaction in the probability that should some cataclysmic disturbance, space ship, or reincarnation deposit us a few million light-years distant from our native planet, we would not need to learn a new chemistry. It should be essentially the same there as here. So far as we have knowledge of it, the chemistry you are learning now is universal chemistry.

With that comforting thought, let us turn now to a consideration of the nature of compounds.

Test Your Memory

1. What were the four "elements" proposed by Aristotle?
2. Who were the alchemists? What kind of chemical information did they leave?
3. Who was Robert Boyle? What was his concept of a chemical element?
4. Name at least ten elements known as individual substances in early times.
5. How many elements were discovered by alchemists?
6. How many elements occur naturally on earth?
7. Identify each of the following and tell something of its elemental composition: lithosphere, hydrosphere, atmosphere.
8. Name the four most abundant elements of the earth's crust in order of decreasing abundance by weight.
9. In what kinds of combinations do the metallic elements occur?
10. Are the elements distributed uniformly throughout the earth's crust?
11. What are the principal elements comprising living matter?
12. Name four natural sources of hydrocarbons. Name four practically useful hydrocarbon products.
13. Name three kinds of compounds that contain only carbon, hydrogen, and oxygen.
14. Answer, as completely as you can, the question: What is the composition of matter?

Test Your Understanding

1. Assume the earth's crust to be 10 miles thick and its average density to be 2.8 lbs per cubic foot. The diameter of the earth is about 8000 miles. The relative abundance of gold is estimated at 0.000004 per cent. How many tons of gold are in the earth's crust?
2. If all the naturally occurring elements have already been discovered, how can so many new compounds be made?
3. What is the effect of chemical combinations on the appearance and properties of the individual elements?

THE ELEMENTAL COMPOSITION OF COMPOUNDS

CHARACTERISTICS OF ATOMS

Any understanding of the nature of chemical compounds must begin with the atoms which compose them. Chapters 6 and 7 are devoted to a detailed discussion of the nature of atoms. For now we will simply assume their existence. This assumption is based on a great abundance of experimental observations.

For the present, let us accept the following facts as being true of all atoms:

All atoms of a given element are similar to one another and significantly different from all atoms of other elements.

All atoms are so extremely small that any sample of matter big enough to be visible must contain an enormously large number of them.

Only whole atoms can participate in or result from any chemical change.

CHEMICAL SYMBOLS

Since all atoms of a given element are essentially alike, any one atom can be represented by a **chemical symbol** which is an abbreviation for the chemical name of the element. The symbol can represent the element in general, one specific atom of the element, or one **mole** of the element. (This important chemical quantity, the mole, is discussed in Chapter 4.)

Most chemical symbols consist of the first letter of the name of the element (capitalized) followed by a second (lower case) letter if necessary to distinguish elements beginning with the same first letter. For example, C is the symbol for carbon, Ca for calcium, Co for cobalt, and Cr for chromium. The Latin name *cuprum* serves as the basis for the symbol for copper, Cu.

Similarly, the symbol for sulfur is S, *samarium,* Sm, and *selenium,* Se; but sodium is Na. An older term for sodium was *natrium,* which was derived from similar words in Arabic and Greek for the mineral called sodium carbonate or soda. Ag, the chemical symbol for silver, comes from the Latin *argentum.* Table 3.1 lists all the known chemical elements with their chemical symbols. Although there is no need to memorize all of them now, you should try to learn each symbol as it is used, for symbols are basic to the language of chemistry. Remember, the symbol may mean either the element in general, one atom of that element, or one mole of atoms of the element (see Chapter 4).

Table 3.1.   The Chemical Elements and Their Symbols

Ac	actinium	Gd	gadolinium	Pm	promethium
Ag	silver	Ge	germanium	Po	polonium
Al	aluminum	H	hydrogen	Pr	praseodymium
Am	americium	He	helium	Pt	platinum
Ar	argon	Hf	hafnium	Pu	plutonium
As	arsenic	Hg	mercury	Ra	radium
At	astatine	Ho	holmium	Rb	rubidium
Au	gold	I	iodine	Re	rhenium
B	boron	In	indium	Rh	rhodium
Ba	barium	Ir	iridium	Rn	radon
Be	beryllium	K	potassium	S	sulfur
Bi	bismuth	Kr	krypton	Sb	antimony
Bk	berkelium	La	lanthanum	Sc	scandium
Br	bromine	Li	lithium	Se	selenium
C	carbon	Lu	lutetium	Si	silicon
Ca	calcium	Lw	lawrencium	Sm	samarium
Cd	cadmium	Md	mendelevium	Sn	tin
Ce	cerium	Mg	magnesium	Sr	strontium
Cf	californium	Mn	manganese	Ta	tantalum
Cl	chlorine	Mo	molybdenum	Tb	terbium
Cm	curium	N	nitrogen	Tc	technetium
Co	cobalt	Na	sodium	Te	tellurium
Cr	chromium	Nb	niobium	Th	thorium
Cs	cesium	Nd	neodymium	Ti	titanium
Cu	copper	Ne	neon	Tl	thallium
Dy	dysprosium	Ni	nickel	Tm	thulium
Er	erbium	No	nobelium	U	uranium
Es	einsteinium	Np	neptunium	V	vanadium
Eu	europium	O	oxygen	W	tungsten
F	fluorine	Os	osmium	Xe	xenon
Fe	iron	P	phosphorus	Y	yttrium
Fm	fermium	Pa	protactinium	Yb	ytterbium
Fr	francium	Pb	lead	Zn	zinc
Ga	gallium	Pd	palladium	Zr	zirconium

The properties of a compound depend on its composition. Since the properties of a compound are uniform, its composition must be uniform also. Furthermore, only whole atoms can enter into combination. We can therefore expect that any compound consisting of hypothetical element A combined with hypothetical element B can be represented by a specific **formula** A_xB_y.

This formula is a combination of chemical symbols that tells us what elements are present and how many atoms of each are involved. The subscripts x and y represent whole numbers and give the relative numbers of atoms of elements A and B in the compound. For example, several different compounds contain only manganese and oxygen. One compound has the formula MnO, which reveals that the compound contains equal numbers of manganese and oxygen atoms. Another compound has the formula MnO_2, indicating that this compound contains two atoms of oxygen for each atom of manganese. A third compound has the formula Mn_2O_3, from which we know that there are three atoms of oxygen for each two atoms of manganese.

You have probably been familiar for years with the chemical formula of water, H_2O, which indicates that each oxygen atom is combined with two hydrogen atoms. You may also know that $NaCl$ is the formula for sodium chloride, or common table salt. The formula tells us that sodium chloride contains an equal number of sodium atoms and chlorine atoms.

> What does the formula for sulfuric acid (H_2SO_4) tell us about the compound itself?

Many compounds have more complicated formulas that include groups of atoms which act as single units. One such group is represented by a water molecule. Some compounds join with water, thus becoming **hydrated,** to form **hydrates.** Calcium chloride ($CaCl_2$) will absorb moisture from the damp air to become a hydrate in which six units of water are combined for each calcium atom. The formula for this hydrate is $CaCl_2 \cdot 6H_2O$. Although this might have been written $CaCl_2H_{12}O_6$, since we know that the water is present as H_2O, the former formula is more informative and, therefore, much preferred.

A group of atoms that occurs as a unit in compounds and is not stable by itself is called a chemical **radical.** A radical like methyl (CH_3) is neutral, while others may carry an electrical charge, as in sulfate ($SO_4^=$) or ammonium (NH_4^+). The origin of these charges is discussed in Chapter 13. Table 3.2 lists some important radicals which occur in many compounds; it should be learned as soon as possible. The formulas of compounds including radicals are written with the radical in parentheses if it occurs more than once. A subscript number following the parentheses indicates how many times the radical occurs in the compound. For example, calcium sulfate is $CaSO_4$, and aluminum sulfate $Al_2(SO_4)_3$. The latter might have been written $Al_2S_3O_{12}$, since the subscript outside the parentheses means that every atom within the parentheses must be multiplied by that number, but since the radical acts as a single element within the compound, it should be designated separately within the formula.

Table 3.2.   Some Common Radicals and Radical Ions

CH_3^-	methyl	SO_4^-	sulfate	ClO^-	hypochlorite
$CH_3CH_2^-$	ethyl	$S_2O_3^-$	thiosulfate	ClO_2^-	chlorite
$C_6H_5^-$	phenyl	HSO_4^-	bisulfate	ClO_3^-	chlorate
^-OH	hydroxyl	$SO_3^=$	sulfite	ClO_4^-	perchlorate
OH^-	hydroxide	HSO_3^-	bisulfite	$PO_4^{\equiv}$	phosphate
NH_4^+	ammonium	NO_2^-	nitrite	HPO_4^-	hydrogen
CO_3^-	carbonate	NO_3^-	nitrate		phosphate
HCO_3^-	bicarbonate	CN^-	cyanide	$H_2PO_4^-$	dihydrogen
					phosphate
				CH_3COO^-	acetate

Since aluminum sulfate does contain sulfate radicals, it is more useful to show this in the formula. The same treatment is given to sodium nitrate ($NaNO_3$), calcium nitrate [$Ca(NO_3)_2$], aluminum nitrate [$Al(NO_3)_3$], copper nitrate [$Cu(NO_3)_2$], and nitric acid (HNO_3).

Aluminum sulfate can become hydrated to form a compound which contains six water units for each aluminum atom, with the formula $Al_2(SO_4)_3 \cdot 12H_2O$. Such a compound contains both radicals and groups of atoms capable of existing independently.

Table 3.3.   Some Sulfates, Nitrates, and Carbonates

	Sulfates	Nitrates	Carbonates
	Na_2SO_4	$NaNO_3$	Na_2CO_3
	$CaSO_4$	$Ca(NO_3)_2$	$CaCO_3$
	$MgSO_4$	$Mg(NO_3)_2$	$MgCO_3$
	$Al_2(SO_4)_3$	$Al(NO_3)_3$	[$Al_2(CO_3)_3$] does not exist
	$FeSO_4$	$Fe(NO_3)_2$	$FeCO_3$
	$Fe_2(SO_4)_3$	$Fe(NO_3)_3$	[$Fe_2(CO_3)_3$] does not exist
	$(NH_4)_2SOS_4$	NH_4NO_3	NH_4CO_3

A formula is not always written with the water shown at the end. Sometimes it is useful to indicate more exactly how the water is attached. For example, consider the hydrate of copper sulfate, a familiar pale blue salt. Analysis shows the formula of this hydrate to be $CuSO_4 \cdot 5H_2O$. X-ray studies show that four units of water surround the copper atom and the fifth is elsewhere in the crystal. This information can be indicated by writing the formula $Cu(H_2O)_4SO_4 \cdot H_2O$.

Chemical nomenclature refers to the naming of chemical substances. Two types of names are used: the common, or **trivial,** name; and the chemical, or **systematic** name. Trivial names are usually nonchemical, often conceived long before anyone wondered about chemical composition. Even after proper scientific terms became available, the greater simplicity or familiarity of the trivial name commonly resulted in its continued use. For example, water, sugar, and salt are the trivial names for dihydrogen oxide, sucrose, and sodium chloride; even chemists will probably never change from the use of the term *water.* The systematic name indicates the chemical composition of a substance, to minimize ambiguity and confusion.

Many compounds consist of hydrogen or a metallic element united with a nonmetallic element. These compounds are named as the hydrogen or metal compound of the nonmetal, to which the suffix *-ide* is added. For example, sodium chlor*ide,* calcium ox*ide,* and hydrogen sulf*ide* are names for the compounds of sodium with chlorine, calcium with oxygen, and hydrogen with sulfur. Metal compounds with radicals such as sulfate and carbonate are named as metal carbonates and metal sulfates—for example, potassium carbonate, copper sulfate, silver nitrate.

Name the following compounds: NaBr, MgO, $FeSO_4$.

Sometimes trivial names which are applied to individual compounds really refer to classes of compounds. For instance, alcohol is a common name for ethyl alcohol, but there are also methyl alcohol, isopropyl alcohol, and hundreds of other alcohols, all different. The need for precision is emphasized by the fact that people have died or been permanently blinded from drinking beverages containing "alcohol" that was not ethyl alcohol. Similarly, although the trivial name *salt* is used for the sodium chloride of the dining table, chemically any combination of a metal with a nonmetal is a salt.

EMPIRICAL AND MOLECULAR FORMULAS

The composition of a compound usually is determined by a chemical analysis which reveals the relative numbers of each kind of atom in the compound. Unless there is some definite reason for doing otherwise, the relative numbers are reduced to the lowest possible combination of whole numbers. For example, we would write NaCl, MnO_2, and $PbCl_4$ instead of Na_3Cl_3 or Na_2Cl_2 or Mn_2O_4 or Pb_2Cl_8. Such chemical formulas, reduced to their lowest terms in whole numbers of atoms, are called the **empirical formulas.** *Empirical* means based on experiment, and here refers to the analysis that determined the composition. Every chemical compound can be designated by an empirical formula.

What are the empirical formulas for $Na_4S_2O_8$, $Al_2(NO_3)_6$, H_2O_2, $C_6H_{12}O_6$, $C_{25}H_{52}O$?

Atoms combine to form compounds in two different ways: they unite to form small equal units called **molecules,** which are all alike for a given compound; or they join together to form a large aggregate, whose size is limited only by the number of atoms available. We therefore distinguish between **molecular** and **nonmolecular** compounds. All liquids and gases, plus many solids, are molecular in nature, whereas nonmolecular compounds are always solids.

Figure 3.1.   Molecular and Nonmolecular Substances.

Chlorine, a gas, is a typical **molecular** substance. Its **molecular formula,** Cl_2, indicates that each molecule consists of two atoms joined together as a single unit—a molecule. Even as a frozen solid, chlorine consists of Cl_2 molecules.

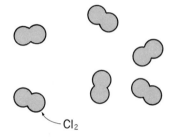
Cl_2

Sodium chloride, a solid, is a typical **nonmolecular** substance. Its **empirical formula,** NaCl, indicates only the relative atomic composition. The crystal contains **no** individual molecules. Each atom is attached equally to six atoms of the other element, throughout the entire crystal.

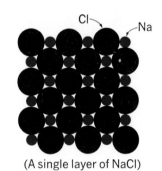
Cl   Na

(A single layer of NaCl)

The six neighboring atoms in NaCl form a regular octahedron around the central atom.

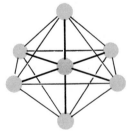

A nonmolecular compound is always represented by its empirical formula. There is no point to writing the formula of nonmolecular sodium chloride, NaCl, as Na_2Cl_2 or Na_8Cl_8 because only the relative numbers of each of the component elements have meaning. Therefore, the formula is best reduced to its simplest form, the empirical formula. Although a molecular compound can be represented by its empirical formula, its molecular formula is more informative. CH is the empirical formula for more than one molecular compound, including both acetylene and benzene, two distinct compounds, the first a gas and the second a liquid. A formula that indicates how many CH units are contained in each molecule is needed to differentiate such compounds. Since there are two such units in acetylene molecules and six in benzene molecules, the molecular formulas are C_2H_2 and C_6H_6, respectively.

Figure 3.2. Empirical and Molecular Formulas.

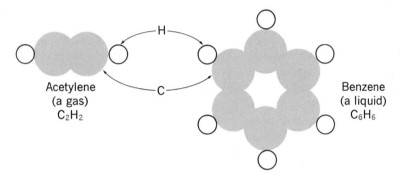

Acetylene
(a gas)
C_2H_2

Benzene
(a liquid)
C_6H_6

The **empirical formula** of each of these two compounds is the same: CH.

The **molecular formula** always equals the empirical formula or some integral multiple of it. For example:

$$C_2H_2 = 2 \times CH$$
$$C_6H_6 = 6 \times CH$$

Sometimes the empirical formula and the molecular formula of a compound are exactly the same. The molecular and empirical formulas for water, which is a molecular compound, are both H_2O, because it has been experimentally determined that each molecule contains one oxygen atom attached to two hydrogen atoms. A molecular formula may be the *same* as the empirical formula or a *multiple* of the empirical formula by a *whole* number. The determination of empirical and molecular formulas of compounds from experimental data is discussed in Chapter 4.

THE COMPOSITION OF THE EARTH'S CRUST

The preceding discussion of compounds and their formulas now provides us with a basis for more specific information about the composition of the material at the surface of the earth. The atmosphere has been described as consisting mostly of nitrogen and oxygen. Both gases occur as diatomic molecules (two atoms per molecule): N_2 and O_2. Other molecules found in the atmosphere include those of carbon dioxide (CO_2) and water vapor (H_2O).

The individual particles of a gas are called molecules even when they are single atoms. This is the case for neon and argon in the atmosphere; therefore, they are represented as simply Ne and Ar. These molecules are **monatomic** molecules, in contrast to the **diatomic** N_2 and O_2 and the **triatomic** CO_2 and H_2O. Nonmolecular compounds occur only in the solid state, so they are not present in the atmosphere, except as dust or smoke.

Ocean water, containing about 3.3 per cent dissolved salts, makes up most of the hydrosphere. Among its numerous salts are sodium chloride (NaCl) and magnesium sulfate ($MgSO_4$).

The lithosphere consists largely of **silicates,** compounds of silicon, oxygen, and different metals which vary widely in composition. Hundreds of formulas would be required to indicate all the mineral silicates that occur in the earth's crust. Most of these formulas, however, can be thought of as some combination of metal oxide, a combination of a metal with oxygen, and silicon dioxide (SiO_2). For example, a silicate of iron has the formula $FeSiO_3$($FeO + SiO_2$), and a silicate of calcium the formula $CaSiO_3$ ($CaO + SiO_2$). Most rocks are mixtures of much more complex silicates. Plain sand, silicon dioxide (SiO_2), is often called silica. Clay consists largely of aluminum silicates. Silicates compose most of the mineral matter used for construction purposes, including gravel, portland cement, concrete, porcelain, glass, and bricks. Other materials of construction use calcium carbonate ($CaCO_3$) from the earth's minerals either directly, as marble, or as a source of lime, plaster, and similar products.

In general, silicates are poor commercial sources of the metals they contain. Although the concentration of metals may be high, the silica binds them so tightly that releasing them through chemical processes can be difficult, expensive, and impractical. Fortunately a major part of the small nonsilicate portion of the lithosphere is composed of other metal compounds, some of which are ready sources of the pure metal. For example, iron ore contains large concentrations of compounds of oxygen and iron in varying proportions (e.g., Fe_2O_3 and Fe_3O_4). Aluminum ore contains Al_2O_3, or $AlO(OH)$, and tin ore contains SnO_2.

In addition to carbonates, silicates, and oxides, the earth's crust also contains sulfates, sulfides, and phosphates, particularly calcium phosphate, $Ca_3(PO_4)_2$. Most of the chemical elements in the crust exist combined with other elements. One exception is sulfur, which occurs in large underground deposits in a remarkably pure state.

Despite the fact that inorganic compounds comprise most of the mass of the earth's crust, ten times as many kinds of organic compounds are known to occur, in molecules ranging from small to very large. Often a very large organic molecule is made up of either one kind or several kinds of small molecules joined together in large numbers. The small molecules are called **monomers.** Combining many of these into a very large molecule, or **polymer,** is called **polymerization.**

Among the important polymeric substances are **cellulose** and **starches.** Their empirical formulas approximate CH_2O and give rise to the name **carbohydrate;** the hydrogen and oxygen are not attached to the carbon in the form of water, however. Many synthetic polymers are known. They include all the familiar materials we call "plastics," and man-made fibers as well. Proteins are polymers of smaller molecules called **amino acids.** They are found in plants and in the hide, claws, hoofs, muscles, and other parts of animals. Leaves and other parts of plants contain starches as well as cellulose, and cellulose is a major constituent of wood, cotton fibers, and plant stalks.

More details of organic chemistry will be discussed in Chapter 34. Note the chemical formulas of some of the more familiar molecular organic compounds. The substance commonly called sugar has the chemical name sucrose $(C_{12}H_{22}O_{11})$, as earlier mentioned. In fact, it is only one of many compounds called sugars. Among the alcohols the most familiar is ethyl alcohol (C_2H_5OH), which is present in liquor. Acetic acid, which gives the sharp taste to vinegar, where its concentration is about three per cent, is CH_3COOH. This formula gives more information than the simpler empirical formula, $C_2H_4O_2$. Chloroform, which knocks out insect specimens and unwary collectors alike, is $CHCl_3$. Acetone (CH_3COCH_3) is a very effective solvent for many organic compounds, dissolving fingernail lacquer and fine wood finishes equally well. An ingredient of gasoline is hexane (C_6H_{14}). These are just a few examples of the more than two million organic compounds which have already been identified.

Test Your Memory

1. What does a *chemical symbol* represent? What does a *chemical formula* represent?
2. How does an *empirical formula* differ from a molecular formula?
3. What is a chemical *radical?*
4. Write formulas for the following radicals: sulfate, ammonium, nitrate, carbonate, phosphate, hydroxyl. Name each of the following radicals: HCO_3^-, NO_2^-, HSO_4^-, $SO_3^=$, CH_3.
5. Define a *molecule.*
6. What is a nonmolecular compound?
7. What are the formulas for sand, water, and carbon dioxide?
8. What is a *silicate?*
9. What is a *metal oxide?*
10. How are the terms *monomer* and *polymer* related?
11. What is the formula for sucrose?
12. What atoms compose one molecule of ethyl alcohol?

Test Your Understanding

1. What is the empirical formula of a compound containing a 2:1 atomic ratio of oxygen to lead?

2. Write the empirical formula of a compound containing one-and-one-half oxygen atoms for every aluminum atom.

3. Write the empirical formula of a compound containing three boron atoms, three nitrogen atoms, and six hydrogen atoms in every molecule.

4. Write the empirical formula of a compound containing two sodium atoms and ten water molecules for every sulfate radical.

5. Write the empirical formula for a compound containing three-and-one-half oxygen atoms for every chlorine atom.

6. How many sulfur atoms are there per formula in the compound $Cr_2(SO_4)_3$?

7. What are the empirical formulas corresponding to the following molecular formulas: C_4H_{10}, H_2O_2, N_2H_4, $Co_2(CO)_3$, $C_{12}H_{22}O_{11}$?

8. How many hydrogen atoms per cobalt atom are indicated in the formula $Co(NH_3)_6Cl_3$?

9. Name the following compounds: $MgSO_4$, $MnSO_4$, Na_2CO_3, $Al(NO_3)_3$, $Cd_3(PO_4)_2$.

4

CHEMICAL FORMULAS AND CALCULATIONS

Two important facts about atoms are the following:

All atoms of the same element are very similar but not necessarily identical to one another and significantly different from the atoms of all other elements;

All atoms are so small that any visible sample of matter must contain an enormously large number of atoms.

Atoms of the same element may differ from others in mass, but usually only slightly. In natural sources of an element, however, the distribution of atoms of different mass is very uniform. All samples of the element that are large enough to see and experiment with have the same *average* mass per atom. A detailed consideration of the structure of an atom is included in Chapters 6 and 7.

Atoms of the same element that differ in mass are called **isotopes.** Most of the elements occur in nature as mixtures of isotopes, the relative abundance of which is usually exactly the same no matter what the source of the element. Therefore, the average mass is nearly always a constant value.

Atoms are so tiny that the average mass of one atom in conventional units would be practically meaningless. However, it is very desirable to be able to compare the different elements in terms of the relative masses of their atoms. The most commonly used relative scale is based on a particular isotope of carbon to which is assigned the relative mass 12.000. On this scale hydrogen, the lightest of all atoms, has an average relative mass of 1.008. Thus, an average hydrogen atom has about one-twelfth the mass of the standard carbon atom. The average relative mass of an oxygen atom on the same scale is 15.999, or about one-third greater than that of a carbon atom and sixteen times as great as that of a hydrogen atom.

Although the property of mass is commonly determined by weighing, weight and mass are not exactly the same in meaning. **Mass** is that quality of matter which causes **inertia,** the tendency to resist change in motion. **Weight** is a measure of mass based on the gravitational forces of attraction between the matter under consideration and a standard mass, usually the earth. Stationary mass does not change, whereas weight changes as the distance between the masses varies the gravitational forces between them. Therefore, strictly speaking we should refer only to relative atomic mass, not atomic weight. However, more than a century-and-a-half of tradition has resulted in the common practice of calling relative atomic masses **atomic weights.** The units are then called **atomic weight units,** abbreviated **awu,** or **atomic mass units (amu).** We must recognize that atomic weights are expressed in atomic mass units, and that the two terms are used interchangeably by most chemists.

Atomic weights are most often used in determining the combining weights of different elements in the formation of compounds, in calculating empirical formulas from analytical data, and in making calculations from masses which have been experimentally determined by weighing. Generally, to determine the mass of anything, we *weigh* it. Since for most purposes *weight* is an accurate measure of mass, in this book we shall follow the practice of speaking of atomic weights rather than masses, and of the weights of chemical substances instead of their masses.

Beginning with an arbitrarily assigned atomic weight of one or two elements forming a compound, we can determine the relative atomic weight of the other element by studying the composition of the compound. For example, if we know that carbon dioxide contains two atoms of oxygen for each atom of carbon, measuring the weight gain of carbon when it burns in oxygen reveals the relative weight of an oxygen atom. Burning 12 g of carbon forms 44 g of carbon dioxide; therefore, $44 - 12$ or 32 g must be the total atomic weight of oxygen. If this is the contribution of two oxygen atoms, each must have the atomic weight of $32/2$ or 16. Since most elements form compounds with oxygen, it has been possible to calculate the atomic weight of an element by determining first the weight of that element which combines with a given weight of oxygen. Thus the atomic weights of all the chemical elements (listed in Table 4.1) have been determined.

Table 4.1.   Atomic Weights and Numbers of the Chemical Elements

Atomic Number	Symbol	Name	Atomic Weight
1	H	hydrogen	1.01
2	He	helium	4.00
3	Li	lithium	6.94
4	Be	beryllium	9.01

Table 4.1.   Atomic Weights and Numbers of the Chemical Elements

Atomic Number	Symbol	Name	Atomic Weight
5	B	boron	10.81
6	C	carbon	12.01
7	N	nitrogen	14.01
8	O	oxygen	16.00
9	F	fluorine	19.00
10	Ne	neon	20.18
11	Na	sodium	22.99
12	Mg	magnesium	24.31
13	Al	aluminum	26.98
14	Si	silicon	28.09
15	P	phosphorus	30.97
16	S	sulfur	32.06
17	Cl	chlorine	35.45
18	Ar	argon	39.95
19	K	potassium	39.10
20	Ca	calcium	40.08
21	Sc	scandium	44.96
22	Ti	titanium	47.90
23	V	vanadium	50.94
24	Cr	chromium	52.00
25	Mn	manganese	54.94
26	Fe	iron	55.85
27	Co	cobalt	58.93
28	Ni	nickel	58.71
29	Cu	copper	63.54
30	Zn	zinc	65.37
31	Ga	gallium	69.72
32	Ge	germanium	72.59
33	As	arsenic	74.92
34	Se	selenium	78.96
35	Br	bromine	79.91
36	Kr	krypton	83.80
37	Rb	rubidium	85.47
38	Sr	strontium	87.62
39	Y	yttrium	88.91
40	Zr	zirconium	91.22
41	Nb	niobium	92.91
42	Mo	molybdenum	95.94
43	Tc	technetium	99
44	Ru	ruthenium	101.07
45	Rh	rhodium	102.91
46	Pd	palladium	106.4

Table 4.1. Atomic Weights and Numbers of the Chemical Elements

Atomic Number	Symbol	Name	Atomic Weight
47	Ag	silver	107.87
48	Cd	cadmium	112.40
49	In	indium	114.82
50	Sn	tin	118.69
51	Sb	antimony	121.75
52	Te	tellurium	127.60
53	I	iodine	126.90
54	Xe	xenon	131.30
55	Cs	cesium	132.91
56	Ba	barium	137.34
57	La	lanthanum	138.91
58	Ce	cerium	140.12
59	Pr	praseodymium	140.91
60	Nd	neodymium	144.24
61	Pm	promethium	147
62	Sm	samarium	150.35
63	Eu	europium	151.96
64	Gd	gadolinium	157.25
65	Tb	terbium	158.92
66	Dy	dysprosium	162.50
67	Ho	holmium	164.93
68	Er	erbium	167.26
69	Tm	thulium	168.93
70	Yb	ytterbium	173.04
71	Lu	lutetium	174.97
72	Hf	hafnium	178.49
73	Ta	tantalum	180.95
74	W	tungsten	183.85
75	Re	rhenium	186.2
76	Os	osmium	190.2
77	Ir	iridium	192.2
78	Pt	platinum	195.09
79	Au	gold	196.97
80	Hg	mercury	200.59
81	Tl	thallium	204.37
82	Pb	lead	207.19
83	Bi	bismuth	208.98
84	Po	polonium	210
85	At	astatine	210
86	Rn	radon	222
87	Fr	francium	223
88	Ra	radium	226
89	Ac	actinium	227

Table 4.1. Atomic Weights and Numbers of the Chemical Elements

Atomic Number	Symbol	Name	Atomic Weight
90	Th	thorium	232.04
91	Pa	protactinium	231
92	U	uranium	238.03
93	Np	neptunium	237
94	Pu	plutonium	242
95	Am	americium	243
96	Cm	curium	247
97	Bk	berkelium	247
98	Cf	californium	251
99	Es	einsteinium	254
100	Fm	fermium	253
101	Md	mendelevium	256
102	No	nobelium	254
103	Lw	lawrencium	254

FORMULA AND MOLECULAR WEIGHTS

The formula weight of a compound is the sum of the atomic weights of all the atoms in the empirical formula. The molecular weight is the sum of the atomic weights of all the atoms in the molecular formula. Formula weights and molecular weights are extremely useful in practical chemistry. Consider a few simple examples of how to determine formula or molecular weights from formulas and atomic weights.

Example 4.1. *What is the molecular weight of water?*

The molecular formula of water is the same as its empirical formula: H_2O. Therefore:

$$\text{atomic weight of H} = 1.008 \times 2 = 2.016 \text{ (contribution by H)}$$
$$\text{atomic weight of O} = 15.999 \times 1 = 15.999 \text{ (contribution by O)}$$
$$\text{Total} = \overline{18.015} \text{ (molecular weight of } H_2O)$$

Example 4.2. *What is the formula weight of copper sulfate pentahydrate* $(CuSO_4 \cdot 5H_2O)$?

The empirical formula can be written $CuSO_9H_{10}$. The formula weight is the sum of these atomic weights:

$$\text{atomic weight of Cu} = 63.54 \times 1 = 63.54 \text{ (contribution by Cu)}$$
$$\text{atomic weight of S} = 32.064 \times 1 = 32.06 \text{ (contribution by S)}$$
$$\text{atomic weight of O} = 15.999 \times 9 = 143.99 \text{ (contribution by O)}$$
$$\text{atomic weight of H} = 1.008 \times 10 = 10.08 \text{ (contribution by H)}$$
$$\text{Total} = \overline{249.67} \text{ (formula weight)}$$

Example 4.3. *What is the formula weight of calcium phosphate,* $Ca_3(PO_4)_2$?

By multiplying each subscript within the parentheses by the subscript 2 outside the parentheses, the empirical formula $Ca_3P_2O_8$ is obtained. Then:

$$\text{atomic weight of Ca} = 40.08 \times 3 = 120.24 \text{ (contribution by Ca)}$$

$$\text{atomic weight of P} = 30.974 \times 2 = 61.95 \text{ (contribution by P)}$$

$$\text{atomic weight of O} = 15.999 \times 8 = \underline{127.99} \text{ (contribution by O)}$$

$$\text{Total} = 310.18 \text{ (formula weight)}$$

WEIGHT-PERCENTAGE COMPOSITION

When the total weight of something and the contribution made by one or more of its components are known, the percentage by weight of these components can be calculated. It is the weight contribution of the component divided by the total weight and multiplied by 100. For example, if a three-pound cake contains one-half pound of sugar, the weight percentage of sugar is 0.5/3 or 0.167, times 100 = 16.7 per cent.

Exactly the same kind of calculation applies to problems of chemical composition. The mathematics is the same for atoms and molecules as for cake and sugar and should be very well known to you. A few examples may be helpful.

Example 4.4. *What is the weight percentage of hydrogen in water?*

In Example 4.1 above, we found that hydrogen contributes 2.016 units to the total molecular weight of water of 18.015. In other words, a sample of water weighing 18.015 units contains 2.016 units of hydrogen. Therefore:

$$\text{weight percentage of H} = \frac{2.016 \times 100}{18.015} = 11.2\%$$

For most purposes, atomic weights accurate to one or two decimal places are satisfactory. Table values given to greater accuracy can be rounded off to make calculations simpler. In working with experimental quantities, however, you must be concerned with the question of **significant figures.** This concept and its application are explained elsewhere. Briefly, the principle is that calculations cannot produce values for physical quantities more precise than the experimental numbers used to make the computations.

Example 4.5. *What is the weight percentage of oxygen in water?*

We can calculate the weight percentage of oxygen in water by observing that oxygen contributes 16.0 amu to a water molecule of 18.0 amu. Therefore:

$$\text{weight percentage of O} = \frac{16.0 \times 100}{18.0} = 88.8\%$$

In this case, however, since the weight percentage of hydrogen in water is already known to be 11.2 per cent, and since the only other component of water is oxygen, then the weight percentage of oxygen must be $100.0 - 11.2$ or 88.8 per cent.

In chemistry, too, the whole is equal to the sum of its parts. Therefore, if we know the percentages of all but one component of a substance, the percentage of that component is easily determined by subtracting the known percentages from 100. This is very useful in determining the percentages of components like oxygen which are hard to measure experimentally.

Example 4.6. *What is the weight-percentage composition of calcium phosphate,* $Ca_3(PO_4)_2$*?*

From Example 4.3, we know that the total formula weight of calcium phosphate is 310.2. Calcium contributes 120.2, phosphorus contributes 62.0, and oxygen contributes 128.0 amu.

$$\text{weight percentage of Ca} = \frac{120.2 \times 100}{310.2} = 38.8\%$$

$$\text{weight percentage of P} = \frac{62.0 \times 100}{310.2} = 20.0\%$$

$$\text{weight percentage of O} = \frac{128.0 \times 100}{310.2} = 41.2\%$$

$$\text{Total} = 100.0\%$$

Such calculations can always be checked by adding the calculated weight percentages together. If they do not add up to 100 per cent, an error has been made.

In summary, the weight-percentage composition of any compound can be determined as follows:

1. Look up the formula of the compound.
2. Look up the atomic weight of each element in the formula.
3. Multiply each atomic weight by the number of atoms of that element in the formula.
4. Add up the total atomic weights for all the atoms in the formula, to find the formula weight.
5. Divide the total weight contribution of each element by the formula weight of the compound, and multiply by 100 to give the weight percentage of that element in the compound.

6. Add up the weight percentages of all the elements in the compound to make sure they total 100 per cent.

WEIGHT RELATIONSHIPS IN A FORMULA

A chemical formula indicates more than the elements present in the compound and the relative number of atoms for each element. If we know the atomic weight for each of the elements present, the formula reveals the relative quantities of these individual elements. Therefore, if the actual weight of a sample of a compound and the formula of the compound are known, the weight of each element in that sample can be calculated. Furthermore, if the weight of only one element in the sample and the formula of the compound are known, the weight of the sample and the amount of each of the other elements present can still be calculated.

Example 4.7. *How much sulfur is needed to produce* 50,000 *tons of sulfuric acid?*

One of the most important of all industrial chemicals is sulfuric acid (H_2SO_4), which is made from elemental sulfur. Manufacturers of sulfuric acid need to know how much sulfur is required to make a certain amount of acid. First, the basic relationships are needed:

$$\text{atomic weight of S} = 32.1 \times 1 = 32.1 \text{ (contribution by S)}$$

$$\text{atomic weight of H} = 1.0 \times 2 = 2.0 \text{ (contribution by H)}$$

$$\text{atomic weight of O} = 16.0 \times 4 = 64.0 \text{ (contribution by O)}$$

$$\text{Total} = 98.1 = \text{formula weight}$$

From this information, the manufacturer can calculate the weight-percentage composition of sulfur, or at least its weight percentage.

$$\text{weight percentage of S} = \frac{32.1 \times 100}{98.1} = 32.7\%$$

Weight percentage means the number of weight units of sulfur in 100 weight units of sulfuric acid. Weight units can be any convenient size. The percentage of sulfur can be represented as a factor, 0.327. This factor, called a **gravimetric factor,** when multiplied by any weight of sulfuric acid, will give the corresponding weight of sulfur needed to make it. Gravimetric means simply *weight measuring*. The corresponding gravimetric factor for converting any quantity of sulfur into sulfuric acid is 1/0.327 or 3.06. Thus, to produce 50,000 tons of sulfuric acid, 0.327 × 50,000 tons, or 16,350 tons of sulfur is needed. From 50,000 tons of sulfur, 50,000 × 3.06 or 151,800 tons of sulfuric acid can be produced. These calculations assume, of course, that the chemical process is able to convert the sulfur quantitatively to sulfuric acid, with no loss along the way.

Example 4.8.   *An iron ore contains 65.40 per cent Fe_2O_3. If it were possible to liberate all the iron by using enough carbon to combine one atom of carbon per atom of oxygen in the iron oxide, how much carbon would be needed to liberate all the iron from a ton of the ore?*

The first problem is to determine how much Fe_2O_3 is in the tone of ore:

$$65.40\% = 0.6540 \text{ (gravimetric factor)}$$
$$0.6540 \times 2000 = 1,308 \text{ lbs of } Fe_2O_3$$

To determine the weight percentage of iron in Fe_2O_3, we must first determine its formula weight:

atomic weight of Fe = $55.85 \times 2 = 111.7$ (contribution by Fe)
atomic weight of O = $16.0 \ \times 3 = \underline{\ 48.0}$ (contribution by O)
$ 159.7$ = formula weight

Then:

$$\text{weight percentage of Fe} = \frac{111.7 \times 100}{159.7} = 70.0\%$$

The weight of iron in the ton of ore is then $0.700 \times 1,308$ lbs or 916 lbs.

If one carbon atom removes one oxygen atom from Fe_2O_3, three carbon atoms will remove the three oxygen atoms, leaving two atoms of iron. To convert this atomic ratio (3 C to 2 Fe) to a weight ratio, it must be multiplied by the ratio of atomic weights:

$$\frac{3}{2} \times \frac{12.01 \text{ (atomic wt. of C)}}{55.85 \text{ (atomic wt. of Fe)}} = \frac{36.03}{111.7}$$

To determine the amount of carbon needed per ton of ore, this weight ratio must be multiplied by the weight of iron per ton of ore:

$$\frac{36.03}{111.7} \times 916 \text{ lbs Fe} = 296 \text{ lbs C}$$

Working with quantitative weight relationships in chemistry is of great practical importance. Therefore, thorough familiarity with such calculations is essential. This familiarity cannot be acquired merely by studying worked-out problems. You must practice performing calculations yourself by solving problems such as those at the end of this chapter. Chemical arithmetic is not difficult, but you must practice to learn which calculations will lead to the desired solution.

SCIENTIFIC WEIGHTS AND MEASURES

Common units of weights and measures are notoriously inconsistent throughout the world. Fortunately, scientists long ago recognized the need for consistent units to communicate with each other about quantitative phenomena. In a scientific supermarket you would never buy eggs by the dozen, butter by the pound, pineapple by the number two can, ribbon by the yard, milk by the quart, carrots by the bunch, or potatoes by the peck. The systems they chose were based on the metric system and were called the **centimeter-gram-second (CGS)** system and the **meter-kilogram-second (MKS)** system.

Length

The standard meter is the distance between lines on a standard bar of corrosion-resistant metal alloy—platinum iridium—in Sevres, France. The **meter (m)** is the standard unit of length in the MKS system. It is exactly 1,650,763.73 times the wavelength of the orange-red light emitted by krypton atoms of atomic mass 86 after they have been excited by the absorption of energy. This wavelength is a value that can be accurately measured and, presumably, can never change.

One hundredth of a meter is called a **centimeter (cm)**, and one tenth of a centimeter, or one thousandth of a meter, is called a **millimeter (mm)**. In English units, a meter is approximately 39.37 inches, and one inch is about 2.54 cm.

How many millimeters are there in one foot? How tall are you in meters?

The diameter of an atom and the distance between the centers of two atoms in a compound are only a few ten-millionths of a millimeter. Therefore, atomic and molecular dimensions are usually given in **angstroms (Å)**, defined as 10^{-8} cm or 10^{-10} m. Intermediate distances are sometimes given in **microns (μ)**, which are 10^{-6} m or 10^4 Å. A **millimicron (mμ)** is 10^{-3} μ or 10Å.

How many millimicrons are there in an angstrom?

Volume

The unit of volume or capacity in the MKS system is the **liter (l).** This is the volume of one thousand cubic centimeters, which could be represented by a cube 10 cm on an edge. One cubic centimeter **(cc)** is, therefore, equal to one thousandth of a liter, or one **milliliter (ml).** One liter is about 1.057 quarts. One teaspoonful is about 5 ml, and 20 drops of water equal approximately one milliliter.

38 Chemical Formulas and Calculations

How many ml are there in one quart? If the kitchen faucet leaks one drop per second, how many gallons of water escape during a 24-hour day?

Mass

The MKS unit of mass is the **kilogram (kg),** which equals one thousand grams. One **gram (g)** is approximately the weight of one ml of water at 4°C. Common laboratory balances can weigh an object to the nearest ten-thousandth of a gram, or tenth of a **milligram (mg).** A milligram is 10^{-3} g. One kilogram equals 2.2046 lbs; the weight of 453.6 g equals about one pound.

What is your weight in kilograms and in grams?

Temperature

In most scientific work, temperatures are measured in degrees **Celsius (C).** This scale was originally called the **centigrade** scale, and although the term Celsius has been recommended by international committee, common usage of *centigrade* continues. Both names refer to the same scale, and are denoted by the common abbreviation C.

On this scale the temperature of boiling water at sea level is taken as 100°C and the melting point of ice as 0°C. The intervening temperature span is divided into one hundred equal units called degrees. One degree Celsius is therefore one hundredth of the temperature difference between melting ice and boiling water.

In everyday American life the **Fahrenheit (F)** scale is commonly used. On this scale the freezing point of water is 32°F and the boiling point is 212°F—there being 180° between freezing and boiling. Thus, one °C is equal to 1.8 or 9/5 °F. One °F is, therefore, 5/9 as large as one °C. It is easy to convert from one scale to the other using the common point −40, at which the two scales intersect. That is, −40°F and −40°C happen to be exactly the same temperature. To convert from one scale to the other, proceed as follows:

1. Add 40°.
2. Multiply by 9/5 if going from °C to °F or by 5/9 if going from °F to °C.
3. Subtract 40°.

Example 4.9.

Convert 25°C to °F.

1. Add 40: 25 + 40 = 65.
2. Multiply by 9/5: 65 × 9/5 = 13 × 9 = 117.
3. Subtract 40: 117 − 40 = 77°F.

Convert 112°F *to* °C.

1. Add 40: 112 + 40 = 152.
2. Multiply by 5/9: 152 × 5/9 = 760/9 = 84.4.
3. Subtract 40: 84.4 − 40 = 44.4°C.

Convert −196°C *to* °F.

1. Add 40: −196 + 40 = −156.
2. Multiply by 9/5: −156 × 9/5 = −280.8.
3. Subtract 40: −280.8 − 40 = −320.8°F.

An alternate method employs the following formulas for conversion from one scale to the other:

$$°F = \frac{9}{5} °C + 32$$

$$°C = \frac{5}{9} (°F - 32)$$

Example 4.10.

Convert 25°C *to* °F.

$$°F = \frac{9}{5} °C + 32$$

$$°F = \frac{9}{5} (25) + 32$$

$$°F = 45 + 32 = 77°$$

Convert 112°F *to* °C.

$$°C = \frac{5}{9} (°F - 32)$$

$$°C = \frac{5}{9} (112 - 32)$$

$$°C = \frac{5}{9} (80) = 400/9 = 44.4°C$$

Convert −196.0°C *to* °F.

$$°F = \frac{9}{5} °C + 32$$

$$°F = \frac{9}{5} (-196.0) + 32$$

$$°F = -1764/5 + 32 = -352.8 + 32 = -320.8$$

If you keep your home at 68°F but it is 100° outside, what are the following temperatures in Celsius: 68°F; 100°F?

Scientific publications throughout the world express quantities in the MKS or CGS system. This standardization of units of measure is very beneficial to science because scientists anywhere in the world are familiar with the units used by any author.

MOLES

Atomic, molecular, and formula weights all are expressed in atomic mass units. Chemists have devised an extremely useful unit of weight by converting these units to grams. This unit is called the **mole.** A mole is simply that quantity for which the number of grams equals the number of atomic mass units. In earlier terminology, the atomic weight of an element in grams was called the **gram-atomic weight,** the molecular weight of a compound in grams the **gram-molecular weight,** and the formula weight of a compound in grams the **gram-formula weight.** Each of these weights is now called a mole. Although it is usually clear whether a mole of atoms, a mole of molecules, or a mole of a nonmolecular solid is meant, it should be specified which is intended, to avoid any possible ambiguity.

For example, one mole of NaCl, formula weight 58.5, is 58.5 g. In this case there is no ambiguity. However, oxygen exists in the free state as a diatomic molecule, O_2. A mole of oxygen may refer to a mole of oxygen gas (O_2 molecules) or a mole of oxygen atoms. It must be specified whether a mole of O_2 molecules, 32 g, or a mole of oxygen atoms, 16 g, is intended.

How many moles of sulfur are there in 100 g?

The importance of a mole is that this weight of any substance contains a specific number of basic units. That number is a fixed constant called **Avogadro's number** after the Italian chemist Amadeo Avogadro (1776–1856). A variety of different experimental procedures have all yielded the same value for this constant, approximately 6.02×10^{23}. Although this constant is a huge number which is difficult to envision, it is a very significant number in chemistry; it is the number of basic units in a mole of anything.

How would the weight of one mole of people (averaging 135 lbs each) compare with the weight of the earth (6.6×10^{21} tons)?

The atomic weight of oxygen is about 16; the molecular weight of oxygen gas, O_2, is about 32. By definition, one mole of oxygen gas is 32 g, the weight of 6.02×10^{23} oxygen molecules. The atomic weight of hydrogen is about 1.

Since hydrogen gas consists of diatomic molecules, H_2, the molecular weight of hydrogen is about 2. One mole, or 6.02×10^{23} molecules of hydrogen, would weigh about two grams. The molecular weight of water, H_2O, is 18. One mole of water molecules, therefore, weighs 18 g.

In chemical reactions, whole numbers of atoms and molecules react, usually in definite proportions. Expressing amounts of chemicals in moles is a very convenient way of describing reacting quantities by weight. A few examples will illustrate the application of this useful concept to chemical problems.

Many such problems become easier to solve if the quantities are first converted to moles. To do this, two simple relationships must be understood:

1. Number of moles = (weight in grams)/(weight of one mole)
2. Weight in grams = (number of moles) × (weight of one mole)

Example 4.11. *What is the weight of 650 moles of sulfuric acid* (H_2SO_4)?

The molecular weight of sulfuric acid is about 98.1. Therefore one mole of sulfuric acid weighs about 98.1 g, and 6.50 moles would weigh 6.50×98.1 or 638 g.

Example 4.12. *What is the weight of 4.300 moles of alum,* $Al_2(SO_4)_3 \cdot 12H_2O$?

First the formula weight must be determined:

$$
\begin{array}{llll}
\text{weight contribution of Al} = 27.0 & \times & 2 = & 54.0 \\
\text{weight contribution of S} = 32.0 & \times & 3 = & 96.0 \\
\text{weight contribution of O} = 16.00 & \times & 24 = & 384.0 \\
\text{weight contribution of H} = 1.01 & \times & 24 = & 24.1 \\
\end{array}
$$

$$\text{Total} = 558.1 = \text{formula weight}$$

Therefore, one mole of alum weighs 558.1 g, and 4.200 moles weigh 4.200×588.1 or 2344 g.

Note that this calculation could have been simplified by recognizing that the molecular weight of H_2O is 18.0 and that of the sulfate radical (SO_4) is 96.0. 54 g Al + (3×96.0 or 288 g SO_4) + (12×18 or 216 g H_2O) = 558 g per mole.

Example 4.13. *How many moles are there in 1000 g of* NaCl?

One mole of NaCl weighs about 58.5 g. Therefore the number of moles in 1000 g is found by dividing 1000 by 58.5:

$$1000/58.5 = 17.1 \text{ moles.}$$

Example 4.14. *One mole of zinc* (Zn) *reacts with one mole of chlorine gas* (Cl_2) *to form the white salt, zinc chloride* $(ZnCl_2)$. *If 100 g Zn is allowed to react completely with 100 g* Cl_2, *then* (a) *which element if any is left over and how much is left?* (b) *What weight of* $ZnCl_2$ *is formed?*

The 100 g Zn is converted to moles as is the 100 g Cl_2. We can assume that they react mole for mole. One mole of Zn equals its atomic weight in grams, or 65.4 g. 100 g Zn is therefore 100/65.4 or 1.53 moles. The molecular weight of Cl_2 is twice its atomic weight, or 70.9. One mole of Cl_2 is therefore 70.9 g, and 100 g is 100/70.9 or 1.41 moles.

Therefore, when all the Cl_2 has reacted, 1.41 moles of $ZnCl_2$ will have been formed and 1.53 − 1.41 or 0.12 moles of Zn will remain. The answer to (a) is 0.12 moles × 65.4 g per mole or 7.8 g Zn. The answer to (b) is that 1.41 moles of $ZnCl_2$ times the weight of one mole (65.4 + 70.9 or 136.3 g) = 193 g $ZnCl_2$.

To determine the number of moles of one substance needed to make a given number of moles of another substance, the formulas of the two substances are compared. For example, how many moles of phosphorus are needed to make five moles of magnesium pyrophosphate ($Mg_2P_2O_7$)? Since the formula shows two phosphorus atoms, five moles of the pyrophosphate would contain ten moles of phosphorus. Observe that knowledge of the formula weight of neither substance is required. Often inspection of formulas gives all the information needed for solving a problem.

> How many moles of nitrogen (N_2) would be needed to make 600 moles of ammonia (NH_3)?

DETERMINATION OF EMPIRICAL FORMULAS

We have been using chemical formulas as if they expressed the actual composition of the substances they represent. We can do this with confidence because the formulas have been determined with precision by the methods of **analytical chemistry.**

Once a thorough study of a given sample of matter establishes that it is a pure substance rather than a mixture, its identity must still be determined. Once this identity is known, the substance can be recognized by its physical properties, but the first time a compound is made or encountered these physical properties are unknown. Therefore, to establish its identity we must find out what elements are in it and in what proportions. This requires a chemical investigation called **analysis.** A chemist causes the compound to change quantitatively, in such a way that the results indicate its composition before its change.

Qualitative Analysis

The purpose of **qualitative analysis** is to discover what elements or groups of elements are present in a compound. Usually it is easier to find a chemical **reagent,** or reacting substance, that will disclose *what* elements are present than it is to find out *how much* of each. A qualitative analysis consists of a series of chemical experiments aimed at detecting each element in a compound by some unique property that no other element could exhibit under the same circumstances.

For example, a particular color appearing as the result of a certain chemical treatment might be an adequate indication; formation of an insoluble substance from solutions mixed together might also suggest the identity of a certain element. The details of qualitative analysis will be studied in Chapter 31 when our background of chemical information is more adequate.

Quantitative Analysis

Once a succession of chemical experiments has established the identity of the elements in a compound through a qualitative analysis, we know what *symbols* to include in its formula but we do not know the correct *subscripts*. To determine these we need a **quantitative analysis.**

In performing a quantitative analysis, a chemist treats an accurately weighed quantity of the compound with exactly measured quantities of reagents and he determines exactly how much of what products is formed. From such procedures, he can calculate exactly *how much* of each component element is present in the sample of compound. In other words, a quantitative analysis is a series of one or more chemical reactions from which the weight-percentage composition of a compound (or mixture) can be calculated.

Empirical Formulas by Synthesis

If the identity and quantity of elements which have reacted to form a compound are known, analysis is unnecessary for determining the empirical formula. For example, a weighed amount of hydrogen might be burned completely in excess oxygen to form water. The formula of the product, the water, could be calculated from a comparison of its weight with that of the hydrogen initially burned. Since the atomic weight of oxygen is 16 and that of hydrogen 1, a 1:1 combination would lead to a ratio of 17 units of water to 1 unit of hydrogen. This would correspond to the empirical formula OH. However, this experiment actually results in a ratio of nine units of oxygen to one unit of hydrogen. In other words, one weight unit of hydrogen joins with eight weight units of oxygen. Consequently, there must be two hydrogen atoms per oxygen atom instead of one. This indicates an empirical formula of H_2O.

The molecular formula *cannot* be determined by controlled synthesis from the constituent elements. Only the empirical formula can be found by this method. If the molecular formula of water were H_4O_2 or H_6O_3 its empirical formula would still be H_2O which would agree with the observations of the experiment. To determine the molecular formula of a compound we must find its molecular weight as well as its empirical formula. We know that the molecular formula of water is the same as the empirical formula—H_2O—because independent experiments have determined that the molecular weight of water is 18. If the molecular formula were H_4O_2 the molecular weight would be 36. The molecular weight of H_6O_3 would be 54.

Empirical Formulas from Weight-Percentage Composition

The empirical formula of a compound can be derived from its percentage composition. For example, an analysis of water shows that it has a weight percentage of hydrogen of 11.2 per cent and a weight percentage of oxygen of 88.8 per cent. The relative numbers of atoms of each element present are determined by dividing the weight percentage of each element by its atomic weight:

$$H = 11.2/1.01 = 11.1$$
$$O = 88.8/16.0 = 5.55$$

What we have determined here is that for every 11.1 atoms of hydrogen in the compound there are 5.55 atoms of oxygen. This is equivalent to determining the number of moles by dividing the total weight by the weight of one mole. To convert these relative numbers of atoms to whole numbers, each relative number is divided by the smallest relative number.

$$H = 11.1/5.55 = 2.00$$
$$O = 5.55/5.55 = 1.00$$

This gives the relative numbers of atoms in whole numbers, the smallest being 1.00. Often some of the relative numbers of other elements are still not in whole numbers, but it is usually easy to determine a small whole number by which all the relative numbers of atoms can be multiplied to change them into whole numbers. Thus are obtained the appropriate subscripts for the formula. In this example, since the relative numbers both come out whole numbers, the job is done. The empirical formula is H_2O.

Example 4.15. *Analysis of a certain mineral compound shows it to contain the following: 38.8 per cent calcium, 20.0 per cent phosphorus, and the rest oxygen. What is its empirical formula?*

First, the weight percentage of oxygen in the compound must be 100.0 − (38.8 + 20.0) or 41.2. The complete composition then is calcium 38.8, phosphorus 20.0, and oxygen, 41.2. To find the relative number of atoms of each element in the compound, we divide through each percentage by the atomic weight:

$$Ca = 38.8/40.1 = 0.968$$
$$P\ \ = 20.0/31.0 = 0.645$$
$$O\ \ = 41.2/16.0 = 2.57$$

We now know that for every 0.968 atom of calcium there is 0.645 atom of phosphorus and 2.57 atoms of oxygen. To convert these to whole numbers we first divide each by the smallest:

$$Ca = 0.968/0.645 = 1.50$$
$$P\ \ = 0.645/0.645 = 1.00$$
$$O\ \ = 2.57/0.645\ \ = 3.96$$

To convert to whole numbers of atoms including calcium it is apparent that each of these relative numbers must be multiplied by 2. Since 7.92 oxygen atoms is close enough to be considered 8.00, this gives $Ca_3P_2O_8$ for the empirical formula. Further investigation of this compound would show that the phosphorus and oxygen atoms occur in the phosphate radical, PO_4. The formula representing calcium phosphate would then be expressed as $Ca_3(PO_4)_2$. However, since the weight-percentage composition alone does not indicate the presence of the phosphate radical, we would normally stop with the empirical formula, $Ca_2P_2O_8$.

Empirical formulas of all known compounds have been determined, most of them in exactly the manner described above.

Test Your Memory

1. Define *atomic weight*.
2. Since all atoms of a given element do not necessarily have the same weight, why are atomic weights still valuable?
3. What is the difference between mass and weight?
4. Define *formula weight*.
5. What is the distinction between formula weight and *molecular weight?*
6. List all the steps to determine weight-percentage composition from formula and atomic weights.
7. How is the weight percentage of one element in a compound related to the amount of compound that might be prepared from a given weight of that element?
8. Give the approximate values for (a) centimeters in an inch, (b) grams in a pound, and (c) milliliters in one quart.
9. What relationship exists between a liter and a kilogram?
10. Which temperature scale, F or C, has larger degrees? What is the ratio of these degrees?
11. At what temperature are °F and °C equal? If you didn't know the answer, how could you determine it?
12. What would be one mole of mosquitoes?

13. What is *Avogadro's number?*
14. What information is needed to calculate the number of moles from the weight of a substance?
15. What information is needed to determine the empirical formula of a chemical compound?
16. What parts of a formula of a compound are determined by (a) qualitative analysis, and (b) quantitative analysis?

Test Your Understanding

1. Determine formula weights for (a) Na_2SO_4, (b) $CaCO_3$, (c) C_6H_6, (d) $Al_2(SO_4)_3 \cdot 12H_2O$, and (e) $BeCl_2 \cdot 4H_2O$.
2. Determine weight-percentage compositions of each of the above compounds.
3. From the weight-percentage compositions calculated in problem 2, calculate empirical formulas of each of these compounds.
4. Assuming 1000 mosquitoes per gram, calculate the weight in tons of one mole of mosquitoes.
5. How many moles are there in 1000 g of (a) O_2, (b) CO_2, (c) $(NH_4)_2SO_4$, (d) $CaCO_3$, and (e) H_2SO_4.
6. During World War II, a research chemist ordered 100 g of a rather expensive compound for use in research on aircraft fuels. The purchasing department thought g stood for gallons (gal) instead of grams (g). By how great a factor did the purchasing department err, if the density of the chemical was 0.8 g per ml?
7. A lady with green eyelids weighing 65 g each is given a diamond ring that contains a two-gram diamond. Diamond is pure carbon. How many carbon atoms does the ring contain?
8. A wealthy king, grateful to a knight for saving his beautiful daughter, offered him his choice of either one pound or two moles of pure gold. The knight chose the latter. Was he smart? Why?
9. In the preparation of sodium metal, NaCl is decomposed to the elements by means of an electric current. From 40 kg of salt how much sodium could be obtained?
10. If 500 g of hexane (C_6H_{14}) were burned completely to form CO_2 and water, what weight of each product would be obtained?
11. A student weighing 65 kg spends 5 hrs and 13 sec in the lab converting 90 per cent of a sample of 50 g of sulfur to calcium sulfate ($CaSO_4$). His source of calcium is limestone ($CaCO_3$). How much limestone does he need if his lab instructor weighs 70 kg?
12. A manufacturer of nitric acid (HNO_3) makes it by converting all the nitrogen in ammonia (NH_3) to HNO_3. What weight of ammonia would be needed for making 10 tons of concentrated HNO_3, a solution containing a weight percentage for HNO_3 of 65 per cent and a weight percentage for water of 35 per cent?
13. A socially prominent gambler is found completely submerged in a steel

drum full of asphalt. A detective discovers some tarry material under a suspect's heel and sends it to the crime lab for analysis. To determine the carbon-to-hydrogen ratio the chemist weighs a sample and burns it, collecting the carbon dioxide and water. He obtains 0.440 g CO_2 and 0.090 g H_2O. (a) What C/H ratio does he report? (b) To what atomic ratio does this correspond? (c) Assuming the material contained only carbon and hydrogen, what was the weight of the sample before burning?

14. A highly reactive liquid compound is analyzed and found to have the following weight composition: 37.8 per cent aluminum, 45.3 per cent boron, and 16.9 per cent hydrogen. (a) What is its empirical formula? (b) Its molecular weight is found to be about 72. What is the molecular formula?

15. A complex salt is found by analysis to have the following weight-percentage composition: 20.0 per cent Cr, 32.2 per cent N, 7.0 per cent H, and the rest Cl. What is its empirical formula?

16. Dry ice (solid CO_2) maintains a temperature of $-78.5°C$ by evaporation. What is this temperature in $°F$?

17. Convert 70° below zero F to $°C$.

5

CHEMICAL EQUATIONS AND ENERGY CHANGES

CHEMICAL REACTIONS

A **chemical equation** is a symbolic representation of a chemical reaction. The substances that react are called **reactants.** The substances formed by the reaction are called **products.** The chemical equation gives the formulas of each of the reactants and each of the products. In addition, it indicates the relative amounts of each substance involved.

For example, hydrogen burns in oxygen to form water. The reactants are H_2 and O_2 and the product is H_2O. We could then begin to write the equation as follows:

$$H_2 + O_2 \rightarrow H_2O$$

The arrow indicates a chemical change and the direction of that change. But by the **Law of Conservation of Matter** *atoms cannot be created or destroyed in a chemical reaction.* Therefore, the number of atoms of each element must be exactly the same on both sides of the equation. To complete the equation the number of molecules of each component must be adjusted to give a material balance. The fact that oxygen gas is bimolecular (O_2) requires that on the right side of the equation there must be at least two water molecules, since only one oxygen atom occurs in each water molecule. If there are two water molecules formed, there must be four hydrogen atoms or two molecules of H_2 in the reactants. The equation is then completed in the form:

$$2\,H_2 + O_2 \rightarrow 2\,H_2O$$

The equation is not complete unless the number of atoms of each element is the same on both sides. The adjustment of coefficients to produce this equality is often called "balancing" the chemical equation, although a more appropriate term is "completing" the equation.

Figure 5.1.   A Chemical Equation.

Hydrogen exists as H_2 molecules:

Nitrogen exists as N_2 molecules:

Ammonia is a compound of hydrogen and nitrogen, each molecule containing three atoms of hydrogen joined to one atom of nitrogen:

Nitrogen + Hydrogen → Ammonia

or, $N_2 + H_2 \rightarrow NH_3$.

But a chemical reaction cannot create or destroy atoms. Therefore the numbers of atoms of each element must be the same in the products as in the reactants.

Since no fewer than two nitrogen atoms can be available as N_2, at least two molecules of NH_3 must be formed to balance the equation. This requires six hydrogen atoms or $3H_2$. The complete equation is:

$$N_2 + 3H_2 \rightarrow 2\,NH_3.$$

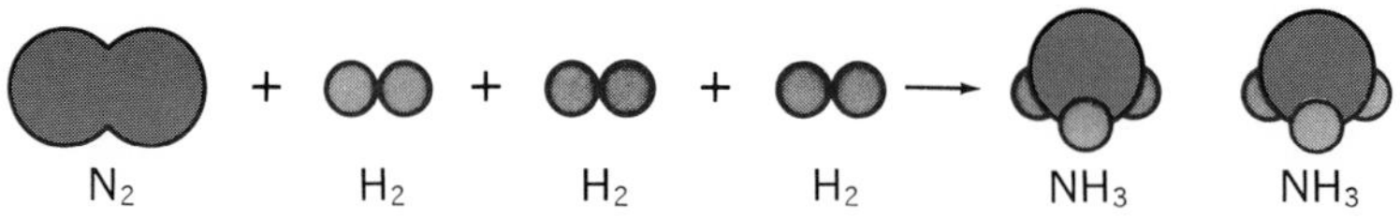

N_2 + H_2 + H_2 + H_2 → NH_3 NH_3

The coefficients of a chemical equation are always reduced to their lowest possible integral values. Although it is not incorrect, there would be no point in writing

$$4\,H_2 + 2\,O_2 \rightarrow 4\,H_2O$$

since it doesn't provide any more information than the simpler form above which results by dividing each coefficient by 2.

Complete this chemical equation: $Al + O_2 \rightarrow Al_2O_3$.

A complete chemical equation tells exactly how many moles of what reactants and what products are involved. Thus, the equation for the burning of hydrogen indicates that two moles of H_2 and one mole of O_2 react to form two moles of H_2O. This is all that the equation tells. It does not reveal anything about the conditions under which the reaction will occur, or even if it will at all. A chemical change is not necessarily possible just because a proper equation can be written to describe it.

A chemical equation tells nothing about the rate or mechanism of a chemical change. It gives only the overall picture of the reaction. As we shall see in Chapter 20, most chemical reactions occur through a series of inter-related steps resulting in intermediate products. The overall chemical equation reveals nothing about these steps, but shows only the initial reactants and final products. There are experimental methods for discovering the steps by which a given reaction probably proceeds. Such information, while available for many reactions, is unknown for most chemical changes.

Types of Reaction

It is not easy to classify all kinds of chemical change, but certain basic types, which include a large number of different individual chemical reactions, can be defined.

Addition reactions include all those in which atoms or molecules simply add to one another to produce larger molecules. In some cases, the addition of atoms or molecules is not quite that simple in that the mechanism may involve initial separation or "dissociation" of atoms before addition. This problem can be disregarded for the present. Examples of addition are:

1. The combination of hydrogen and oxygen to form water:

$$2 H_2 + O_2 \rightarrow 2 H_2O$$

2. The combination of zinc and sulfur to form zinc sulfide:

$$Zn + S \rightarrow ZnS$$

3. The combination of calcium oxide and water to form calcium hydroxide:
$$CaO + H_2O \rightarrow Ca(OH)_2$$

Decomposition is the opposite of addition. Examples are:

1. Calcium carbonate decomposing to calcium oxide and carbon dioxide:
$$CaCO_3 \rightarrow CaO + CO_2$$

2. Ammonium chloride decomposing to ammonia and hydrogen chloride:
$$NH_4Cl \rightarrow NH_3 + HCl$$

3. Mercuric oxide decomposing to mercury and oxygen:

$$2 HgO \rightarrow 2 Hg + O_2$$

Displacement reactions involve one element or group of elements replacing another element or group of elements in a molecule. Examples are:

1. Sodium and hydrogen chloride forming hydrogen and sodium chloride:

$$2\,Na + 2\,HCl \rightarrow H_2 + 2\,NaCl$$

2. Calcium carbonate and silicon dioxide forming calcium silicate and carbon dioxide:

$$CaCO_3 + SiO_2 \rightarrow CaSiO_3 + CO_2$$

3. Chlorine and magnesium iodide forming magnesium chloride and iodine:

$$Cl_2 + MgI_2 \rightarrow MgCl_2 + I_2$$

Double displacement or **metathesis** might be termed partner swapping, as will be seen from the following examples:

1. Sodium sulfate and barium chloride form barium sulfate and sodium chloride:

$$Na_2SO_4 + BaCl_2 \rightarrow BaSO_4 + 2\,NaCl$$

2. Calcium sulfide and hydrogen chloride form hydrogen sulfide and calcium chloride:

$$CaS + 2\,HCl \rightarrow H_2S + CaCl_2$$

3. Sodium hydride and water form sodium hydroxide and hydrogen:

$$NaH + H_2O \rightarrow NaOH + H_2$$

Weight Relationships

Chemical equations are quantitative in nature. They tell exactly how many moles of each reactant are needed and how many moles of each product are formed in a given reaction. Since moles refer to a specific weight of a substance, an equation indicates the relative weights of each component involved. No change in total weight can occur in a chemical reaction, because of the Law of the Conservation of Matter stated above. Consequently, if the weight of only one of the reactants or products is known, the weights of all the other reactants and products can be calculated. If any reactant is present in excess, it can be identified, and exactly how much will be left over at the end of the reaction can be calculated.

Example 5.1. *What is the maximum amount of magnesium chloride* ($MgCl_2$) *which could be formed from 50 g of chlorine? How much magnesium would be required?*

$$Mg + Cl_2 \rightarrow MgCl_2$$

One mole of magnesium requires one mole of chlorine to form one mole of $MgCl_2$. Therefore, we need to know how many moles of chlorine are in 50 g. The molecular weight of chlorine is about 71, therefore 50 g is 50/71 or 0.71 mole of chlorine.

One mole of magnesium weighs about 24 g. Therefore, 0.71 mole weighs 17 g. One mole of $MgCl_2$ weighs about 24g + 71g or 95 g. From this, 0.71 mole weighs 67 g. The weight of products (17 g + 50 g or 67 g) thus equals the weight of reactants when expressed to the nearest significant figure.

Example 5.2. *Reaction between sulfur trioxide (SO_3) and aluminum oxide (Al_2O_3) produces aluminum sulfate, $Al_2(SO_4)_3$. Starting with one gram of aluminum, what is the maximum amount of sulfate that could be produced, and how much SO_3 would be needed?*

$$3 SO_3 + Al_2O_3 \rightarrow Al_2(SO_4)_3$$

It is apparent from the formula of aluminum oxide that two moles of aluminum are required to produce one mole of the compound. Since one mole of aluminum weighs about 27 g, one gram equals 1/27 or 0.037 mole. The number of moles of Al_2O_3 and of the sulfate must be half the number of moles of aluminum, or 0.0185 mole. The number of moles of SO_3 must be 3 × 0.0185 or 0.0555 mole. Rounded to significant figures these become 0.019 mole and 0.056 mole.

The formula weight of Al_2O_3 is (2 × 27) + (3 × 16) or 102; (0.019 mole) × (102 g per mole) = 1.9 g. The formula weight of $Al_2(SO_4)_3$ equals Al_2O_3 + 3 SO_3 or 102 + 240 or 342; 342 × 0.019 = 6.3 g. The formula weight of SO_3 is 80; 80 × 0.056 = 4.4 g. The total weight of the products, 6.3 g, must equal the total weight of the reactants, which is 4.4 + 1.9 or 6.3 g.

ENERGY RELATIONSHIPS

Atoms remain combined in stable compounds because atoms are more stable together than apart. In other words, the potential energy of a system of the atoms joined together is less than if they were separated and unattached. A **chemical bond** consists of the attractive forces between two adjacent atoms that must be overcome to cause the atoms to separate. **Bond energy** is the difference in total potential energy between the attached and the separated atoms.

Chemical changes occur through a breaking of bonds in the reactants and the formation of new bonds in the products. Almost always, different bonds have different bond energies. Therefore, an energy difference exists between reactants and products which can be measured by direct experiment. The reaction is conducted inside a **calorimeter,** a device for measuring exact quantities of heat. To understand the use of this instrument to determine energy differences of reactants and products, it is first necessary to know more about principles and units of heat measurement.

Heat Measurement

The name calorimeter comes from the **calorie** (**cal**) the unit of heat needed to raise the temperature of one gram of water from 15 to 16°C. A thousand calories is one **kilocalorie** (**kcal**), the unit in which most chemical energy is expressed. Most chemical reactions result in heat changes greater than one kilocalorie per mole of reactants. Individual bond energies may range from about 10 to more than 200 kcal per mole.

Specific heat, a characteristic property of any substance, is the quantity of heat required to raise the temperature of one gram of the substance by one degree Centigrade. When two bodies of matter that differ in temperature are placed in contact, heat flows from the warmer body to the cooler until both are equal in temperature. The new intermediate temperature of both bodies depends on the heat capacity of each body, which is the product of its specific heat times its weight in grams.

For example, suppose body A has a specific heat of 0.5 cal/g/°C, weighs 20 g, and has an initial temperature of 20°C. Body B has a specific heat of 1 cal/g/°C, weighs 40 g, and has an initial temperature of 60°C. The final temperature of both A and B will be determined by the fact that the quantity of heat lost by B must equal the quantity of heat gained by A. This total heat transfer assumes that the two bodies are completely insulated from the rest of the universe, but complete insulation is an ideal only imperfectly realized in any actual calorimeter. For A, (0.5 cal/g/°C) $\times$ 20 g = 10 cal/°C total heat capacity; for B, (1 cal/g/°C) $\times$ 20 g = 40 cal/°C total heat capacity. Thus B must cool 10/40 or one fourth as many degrees as A must gain during the heat transfer. The original temperature difference between the two bodies is 60 − 20 or 40°C. If A warms $4X$ degrees while B cools X degrees, the total temperature change, $4X + X = 5X$, equals 40°C; therefore, $X = 40/5 = 8°C$.

A absorbs enough heat to warm it to 20 + 4(8) or 20 + 32 or 52°C while B loses enough heat to warm A to 52°C and cool itself to 60 − 8 or 52°C. To warm A by 32° takes 10 cal/°C or 320 cal; to cool B by 8°, 40 cal/°C or 320 cal must be removed. The heat gained by A equals the heat lost by B as the two bodies become equal in temperature.

To a container having a heat capacity of 100 cal/°C, 50 ml of water at 80°C is added. What is the final temperature?

The Calorimeter

An isolated system must reach for and remain at *thermal equilibrium,* a condition of equal temperature throughout the system. Any temperature change must be the result of some change in the system that alters its heat content. Therefore, any chemical reaction involving a change from one potential energy to a lower one, must release this energy difference as kinetic energy, or heat.

In the isolated system, this heat cannot escape so it raises the temperature of all parts of the system. Using the initial and final temperatures of the system and the heat capacity of each component of the system, we can calculate the exact amount of heat needed to produce the observed temperature change. This is the principle of the calorimeter. Chemical reactants of known weight and known heat capacity are placed in a calorimeter and allowed to react to form new products of known weight and heat capacity. The net heat absorbed or evolved in the reaction can thus be calculated. This heat is called the **enthalpy** of the reaction.

Enthalpy of Reaction

It is not necessary to measure the heat of reaction experimentally if the heats of formation of each individual compound from its component elements are known. The **standard heat of formation,** $\Delta H_f{}^\circ$, is the heat that is absorbed or evolved, in kilocalories per mole at 25°C, when a compound is formed from its constituent elements each in its standard state. The standard state of an element is its state at 25°C under ordinary conditions. For a gas, the standard state is its condition under a pressure of one atmosphere. For a solid, the standard state is its usual crystalline form. The standard heat of formation of each *element* is arbitrarily assigned the value of zero. The standard heat of formation of any compound, then, is the same as the heat of the reaction, ΔH°, between the elements to form the compound.

The heat of any reaction can be evaluated as the sum of the heats of formation of all the products minus the sum of the heats of formation of all the reactants. Thus, heat evolved is a negative quantity and heat absorbed is positive. If the heat evolved in forming all the products is gerater than the heat evolved in forming all the reactants, heat is evolved in the reaction and the enthalpy is negative. A reaction that evolves heat (negative enthalpy) is called **exothermic,** whereas a reaction that absorbs heat (positive enthalpy) is called **endothermic.**

Example 5.3. *How much heat is evolved when the common fuel gas, methane* (CH_4)*, is burned? In the chemical reaction, all of the carbon is converted to carbon dioxide and all of the hydrogen is converted to water:*

$$CH_4 + 2\,O_2 \rightarrow CO_2 + 2\,H_2O$$

The heat of formation of CH_4 is the heat of the reaction

$$C(graphite) + 2\,H_2\,(g,\,1\,atm) \rightarrow CH_4\,(g,\,1\,atm)$$

The value of this heat of reaction is -17.9 kcal/mole. The minus sign indicates that the heat is evolved in the reaction as written from left to right; the carbon and hydrogen atoms are more strongly held together in CH_4 than they are (on the average) in graphite and H_2 molecules. (Graphite is the standard or usual form of carbon at 25°C.)

Since O_2 represents oxygen in its standard state, its standard heat of formation is defined as zero.

The standard heat of formation of CO_2 is the heat of the reaction:

$$C(graphite) + O_2 \text{ (g, 1 atm)} \rightarrow CO_2 \text{ (g, 1 atm)}$$

which is -94.0 kcal/mole. This represents the heat evolved when carbon burns; carbon and oxygen atoms are more strongly held together in CO_2 gas than they are (on the average) in graphite and O_2 molecules.

Finally, the heat of formation of water is obtained from the reaction:

$$2 H_2 \text{ (g, 1 atm)} + O_2 \text{ (g, 1 atm)} \rightarrow 2 H_2O \text{ (liq)}$$

The heat of reaction is -136.6 kcal for the reaction as written, but producing two moles of water, thus making the heat of formation of one mole of water -68.3 kcal/mole. Hydrogen and oxygen atoms are more stable on the average when combined in water than in H_2 and O_2 molecules.

Now if the standard heat of formation of each reactant and each product of a chemical change is known, the net heat content change in the reaction can be easily determined. It is the difference between the heats of formation of all the products and of all the reactants:

$\Delta H_f°$ products (kcal/mole)		$\Delta H_f°$ reactants (kcal/mole)	
CO_2	-94.0	CH_4	-17.9
$2 H_2O$	-136.6	$2 O_2$	0.0
total	-230.6	total	-17.9

$$\Delta H° \text{ (for the reaction)} = (-230.6) - (-17.9) = -212.7 \text{ kcal/mole}$$

The calculated *heat of combustion* of methane, which is the heat of reaction between methane and oxygen, is thus found to be approximately -213 kcal/mole.

In this particular example, we would in practice have measured this heat directly by burning methane in a calorimeter. From this value the heat of formation of methane could then be calculated. In fact that is how the heat of formation of methane was determined since it is not possible to cause carbon and hydrogen to unite directly to form only methane or any other specific hydrocarbon. Nevertheless, the indirect source of information is reliable because differences in energy between compounds in their standard states are constant. Thus, accurate heats of formation are obtained by measuring the heat of combustion of a hydrocarbon and calculating backward.

The heat of any reaction can be predicted accurately by following the procedures illustrated above. Such calculations are greatly facilitated by the existence of tabulations of standard heats of formation for a large number of compounds prepared by the U.S. Bureau of Standards and others. In addition, if the heat of reaction is known and the heats of formation of all but one of the reactants or products are known, the single unknown $\Delta H°$s can be calculated.

The energy of a chemical reaction is sometimes written as part of the chemical equation. For example:

$$CH_4 + 2\,O_2 \rightarrow CO_2 + 2\,H_2O + 213\ kcal$$

In this equation $+213$ is written because the heat is shown as a product. However, the $\Delta H°$ for this reaction is -213 kcal per mole of methane, indicating that heat is evolved.

Heats of formation are especially useful because they give a fair indication of whether a compound is stable with respect to the elements or is likely to decompose to its elements if the appropriate conditions occur. A compound that has a high negative heat of formation is stable toward decomposition. For NaCl, which is extremely stable toward heat, $\Delta H_f° = -98.2$ kcal/mole. Nitrogen trichloride (NCl_3), on the other hand, has a $\Delta H_f°$ of about $+55$ kcal/mole. Even at 25°C (about room temperature) this compound tends to revert to the elements N_2 and Cl_2, usually with explosive violence.

Heats of reaction are important because they give a fair indication of whether a reaction as written in an equation will indeed occur. In general, a highly exothermic reaction, one of large negative heat of reaction, tends to proceed readily once started. Conversely, a large positive heat of reaction suggests that the reaction is unlikely to occur. Strong chemical bonds are not likely to be broken in order to form new bonds that are weaker. For example, from the equation for the burning of methane discussed above, water and carbon dioxide might react to form methane and oxygen, but this would be a highly endothermic reaction. There is no reason to expect it to proceed.

Test Your Memory

1. What determines whether a chemical equation is complete?
2. What information does a chemical equation alone provide?
3. What is meant by an *addition reaction?* By *decomposition?* By a *displacement reaction?*
4. Define *metathesis.*
5. How do the total weight of original reactants and the total weight of products compare after complete reaction?
6. Define *kilocalorie.*
7. For what is the *calorimeter* used?
8. Define *standard state* and *standard heat of formation.*
9. What is the significance of a negative heat of reaction?

10. Define *exothermic* and *endothermic*.
11. What information about a chemical reaction is needed to calculate the heat of formation of one of the reactants or products?
12. How is the heat of reaction calculated?
13. What relationship exists between heat of formation and thermal stability?
14. What does heat of reaction indicate about the reaction?

Test Your Understanding

1. Write completed equations for each of the following:
   a) NaCl and H_2SO_4 form $NaHSO_4$ and HCl
   b) HCl and $Ca(OH)_2$ form $CaCl_2$ and water
   c) iron and oxygen form Fe_2O_3
   d) Cl_2 and methane form carbon tetrachloride and HCl
   e) C_3H_8 and O_2 burn to carbon dioxide and water
2. For each of the above reactions, start with one gram of one reactant and calculate the quantities of the other reactant required and the amount of each product which would result. Repeat this, assigning the one-gram weight to each of the other reaction components in turn.
3. Starting with 6.5 moles of the first compound listed in each of the above equations, calculate the weights of each of the other compounds involved.
4. Classify each of the following reactions:
   a) $H_2 + Cl_2 \rightarrow 2 HCl$
   b) $Na_2SO_4 \rightarrow Na_2O + SO_3$
   c) $AgNO_3 + KCl \rightarrow AgCl + KNO_3$
   d) $TiCl_4 + 4 Na \rightarrow Ti + 4 NaCl$
5. What is the heat of reaction for 4(d), if the heats of formation are: -192.3 kcal/mole for $TiCl_4$ and -98.2 kcal/mole for NaCl?

6

THE GROSS STRUCTURE OF ATOMS

ATOMIC THEORY

Many discussions of atomic structure begin with an attempt to prove that atoms exist. In fact, the whole science of chemistry provides the proof of their existence, so for complete proof you will have to be patient. The basic idea that all matter consists of tiny, indivisible, component-building blocks called atoms occurred to many of the early philosophers in various lands many centuries ago. But it was not until around A.D. 1800 that modern atomic theory started to develop. An English schoolmaster named John Dalton (1766–1844) traditionally receives major credit for originating this theory, although he was neither the first nor the only person to think along such lines.

Since the time of Dalton, the accumulation of a vast amount of supporting evidence has led to general acceptance of the atomic theory as fact. Thus we shall accept it here, although like all theories devised to explain experimental observations, it is subject to continual revision as new observations are made and new interpretations developed. Only a truly unforeseen development could cause abandonment of the basis of atomic theory: the conception of matter as a composite of tiny basic particles, or atoms.

You see, science is not just a collection of facts that people have observed and discovered and reported. It is also an *active process of new discovery* which is subject to change whenever new data indicate the need for change. Now if experiments have been performed accurately, with materials of proven identity and purity, and if observations have been made intelligently, skillfully, and without bias, then any other person in the world, now or at any time in the future, should be able to duplicate the work and obtain identical results. Such results are therefore considered to be "facts." But even a "fact" might be in error because of unforeseen and unrecognized factors influencing the experiment that produced it. We should therefore expect that in the course of time at least a few of the experimental facts that we have learned will be found to be erroneous. We must be prepared to revise our store of facts continuously throughout life.

Interpretation of the facts is quite another matter. Man as interpreter thinks subjectively. He bases his thoughts on his own particular knowledge, his own special prejudices, his own intuition, and his own hunches, trying to decide exactly what the facts *mean.* When he succeeds in dreaming up an explanation that seems to fit a few facts without notable exceptions, he generally calls this explanation a **hypothesis.** It gives him a clue as to where to look for additional information, by suggesting other facts with which to test the hypothesis. Such information might shed light on the problem. It might tell him whether his explanation is adequate as it is, needs revision, or ought to be quickly forgotten. But if further evidence, either from earlier or newer experimentation, seems to confirm his hypothesis, he may then develop it into a more detailed, thorough, and comprehensive set of ideas and explanations. This he may call a **theory.** Further information will then either suggest changes in the theory or support it as it is. If enough information appears to support the theory, the explanation may come to be accepted as **fact.**

A very interesting philosophical problem is that of deciding what constitutes proof of a fact. No two people are likely to agree on how much evidence is necessary to establish a theory as a fact. If it were just a matter of measuring the melting point of an easily prepared, easily purified substance, ten competent scientists in different parts of the world might, independently of each other, make measurements in close agreement. Practically everyone would then be willing to accept this work as ample proof of the accuracy of that particular melting point. But if the same ten scientists were asked *why* that substance should melt at that particular temperature, one could expect as many as ten different answers. At least some of these would be, "I haven't the faintest idea." Usually it is much more difficult to explain why than to measure what or how much. Good solid facts are much easier to acquire than good solid theories.

In the natural development of science, therefore, theories change much more rapidly than facts. Even theories long accepted as truth, for which alternative suggestions seem heresy, are often shown to need revision. Sometimes they have only a germ of truth imbedded in a heavy shell of fallacy. They could even be completely wrong. However, in our modern world of widespread communication among many active researchers, any widely accepted theory must have some validity, though it may not be perfect. New theories do not usually completely replace older theories, although the possibility exists that they might. What we must become accustomed to is the necessity of continuous revision of the *explanations* of facts. Our present concept of what atoms are made of and how they are put together provides important understanding of chemical behavior. The invisibility of atoms requires that all knowledge of their structure be inferred from indirect evidence. Consequently, the current theory of atomic structure represents one of the most impressive intellectual and experimental accomplishments in the history of man.

The Components of Atoms

The mysteries of matter and the mysteries of electricity have long been thought to be related. Even in the early 1800's, electrical "forces" were thought to play an active role in holding atoms together in molecules and compounds. Scientists discovered that electricity was capable of effecting chemical reactions, such as the isolation of sodium metal from its salts, which seemed impossible to produce in any other way. Michael Faraday (1791–1867), one of the founders of **electrochemistry,** discovered quantitative relationships between chemical change and quantities of electricity which are now considered some of the most important relationships in chemistry. Thus, the essentially electrical nature of matter was recognized even before the fundamental electrical particles were discovered about a century ago.

Originally, scientists thought that the atom could not be divided into smaller particles. Physicists today have discovered more than a hundred subatomic particles. Fortunately, most current chemical theory classifies only three of these as the fundamental components of atoms: **electrons, protons, and neutrons.**

Electrons and protons, recognized about a century ago, still have that mysterious quality which we call **electrical charge.** They possess the smallest unit of electrical charge known. There are two kinds of electrical charge, distinguished by the fact that they attract one another. Two charges of the same kind repel one another. The electron holds a single unit charge of one kind; the proton holds a single unit charge of the opposite kind. Arbitrarily, the charge on the **electron** has been labeled **negative** and that on the **proton, positive.** The two charges have been found to be exactly equal in quantity but opposite in sign. Equal but opposite charges which occur at the same point balance each other, so that no electrical effect is detectable from a distance.

Since attraction or repulsion between electrical charges can be easily detected experimentally, electrons and protons were discovered first and studied more easily. Then the neutron was discovered by James Chadwick (1891–   ) in 1932, long after electrons and protons were known. The discovery of the neutron necessitated a revision of an earlier theory of atomic structure which did not include neutrons. A neutron is a neutral particle of about the same size and mass as a proton. The electron is much lighter, having a mass only about 1/1840 as great as that of a proton or neutron.

Atomic Number

The charge of an electron is equal and opposite to that of a proton. Since atoms are electrically neutral, the number of protons in each atom must exactly equal the number of electrons. The number of electrons, which is equal to the number of protons, is called the **atomic number** of an atom. The property of atomic number was discovered by a brilliant young British scientist, H. G. J. Moseley (1887–1915), who soon thereafter lost his life in battle in World War I.

Each element has a different atomic number. For hydrogen the atomic number is 1. For oxygen the atomic number is 8, for iodine it is 53, for lead, 82. *The identity of an element is positively established by its atomic number.* If an atom has 53 protons in it, it must be an atom of iodine; there is no other chemical element which it could possibly be. If it has only 8 electrons and 8 protons per atom, it is oxygen. There is no alternative.

Atomic numbers of all the chemical elements are given with their symbols and atomic weights inside the back cover of this book.

Coulomb's Law

The interaction of electrostatic charges is expressed quantitatively by Coulomb's Law. According to this law:

> The force of attraction or repulsion between two charges is equal to the product of the charges divided by the square of the distance separating them.

This is true only in a vacuum, which has no influence on the electrical field between the charges. Because of its electrical nature, intervening matter influences such a field, reducing the forces to an extent measured by the **dielectric constant,** k, which is unity (1.0) for a vacuum but larger for any substance. Therefore, the expression for Coulomb's Law is usually written:

$$F = \frac{z_1 z_2}{kr^2}$$

where z_1 and z_2 are the separate charges, k the dielectric constant, and r the distance of separation. For example, the electrostatic force (coulomb force) between charges separated by water (dielectric constant about 80) would be only about 1/80 as great as in a vacuum.

Coulomb's Law is usually applied in chemistry to determine the *energy* required to overcome attractions or repulsions among electrostatic charges. This energy is equal to the force to be overcome multiplied by the distance between the charged particles, $E = Fr$. The coulomb energy, therefore is:

$$E = Fr = \frac{z_1 z_2}{kr}$$

To obtain this energy in the chemically useful unit **kcal per mole,** the factor 332 is employed, which gives the expression:

$$E = \frac{332 z^+ z^-}{r} \text{ kcal per mole}$$

where z^+ and z^- are the electronic charges in unit charges and r is the distance between charges (in angstroms $1\text{Å} = 10^{-8}$ cm). Coulombic energy, about 10^{40} times greater than gravitational energy, is probably the single most important factor in determining the structure of a chemical substance.

THE NUCLEAR ATOM

Inside an atom, no dielectric constant is involved. Coulomb's Law is applied as it would be in a vacuum. Since like charges repel one another and unlike charges attract one another, we might think that the equal numbers of electrons and protons of an atom would arrange themselves so that like charges would be as far apart as possible, consistent with unlike charges being as close together as possible. In two dimensions, this would correspond to a checker-board arrangement, the electrons sitting on the black squares and the protons on the red squares, each most directly surrounded by the other. But electrons and protons are extremely small, having diameters about $1/100,000$ as great as those of atoms. If they were spread out uniformly, as Coulomb's Law suggests they might be, an atom would be an extraordinarily porous particle, and all atoms would attract each other strongly.

In early twentieth-century England, Lord Rutherford and his students were investigating the radiation emitted by certain radioactive substances. This radiation was in the form of double-positive alpha particles which had an atomic mass of four. When they directed a stream of these particles at very thin gold foil which was nevertheless many atoms thick, they found that the foil offered no resistance to these alpha particles and allowed them to whiz right through. This suggested that the atoms were mostly empty space, with the components widely separated from one another, relative to their diameters. Careful studies showed, however, that although most of the alpha particles did go straight through the foil, some were deflected as though they had bounced off something relatively heavy or highly positive. A few even bounced back in the direction from which they had come. This was certainly not the behavior expected of an alpha particle after colliding with a proton only one-fourth its mass and half its charge. It was then postulated that the atoms of the gold foil consisted not of electrons and protons spread out evenly, but of tiny, positively charged particles of high mass, as well as the low-mass electrons. This was the origin of the concept of the **nuclear atom,** which has since been the basis for the model of the structure of atoms.

According to this model, each atom consists of a tiny, relatively heavy, solid particle, called the **nucleus,** which contains all the protons and is surrounded by a cloud of electrons. Since a proton outweighs an electron by a factor of nearly 2000, any atom composed of protons and electrons must derive practically all its mass from the protons. Hydrogen, with an atomic weight of 1.0 contains one electron and one proton per atom. If the electron provides only a negligible contribution to the mass, the atomic weight of one proton must also be 1.0.

The element with the next largest atomic number is helium, with atomic number two, but atomic mass of four. Reasoning that atoms were composed only of protons and electrons, in the nuclear model arrangement, and recognizing that the atoms are electrically neutral, chemists as late as 1932 thought

Figure 6.1. The Nuclear Model of the Atom (not to scale).

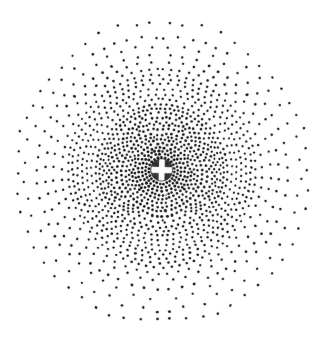

The **nucleus** concentrates all the positive charge and practically all the mass within a tiny region $1/100,000$ (or 10^{-5} times) the diameter of the entire atom. Its protons and neutrons are called *nucleons.*

The **electrons,** individually comparable to the nucleus in size, move so rapidly about the nucleus that they effectively occupy a volume billions of times larger, forming a thin cloud. This cloud has no definite boundary except with reference to its approach to another atom.

the higher atomic weight of helium must be the result of having four protons in the nucleus. In order to keep the number of cloud electrons at two yet maintain the electroneutrality of the atom, they postulated that the nucleus must consist of four protons and two electrons. When the **neutron,** an electrically neutral particle with a mass similar to that of the proton, was discovered in 1932, the need for nuclear electrons disappeared. The extra two units of mass in a helium atom, for example, could be accounted for by two neutrons.

Each particle in the nucleus of an atom, whether a proton or a neutron, is called a **nucleon.**

ISOTOPES

For practically all atoms with the exception of hydrogen, the number of neutrons in the nucleus equals or exceeds the number of protons. The number of neutrons in an atom is obtained merely by subtracting the atomic number from the atomic weight, because the masses of both neutrons and protons are approximately 1.0 on the atomic weight scale. The atomic weight is almost the same as the number of nucleons: the number of protons plus neutrons.

Applying this rule to a number of different elements, we find that sometimes it seems to work well and sometimes not. For example, the atomic weight of oxygen is almost 16, and the atomic number is 8, the difference of 8 being the number of neutrons. The atomic weight of sulfur is about 32, and the atomic number is 16, suggesting that the difference of 16 is the number of neutrons. But the atomic weight of chlorine is almost 35.5, and if we subtract the atomic number, 17, we get 18.5. Does this mean that each chlorine atom contains 18.5 neutrons? The answer is no. Clearly, since neutrons are basic particles and cannot be divided into fractions (any more than we can have fractions of electrons or protons) this atom can't contain 18.5 neutrons. Consequently, there must be chlorine atoms that differ in their number of neutrons although each absolutely must possess 17 protons. In fact, it has been discovered that most of the chemical elements can occur each as atoms differing somewhat in the number of neutrons. Forms of an element that differ only in the number of neutrons per atom, and hence in nuclear mass, are called **isotopes.**

> How many neutrons per atom in the oxygen isotope of atomic weight 17? In the hydrogen isotope of atomic weight 3?

The mixture of isotopes that makes up a natural element may have an average atomic weight that differs appreciably from a whole number. An atomic weight that is approximately a whole number may represent a single isotope, but it may also represent a mixture of isotopes that happens to have an integral average value for the atomic weight. In chlorine, the most abundant isotopes are those of mass 35 and those of mass 37 (indicated symbolically by $^{35}_{17}Cl$ and $^{37}_{17}Cl$, where 17 is the atomic number and the 35 and 37 are the "mass numbers" representing the number of nucleons per nucleus). The atomic weight of about 35.5 for chlorine represents a mixture of about 75 per cent of the lighter isotope and 25 per cent of the heavier one.

The "Constancy" of Atomic Weights

If the isotopic composition of any one element varied from place to place geographically, atomic weight determinations would disagree. We would not be justified in assigning a particular atomic weight to each element, especially if expressed to fractions of a mass unit. Fortunately, this composition remains quite constant for most elements. The particular distribution of isotopes for any one element evidently occurred quite uniformly when the earth was formed. Therefore, the atomic weights of the elements accurately represent the average relative mass of the atoms as they exist on earth, even though the individual atoms in any given sample show some variance.

Properties of Isotopes

The chemical properties of atoms are almost entirely the result of their electron clouds and nuclear charges which are *identical for all isotopes of the same element*. The only properties, physical or chemical, in which we may expect to observe significant differences among isotopes, are those affected by mass, and even the mass differences are usually relatively small. Isotopes are usually extremely similar to one another. For the elements of low atomic number, however, the effect on the mass of changing the number of neutrons in the nucleus is proportionately much larger.

The isotopes of hydrogen are especially interesting in this respect. The addition of one neutron to the proton which already comprises the nucleus *doubles* the mass. A second neutron triples it. The properties of these hydrogen isotopes, which we may designate as $_1^1H$, $_1^2H$, and $_1^3H$, are sufficiently different from one another that special names have been assigned to the **heavy hydrogen** isotopes. The hydrogen atom of mass 2 is called **deuterium.** The one of mass 3 is called **tritium.** Water containing these isotopes (more commonly deuterium since this is much more abundant) is called **heavy water.**

SUMMARY

In this chapter we have developed a picture of the structure of atoms which is worth summarizing and perhaps elaborating a little before proceeding to more complex concepts. Every atom consists of a central particle called the nucleus, which contains protons and usually neutrons and which thus has a relatively high mass and a positive charge. This nucleus is imbedded in a cloud of negatively charged electrons, equal in number to the protons in the nucleus, individually of very low mass and collectively spread out through a relatively large volume of space around the nucleus. If the electron and nucleus of a hydrogen atom were each to be enlarged to the size of a baseball (both are about the same diameter), the baseball electron would be whizzing around the baseball proton at distances up to half a mile or more. The two baseballs would then be the only matter occupying a sphere one mile in diameter.

You may well wonder then how matter can seem so substantial and solid. How can a footstool dent your shin if it is mostly empty space? Presumably it is because the electrons travel with such tremendous speed that, in effect, they occupy all the space at once. It has been calculated that the electron of a hydrogen atom encircles the proton more than six billion times within each millionth of a second. So you could never see the electron in our baseball model of a hydrogen atom. But if you should happen to thrust your head momentarily within that spatial sphere one mile in diameter, you would soon discover a clean round hole through your skull remarkably close to the diameter of a baseball. The electron does indeed effectively occupy the space of a hydrogen atom.

Since the gross structure of all atoms can be described in this same way, it affords no clue to differences among the different elements except in their atomic number. It does little to explain why matter that is made up of different kinds of atoms has the different properties that we observe. We must therefore examine the structure of atoms more closely.

Although a knowledge of the structure of the atomic nucleus has extremely useful applications, as shown by the development of nuclear energy, it does not seem to lead to a better understanding of the general physical and chemical properties of a substance. Thus, although we are beginning to interpret many chemical properties in terms of various nuclear properties with which we are now familiar, the most important properties of the nucleus, from the standpoint of understanding chemical change and other atomic properties, are mass and charge. For our present purposes, we shall consider the nucleus of every atom as occupying only a point in space, containing most of the mass of the atom, and bearing all of the positive charge. A more detailed description of the electron cloud is discussed in the next chapter.

Test Your Memory

1. Who was John Dalton and for what is he remembered?
2. What are the characteristics of electrons?
3. How does a *proton* differ from an *electron?*
4. What are the properties of a *neutron?*
5. Which of the component particles of an atom was discovered most recently? When? By whom?
6. Define *atomic number.*
7. What single property distinguishes each of the chemical elements?
8. Give the mathematical expression for calculating coulomb energy, and state it in words.
9. What is meant by the term *nuclear atom?*
10. Where are each of the three kinds of basic particles located in an atom?
11. What is a *nucleon?*
12. Define *isotope.*

13. Why are not all atomic weights whole numbers?
14. Which particles contribute most to atomic weights?
15. What is there about the natural distribution of isotopes that keeps atomic weights reliable?
16. How do isotopes of a given element differ in physical or chemical properties?
17. Describe the *gross structure* of an atom.

Test Your Understanding

1. Calculate the contribution made by the electrons to the atomic weight of element 100.
2. Using the data from the inside of the back cover, calculate the average number of neutrons in each of the first 30 elements, hydrogen through zinc.
3. No one understands perfectly the nature of the forces inside an atomic nucleus, but what do you think might permit many protons, with their mutually repulsive positive charges, to remain as close together as they do in a nucleus?

7

ELECTRONIC CONFIGURATIONS OF ATOMS

SOME REMARKS ABOUT MODELS

The kind of model you are probably most familiar with is the small-scale exact replica that shows you what something looks like. If you were to carve a model of an old sailing vessel, you would probably judge your success by seeing how faithfully you could reproduce the lines of the ship, the masts, all the ropes, and even the lifeboats. If you were trying to make a miniature model of an early Model T, again you would be most pleased if you could succeed in making your model exactly resemble the real object. If you could make it a working model as well, so much the better.

Scientists also use models such as these. But many aspects of nature are so complex that it would be impossible to construct an accurate model in the first place. Furthermore, even if an accurate model were available, it would not be helpful. For example, how would we build a scaled working model of a hydrogen atom? Suppose we chose a marble for the one electron and a marble for the proton. How would we construct and mechanize it so that one marble would be two or three hundred yards away and traveling around the other one six billion times every millionth of a second? And if we could succeed in building such a model and placing it in operation, what would the model be good for? All we could see would be the nucleus, and we couldn't get closer than a quarter of a mile or more to that. No, this is not the kind of model that would be helpful to a chemist, and especially as a model of an atom.

What a chemist needs is an imaginary model that will help him to *understand* the atom. Then he may also find a visual model helpful, but only if the model is not a replica of an actual atom but a depiction of the *idea* of the atom. The components of atoms are of definite relative sizes which can be shown by a three-dimensional model or even by circles drawn on paper. Beyond showing the relative size, however, such a model can be helpful only if it *represents* those qualities of an atom which aid in understanding its properties. We will consider this type of atomic model later. First we need to study the intellectual explanation which constitutes the modern idea of the atom.

QUANTUM THEORY

Much of what has been deduced about the structure of atoms has come from studies of the interaction of matter with energy. In particular, when different substances are exposed to electrical energy or heat energy, they emit light. Ordinary white light is actually a wide spectrum of electromagnetic radiation. Light can be separated by a prism into a visible spectrum of component frequencies: a rainbow-like pattern of colors ranging from red through orange, yellow, green, and blue to violet. A device more effective than a prism for separating electromagnetic radiations is called a **diffraction grating.** This can be a flat surface of glass upon which have been engraved many thousands of parallel lines per inch.

The light emitted from gaseous substances which have become incandescent by absorbing energy can be separated into its component frequencies by using a diffraction grating in a device called a **spectroscope.** Such light consists not of a continuous spectrum but rather of only relatively few wavelengths or frequencies. Furthermore, the wavelengths of these rays of light of the **emission spectrum** of each substance are characteristic of the elements in that substance. Each element gives its own highly specific and characteristic spectrum, just as every individual person has his own distinctive fingerprints. A properly designed spectroscope can be a very sensitive device for recognizing elements present only in trace quantities. A substance that is spectroscopically pure is very pure indeed.

Figure 7.1. Diagram of Spectroscope.

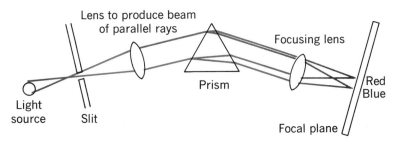

The Bohr Atom

Since each frequency of light represents a specific amount of energy, atomic spectra can be interpreted as representing quantities of energy released by excited atoms. A physicist named Max Planck (1858–1947) had earlier proposed the theory that energy could not be transmitted continuously but only in tiny bundles or packets called **quanta** (singular, **quantum**). This is the basis of the quantum theory. The great Danish physicist Niels Bohr (1885–1962) later applied Planck's quantum theory to the interpretation of the hydrogen spectrum, which is simplest of all yet surprisingly complex. Bohr set himself to the task of imagining what in the nature of hydrogen atoms would cause them to give out only light of certain frequencies when excited by the absorption of energy. He assumed that the electron normally travels around the proton in the most stable energy level possible. He postulated that an infinite number of higher energy levels is *not* available. According to the quantum theory, only certain distinct energy levels exist for an electron or an atom. He imagined such an energy level as a circular path he called an **orbit.** The electron was prevented from flying off at a tangent by the coulombic attraction between it and the proton at the center of the orbit. The electron's energy remained constant as long as it remained in any particular orbit.

Figure 7.2.   Origin of Hydrogen Spectrum.

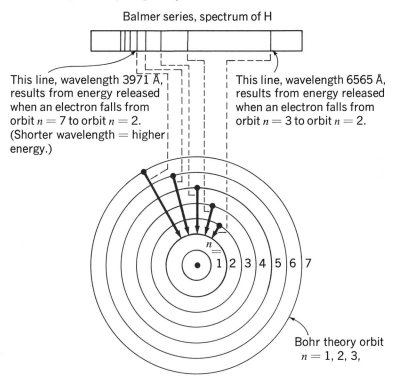

Balmer series, spectrum of H

This line, wavelength 3971 Å, results from energy released when an electron falls from orbit $n = 7$ to orbit $n = 2$. (Shorter wavelength = higher energy.)

This line, wavelength 6565 Å, results from energy released when an electron falls from orbit $n = 3$ to orbit $n = 2$.

$n = $ 1 2 3 4 5 6 7

Bohr theory orbit $n = 1, 2, 3,$

The Balmer series of spectral lines results from energy released by electrons falling from orbits of higher energy to the orbit $n = 2$. Other series of lines result from falls to $n = 1$, $n = 3$, $n = 4$, and so on.

Bohr postulated that the hydrogen spectrum originated in the absorption by the hydrogen electron of energy from some outside source. This energy promoted the electron to some discrete, definite higher level or orbit. Unstable with this extra energy, the electron would almost immediately return to its most stable position again. It would rid itself of the extra energy by emitting this excess as light of the frequency corresponding to the energy. He further postulated that the electron need not necessarily return to its most stable orbit, the **ground state,** all in one jump, but might travel in steps. Thus, each individual line of the hydrogen spectrum was explained as the result of a particular quantum jump downward to a more stable level. Suppose the electron jumped all at once to the fifth energy level. It might return by one jump, which would correspond to one particular line of the spectrum, or it might return by jumping from level five to level four, then to level three, then to level two, and finally back to level one. Or it could make the return trip by any combination of jumps, all downward toward the ground state. Each of these separate jumps would correspond to a different line in the spectrum.

When Bohr carried out the relatively simple mathematics involved in this picture, he found that he could account almost exactly for the origin of all the spectral lines for hydrogen. The great value of this work is that it showed that the electrons around an atomic nucleus cannot have just any amount of energy. They are restricted to certain very specific energy levels. It also showed a way in which the values of these individual energy levels could be calculated, as well as measured experimentally. In other words, the electron cloud has a definite structure.

Wave Properties of Electrons

The Bohr theory of the hydrogen atom was remarkably successful in application. Unfortunately, it was inapplicable to more complex atoms in which electron-electron repulsions had to be taken into account. Something more was needed, the nature of which became evident when a French physicist named Louis de Broglie (1892–   ) recognized that moving particles should have wave characteristics associated with their motion. Since an electron moving around the nucleus is a moving particle, it should have wave characteristics, as well as mass and velocity. The exact nature of these *matter-waves* associated with the electrons of an atom cannot be described here. In general they are somewhat analogous to visible waves such as those in water.

The fact that waves associated with electrons in an atom must exist and operate within a very limited space places restrictions upon them. If you were to operate a plunger in the middle of an infinitely large ocean by pumping it up and down in a regular manner, a succession of circular waves would spread out continuously and indefinitely far. Each crest would be followed by a trough and then another crest. As long as the speed of the plunger were not changed, the waves would roll away one by one without interfering with each other.

If you tried the same thing inside a circular tub of water, however, each wave would spread and move outward until it reached the walls of the tub. The walls would reflect it inward. If the frequency of the wave motion and the tub radius were exactly right, the crest of each returning wave and the crest of each new wave would coincide. As a result standing waves (standing crests and standing troughs) would be created. But if the returning waves and the new waves were out of phase, a given portion of water would be subjected simultaneously to upward and downward forces. In effect its motion would be greatly restricted or stopped. This is the phenomenon of wave interference. It occurs whenever two or more similar wave motions that are out of phase are applied to the same medium simultaneously.

This type of phenomenon places an important restriction on an electron in orbit. Its wave properties must reinforce rather than interfere with those of other electrons or itself. For example, in the hydrogen atom there is only one electron, but it is traveling in a periodic or cyclic manner since it is going around the nucleus. The wave properties of this moving electron require that the circumference of its path around the nucleus have a length that is exactly equal to some whole multiple of the length of the particle-wave. In other words, the length of the path once around the nucleus may be equal to one, two, three, or four electron wavelengths, but nothing intermediate. Intermediate values would result in mutual cancellation. This picture of the hydrogen atom agrees with Bohr's. In his theory the different energy levels available to the electron turn out to be exactly the same as those calculated for whole numbers of electron wavelengths. That is, the circumference of the circular orbit, $2\pi r$, must equal $n\lambda$ where n is a whole number and λ is the wavelength.

In general, we may think of the various electrons of an atom interacting in such a way as to create **standing waves** wherever the electron-waves are in phase with one another. These various standing waves correspond to the various energy levels that are involved in the production of spectra.

Wave Mechanics

The theory of atomic structure that is expanded to take into account the wave nature of the moving electrons is called **wave mechanics,** which gives rise to the **quantum mechanical** or the **wave mechanical** model of the atom. The wave mechanical picture is not simple because the nature of matter is not simple. One of the unhappy consequences of this newer picture is that it cannot be brought into focus, but remains forever blurred. The specific location or orbit for a given electron cannot be defined exactly, rather only the *probability* of finding the electron at any given spatial coordinates. This probability is proportional to the square of the **wave function,** a mathematical expression defining the condition of an electron. Thus, we can define a certain region in space around the nucleus within which the probability of finding the electron is, for example, 90 per cent. An atom can be accurately described only in complex mathematical terms that cannot be visualized.

In principle, the methods of wave mechanics are adequate for the calculation of all of the properties of any atom. If this is true, why are there chemistry laboratories? Why bother to experiment when all the answers can be calculated on paper? First, the immense labor of making such calculations, even with the help of the most modern of computers, is far too great. Complete calculations on any but the simplest of chemical systems are a practical impossibility unless grossly simplifying assumptions can be made. Second, mere knowledge of structural and energetic requirements for a certain compound does not reveal the experimental process which will lead to making it. Experimental chemistry is important to the study and design of chemical reactions also.

Although at our present stage in the study of chemistry the prospects of reaching a complete understanding do not seem great, it seems to be a curious characteristic of nature that a revealing simplicity is often associated with obscure complexity. We can hold more than one viewpoint on the problem of understanding the properties of matter without being self-contradictory. We may view the vastly confusing complexity of physical reality and throw up our hands in dismay, knowing that the ultimate truth is forever out of reach and out of sight. Or we may accept the complexity but seek to recognize the underlying simplicity. If we adopt a favorable attitude, the second view can provide a degree of understanding that will be extremely useful and reasonably satisfying as an approximation of the unknowable real truth.

The latter course is that followed to a greater or lesser degree by most chemists. It has led to a faster and richer development of a practical science than would ever have been possible if we refused to accept the limitations of human intelligence and to compromise. This is the course we shall try to follow in this book. We will try to be as precise and exact as is possible at this level of chemistry. We will keep in mind that professional chemists usually operate on a higher, more sophisticated level of ignorance than we do, but that compared with the ultimate truth, it is ignorance just the same.

ENERGY LEVELS OF ELECTRONS

Although exact calculations of energies for the more complicated atoms are not practically possible, it is useful to assume that such atoms have much in common with hydrogen atoms. On this basis, and also by applying wave mechanical concepts, we can describe the energy level of each electron in any atom in terms of four **quantum numbers:** the principal quantum number, the orbital quantum number, the orbital magnetic quantum number, and the spin magnetic quantum number. Although a detailed explanation of these numbers is not possible at this point, we should be able to gain an approximate idea of what they represent.

Principal Quantum Number

Let's imagine the electrons as distributed among various major energy levels or **shells** around the nucleus. Each particular shell is identified by a **principal quantum number,** n, which may have any positive, whole-integer value beginning with 1. We may imagine a series of concentric spherical shells surrounding the nucleus. Shell number one, lowest in energy, lies closest to the nucleus, number two is higher in energy, number three still higher, and so on. On the average, the electrons of the first shell may be considered held most tightly, those of the second, next most tightly. On the average, as predicted by Coulomb's Law, the farther the electrons are from the nucleus, as suggested by larger values of n, the less strongly they are attracted to it. The shells are sometimes designated by letters: K for $n = 1$, L for $n = 2$, M for $n = 3$, N for $n = 4$, O for $n = 5$, and P for $n = 6$.

Orbital Quantum Number

Within a given principal quantum shell, electrons have different energies depending on the shape of the particular kind of region they occupy. These regions are called **orbitals.** The most stable orbital within a given principal quantum shell, the s orbital, occupies a spherical region around the nucleus. The next most stable orbitals are the three p orbitals, each shaped somewhat like a dumbbell. Imagine the usual three axes at right angles to one another with the atomic nucleus as the origin. One of these dumbbells runs along the X axis, extending on both sides of the nucleus, one along the Y axis, and the third along the Z axis. Although together their distribution in space is spherically symmetrical about the nucleus, individually these three orbitals are not. Although differently oriented, they are of equal energy, a condition described by the term **degenerate.**

The next most stable orbitals within a given principal quantum shell are the five d orbitals. Four of these are identical in shape, each looking something like a pair of crossed p orbitals, or a four-leaf clover in three dimensions. Three of these are located between two axes but intersected by their plane. A fourth lies along the X and Y axes. The fifth, necessarily of somewhat different shape, lies along the Z axis occupying the only space not otherwise designated for another d orbital. The s, p, and d orbitals are shown in Figure 7.3.

A fourth kind of orbital is called an f orbital. These come in a set of seven but are too complex in shape to be very meaningful in illustration, and relatively less important anyway.

The kind of orbital occupied by an electron is designated by the **orbital quantum number,** l, which can have any positive, whole-integer value from 0 to $(n - 1)$. When $l = 0$, this denotes an s orbital. When $l = 1$, a p orbital is indicated, when $l = 2$, a d orbital, and when $l = 3$, an f orbital.

Figure 7.3. Approximate Shapes of Atomic Orbitals.

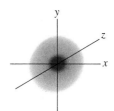

Shaded areas on the drawings represent the shape of the region in which there is a 90% chance that an electron in the particular orbital will be found at any given instant.

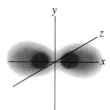

s **orbital.** This represents the time-average electron distribution which is spherically symmetrical with respect to the nucleus. In other words, the chance of finding the electron at a given distance is equal in all directions from the nucleus.

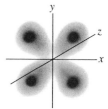

p **orbital.** This region is concentrated along one axis. The one designated p_x lies along the X axis, the p_y orbital along the Y axis and the p_z orbital along the Z axis. All three are degenerate (meaning equal in energy). They differ only in direction. Individually they are not symmetrical with respect to the nucleus but as a set of three, they are.

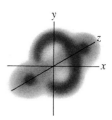

d **orbital.** The one centered between the X and Y axes and in the XY plane is called the d_{xy} orbital. Three others are identical in shape. One, d_{xz}, is centered in the XZ plane between the axes. One, d_{yz}, is centered in the YZ plane between the axes. The fourth, called $d_{x^2-y^2}$, is centered in the XY plane along the X and Y axes. A fifth orbital, d_{z^2}, extends along the Z axis. As a set of five, the *d* orbitals are spherically symmetrical around the nucleus. All five are degenerate.

Orbital Magnetic Quantum Number

For most purposes, the first two quantum numbers give the most useful information. They tell which principal quantum level contains the electron under discussion, and in what shape orbital it is located. But to describe more fully the energy situation of a given electron in an atom, two more quantum numbers, both based on magnetism, are needed.

The first is called the **orbital magnetic quantum number.** It specifies which of the several orbitals of a given type holds a given electron. Normally, the several orbitals of a given type that are in the same principal quantum level are exactly alike in energy but do not all point in the same direction. Remember how an electric current creates a magnetic field around the conductor it flows through? This is the basic principle of the electromagnet. The electron traveling around the nucleus is a charge in motion and therefore a tiny current. It too generates a magnetic field which can interact with any external magnetic field in which the atom may be placed. Since the orbitals are pointed in different directions, they cannot possibly line up in the same way with the external field. The orbital magnetic quantum number represents the particular orientation of the orbital with respect to the others.

Designated m_l, these numbers can have values 0 to $+l$. If $l = 1$, as for p orbitals, there can be as many orbitals as there are values possible for m_l: 0, $+1$, and -1, which make three. If $l = 2$, the values possible for m_l are: 0, -1, -2, $+1$, $+2$, or five in all which correspond to the five d orbitals. If $l = 3$, the values possible for m_l are: 0, $+1$, $+2$, $+3$, -1, -2, -3, or seven values corresponding to the seven f orbitals.

Spin Magnetic Quantum Number

The second magnetic quantum number needed is called the **spin magnetic quantum number.** It is necessary because each electron, independent of its orbital motion, has the properties of a tiny magnet. If this magnet is oriented in one way, the spin magnetic number m_s equals ½; if oriented in the opposite way, it equals $-½$. These are the only two values possible for this number. If two electrons occupy the same orbital, their magnets must be opposed, and they are said to have **opposed spins.**

BUILDING ATOMS

Principles

The description above must seem unduly complicated. Nevertheless, it is important to have some idea about these quantum numbers because they are directly related to the electronic structure of an atom. Two basic rules guide the assignment of electrons to the various sets of quantum numbers (energy levels) available. The first, the **Pauli Exclusion Principle,** states that: No two electrons within the same atom may have the identical set of four quantum numbers. If n indicates which principal quantum shell the electron is in, l tells what kind of an orbital it occupies, and m_l indicates which one of the orbitals of this kind is occupied, then three of the four quantum numbers are already specified. The fourth number must be different for two electrons or they cannot occupy the same orbital. In other words, although each orbital has a maximum capacity of two electrons, it can hold two electrons only if their spins are opposed.

The second rule is called the **aufbau** or **building-up principle:** Each successive electron added to a bare nucleus occupies the most stable position available to it. With few exceptions, this means that each atom has an electronic configuration exactly like that of the atom preceding it in atomic number, but with one more electron added.

Shell Capacities

Before considering the electronic configurations of the elements, let us examine the restrictions placed upon the capacities of each successive principal quantum shell. The K shell, where $n = 1$, can have only the value 0 for l, which means only one orbital, the $1s$ orbital. This can hold two electrons. Thus the total capacity of this first shell is only two.

The L shell, where $n = 2$, can have $l = 0$ or 1. For $l = 0$, m_l can only equal 0, which means only one orbital, the $2s$. But for $l = 1$, m_l may have the values 0, $+1$, -1, allowing for three p orbitals. Each of these can hold two electrons. With two electrons in the $2s$ orbital and two more in each of the three $2p$ orbitals, the maximum capacity of the second principal quantum shell is eight. Stated briefly, the second shell includes only eight different combinations of the four quantum numbers.

In a similar manner we could show that the capacity of the third principal quantum shell is 18. Included are five d orbitals with their capacity of 10 electrons in addition to the eight in the three p and one s orbitals. Similarly, the capacity of the fourth principal shell is 32, adding the seven f orbitals with their capacity of 14 to the previous 18. Beyond this shell, no atom ever holds more than 32 electrons in one shell even though, in principle, the capacity could be greater.

In summary, the number of different orbitals present in any principal quantum level is indicated by the square of the principal quantum number n. When $n = 1$, only one orbital, the s orbital, is possible. When $n = 2$, four orbitals are present: the one s and three p. When $n = 3$, nine orbitals are present: the s, three p, and five d. When $n = 4$, sixteen orbitals are present: the s, three p, five d, and seven f. Naturally, since each orbital can hold two electrons, the total electron capacity of any principal quantum level is given by $2n^2$, because the number of orbitals is n^2.

The Electronic Theater and the Nuclear Stage

Let us imagine that in building the different atomic structures, we begin each atom with a bare nucleus which holds a charge and is surrounded by imaginary energy levels (orbitals) capable of accommodating electrons. We will feed the electrons in, one by one, and see where they go. Before you become panicked by the strangeness of quantum numbers and the energy levels they designate, think of a large theater. It may contain thousands of seats, but an usher, with only a little experience, can locate any seat just by noting its designation on the ticket: Section A, Row 19, Seat 4. The description of the energy location of an electron in an atom, by means of four quantum numbers, is not very different from the description of the seat location by means of numbering the section, row, and seat. To understand what goes on in this building up of the elements, let us consider further the analogy of the theater and the stage.

Let us suppose that a given atomic nucleus is the stage of a theater. This is not a very conventional theater, for although the seats are arranged in different sections, the number of seats in a given section may be very small, and all the seats are in pairs. Never mind that; the rest of the analogy works out quite well. Just outside, in an electrifying atmosphere of excitement, a crowd of electrons eagerly awaits admittance. Each electron feels attracted toward the stage, and knows he will get a positive charge out of sitting as close to it as he can. Seats are not reserved, but may be occupied on a first-come, first-serve basis. One by one, the electrons are admitted to the theater.

The first electron naturally takes the best seat in the house, front and center, in Section 1 (the $1s$ orbital). The second electron looks around, finds the first electron repulsive but sits beside him anyway because no other seat offers as good a view of the stage. This fills Section 1. The third electron must find the next best seat, which is in Section 2, where there are a total of 8 seats. Two seats in this section (the $2s$ orbital) afford a better view than any of the other six. These two seem equal so the third electron sits down in the nearest one. The fourth electron acts as though he would rather be alone. Nevertheless he sits beside the third because it seems to be a better seat. The fifth electron goes also to Section 2, where he finds a choice of three equal pairs of seats left (the $2p$ orbitals). He arbitrarily chooses one, for they give equally good views of the stage. The sixth electron finds five of these seats unoccupied, one of them beside the fifth electron and the other four in the two separate pairs. Being repelled by the fifth electron, he takes one of the empty pairs since the view is just as good from there. The seventh electron also would rather sit alone, so he takes one of the seats of the last remaining unoccupied pair in this section. The eighth, ninth, and tenth electrons fill up this section, to the disgust of the earlier arrivals and despite their preference for solitary seating, because they recognize that these seats give a better view of the stage than do any of the seats in Section 3. And now Section 2 is filled to its capacity.

The eleventh electron must begin to fill Section 3, since the first two sections are completely filled. From the eleventh through the eighteenth electron, the pattern of filling resembles exactly that used for Section 2. A new situation, however, confronts our nineteenth electron. He sees that there are still five pairs of seats left in Section 3, but that these are in the back of the section. A front seat in Section 4 would really be superior to a back-row seat in

Section 3. He therefore leaves the back row of Section 3 empty and sits down in the front row (4s orbital) of Section 4. Here he is soon joined by electron number twenty, to their mutual annoyance.

Electron twenty-one looks at the second row of Section 4 and compares it with the still-empty last row in Section 3, which he decides will afford him a better view of the stage. Instead of continuing to fill Section 4 he sits down in Section 3 (3d orbital). The filling of Section 4 is thus interrupted until all ten seats of the back row of Section 3 are filled. Electron thirty-one, admitted next, has little difficulty in deciding what is best. He sits in the second row of Section 4 (4p orbitals). So do the next five electrons, until this row is filled.

The thirty-seventh electron finds a situation very similar to that which faced the nineteenth. That is, Section 4 is not filled but it looks as though he could see better from the front row of Section 5 (5s orbital). He sits there and is soon joined by the thirty-eighth electron. But the thirty-ninth electron sees that the left-over seats in the third row of Section 4 (the 4d orbitals) afford a better view than the second-row seats of Section 5 (the 5p orbitals). So do the next nine electrons which follow. Once again the filling of a section (Section 5 this time) is interrupted, here by the filling of the third row of Section 4.

Although in general an electron will find its best seat in the section of *lowest* number, the front-row seats of the section of *next highest* number afford a better view of the stage than do the ninth and subsequent seats of the section of lowest number available. Therefore, a section never has more than eight seats occupied until the front row of the next highest section is occupied.

Figure 7.4. Electron Energy Level Diagram (not to scale).

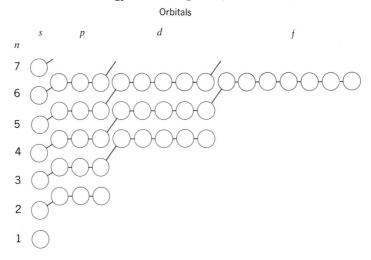

Energy increases upward. In building up of elements, each successive electron occupies the most stable orbital (lowest energy level) available to it.

The best seats of the higher section are better than the worst seats of the lower section. In other words, electrons always occupy the $(n + 1)$ s orbital before they begin to fill the n d orbitals.

The principal quantum shells of the atoms thus overlap in energies such that the lowest energy of the higher shell is less than the highest energy of the lower shell. The extremely significant consequence of this is that *the outermost shell never holds more than eight electrons.* The ninth electron always finds greater stability in the next higher principal quantum level, beginning the filling of a *new* outermost shell. As will be explained in greater detail in the

Figure 7.5. Electronic Configurations of the First 36 Elements.

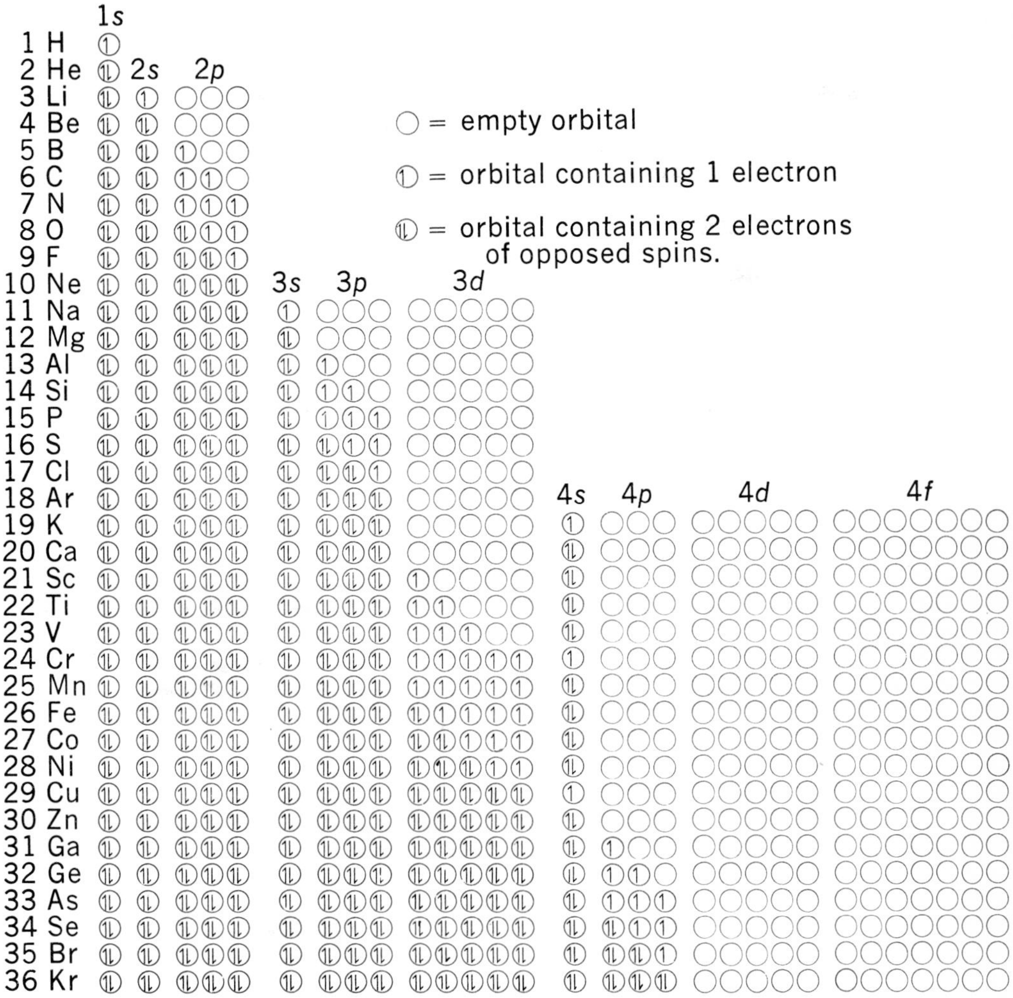

```
      1s
 1 H   ⊙
 2 He  ⊕  2s    2p
 3 Li  ⊕  ⊙  ○○○
 4 Be  ⊕  ⊕  ○○○            ○ = empty orbital
 5 B   ⊕  ⊕  ⊙○○
 6 C   ⊕  ⊕  ⊙⊙○            ⊙ = orbital containing 1 electron
 7 N   ⊕  ⊕  ⊙⊙⊙
 8 O   ⊕  ⊕  ⊕⊙⊙            ⊕ = orbital containing 2 electrons
 9 F   ⊕  ⊕  ⊕⊕⊙                  of opposed spins.
10 Ne  ⊕  ⊕  ⊕⊕⊕   3s   3p      3d
11 Na  ⊕  ⊕  ⊕⊕⊕   ⊙  ○○○  ○○○○○
12 Mg  ⊕  ⊕  ⊕⊕⊕   ⊕  ○○○  ○○○○○
13 Al  ⊕  ⊕  ⊕⊕⊕   ⊕  ⊙○○  ○○○○○
14 Si  ⊕  ⊕  ⊕⊕⊕   ⊕  ⊙⊙○  ○○○○○
15 P   ⊕  ⊕  ⊕⊕⊕   ⊕  ⊙⊙⊙  ○○○○○
16 S   ⊕  ⊕  ⊕⊕⊕   ⊕  ⊕⊙⊙  ○○○○○
17 Cl  ⊕  ⊕  ⊕⊕⊕   ⊕  ⊕⊕⊙  ○○○○○
18 Ar  ⊕  ⊕  ⊕⊕⊕   ⊕  ⊕⊕⊕  ○○○○○   4s  4p      4d          4f
19 K   ⊕  ⊕  ⊕⊕⊕   ⊕  ⊕⊕⊕  ○○○○○   ⊙  ○○○  ○○○○○  ○○○○○○○
20 Ca  ⊕  ⊕  ⊕⊕⊕   ⊕  ⊕⊕⊕  ○○○○○   ⊕  ○○○  ○○○○○  ○○○○○○○
21 Sc  ⊕  ⊕  ⊕⊕⊕   ⊕  ⊕⊕⊕  ⊙○○○○   ⊕  ○○○  ○○○○○  ○○○○○○○
22 Ti  ⊕  ⊕  ⊕⊕⊕   ⊕  ⊕⊕⊕  ⊙⊙○○○   ⊕  ○○○  ○○○○○  ○○○○○○○
23 V   ⊕  ⊕  ⊕⊕⊕   ⊕  ⊕⊕⊕  ⊙⊙⊙○○   ⊕  ○○○  ○○○○○  ○○○○○○○
24 Cr  ⊕  ⊕  ⊕⊕⊕   ⊕  ⊕⊕⊕  ⊙⊙⊙⊙⊙   ⊙  ○○○  ○○○○○  ○○○○○○○
25 Mn  ⊕  ⊕  ⊕⊕⊕   ⊕  ⊕⊕⊕  ⊙⊙⊙⊙⊙   ⊕  ○○○  ○○○○○  ○○○○○○○
26 Fe  ⊕  ⊕  ⊕⊕⊕   ⊕  ⊕⊕⊕  ⊕⊙⊙⊙⊙   ⊕  ○○○  ○○○○○  ○○○○○○○
27 Co  ⊕  ⊕  ⊕⊕⊕   ⊕  ⊕⊕⊕  ⊕⊕⊙⊙⊙   ⊕  ○○○  ○○○○○  ○○○○○○○
28 Ni  ⊕  ⊕  ⊕⊕⊕   ⊕  ⊕⊕⊕  ⊕⊕⊕⊙⊙   ⊕  ○○○  ○○○○○  ○○○○○○○
29 Cu  ⊕  ⊕  ⊕⊕⊕   ⊕  ⊕⊕⊕  ⊕⊕⊕⊕⊕   ⊙  ○○○  ○○○○○  ○○○○○○○
30 Zn  ⊕  ⊕  ⊕⊕⊕   ⊕  ⊕⊕⊕  ⊕⊕⊕⊕⊕   ⊕  ○○○  ○○○○○  ○○○○○○○
31 Ga  ⊕  ⊕  ⊕⊕⊕   ⊕  ⊕⊕⊕  ⊕⊕⊕⊕⊕   ⊕  ⊙○○  ○○○○○  ○○○○○○○
32 Ge  ⊕  ⊕  ⊕⊕⊕   ⊕  ⊕⊕⊕  ⊕⊕⊕⊕⊕   ⊕  ⊙⊙○  ○○○○○  ○○○○○○○
33 As  ⊕  ⊕  ⊕⊕⊕   ⊕  ⊕⊕⊕  ⊕⊕⊕⊕⊕   ⊕  ⊙⊙⊙  ○○○○○  ○○○○○○○
34 Se  ⊕  ⊕  ⊕⊕⊕   ⊕  ⊕⊕⊕  ⊕⊕⊕⊕⊕   ⊕  ⊕⊙⊙  ○○○○○  ○○○○○○○
35 Br  ⊕  ⊕  ⊕⊕⊕   ⊕  ⊕⊕⊕  ⊕⊕⊕⊕⊕   ⊕  ⊕⊕⊙  ○○○○○  ○○○○○○○
36 Kr  ⊕  ⊕  ⊕⊕⊕   ⊕  ⊕⊕⊕  ⊕⊕⊕⊕⊕   ⊕  ⊕⊕⊕  ○○○○○  ○○○○○○○
```

following chapter, this is the fundamental basis for the periodic law and the periodic table.

Electronic configurations of some of the elements are represented in Figure 7.5.

Test Your Memory

1. Why is an exact physical replica of an atom impossible?
2. What mechanism did Bohr suggest for the production of the different lines emitted in the hydrogen spectrum?
3. What is a *quantum?*
4. What concept did de Broglie add to the picture of an atom?
5. What is a *standing wave?*
6. How does the wave mechanical picture of an atom differ from the model of the hydrogen atom proposed by Bohr?
7. What is represented by each of the four quantum numbers?
8. What does the Pauli principle say about there being two electrons with identical quantum numbers in a given atom?
9. What is the order of orbital filling within any given principal quantum level?
10. Under what conditions can a second electron add to an orbital already containing one electron?
11. Why can there never be more than eight outer-shell electrons in a solitary atom?
12. How many kinds of orbitals are important?
13. How many orbitals of each kind can there be in a given principal quantum level?
14. What is the formula for shell capacity?

8

THE PERIODICITY OF ATOMIC STRUCTURE

THE BUILDING UP OF ELECTRONIC STRUCTURES

Chemists sometimes represent the complete electronic configuration of an atom by a sort of shorthand called **spectral notation.** The principal quantum number of each shell is followed by the letter indicating the kind of orbital, with a superscript number telling how many electrons are in that particular set of orbitals. For example, the structure for hydrogen is given as $1s^1$, or $1s$. (When the number of electrons is only 1, the superscript number is usually omitted.) For helium, the structure is represented as $1s^2$, meaning that two electrons occupy the s orbital of principal quantum level 1. Lithium has the structure $1s^2 2s$. The structure of carbon is represented by $1s^2 2s^2 2p^2$. For fluorine it is $1s^2 2s^2 2p^5$. For lead (compare with Figure 7.1) it is

$$1s^2 2s^2 2p^6 3s^2 3p^6 3d^{10} 4s^2 4p^6 4d^{10} 4f^{14} 5s^2 5p^6 5d^{10} 6s^2 6p^2.$$

However, such complete notation is unnecessary, since the order of decreasing stability of orbitals, *within* each principal quantum level of an atom, is always *s-p-d-f*. The order of occupancy by electrons is the same as the order of decreasing orbital stability. Therefore, the description of the electronic configuration can be simplified by merely giving the total number of electrons in each principal quantum level, beginning with $n = 1$ and continuing upward in n values.

For example, if a given shell has six electrons, the first two of these must be in an s orbital, and the p orbitals have plenty of room for the remaining four. We would interpret 6 as $s^2 p^4$. If there are nine electrons in a given shell, the first two must be s electrons and the next six must be p electrons. That leaves one more which therefore must go into a d orbital. In other words, we would interpret 9 as meaning $s^2 p^6 d$. A shell containing 21 electrons must have them distributed two in an s orbital, six in the three p orbitals, ten in the five d orbitals, and the remaining three in the f orbitals, so we would interpret the 21 as $s^2p^6d^{10}f^3$. Therefore, unless there is special need for the complete configuration, we shall simply write, for example, 21. The distribution cannot be other than that just described. For lead, instead of the lengthy spectral notation given above, we can write: 2-8-18-32-18-4.

When a given shell of an atom holds 16 electrons, how are they distributed?

Using the abbreviated notation for electronic configurations, let us now study how the configurations change as the atomic number progressively increases. Refer to Figure 7.5 whenever it can be helpful. Hydrogen is represented simply as 1, and helium as 2. Two electrons completely fill the first shell, so with lithium a new shell must be begun: 2-1. There follow beryllium 2-2, boron 2-3, carbon 2-4, nitrogen 2-5, oxygen 2-6, fluorine 2-7, and neon 2-8. With these eight electrons, the second shell is filled, so the eleventh electron in sodium must occupy a new, third shell: 2-8-1. Magnesium follows with 2-8-2, aluminum 2-8-3, silicon 2-8-4, phosphorus 2-8-5, sulfur 2-8-6, chlorine 2-8-7, and argon 2-8-8.

At this point the s orbital of the fourth shell offers greater stability than a d orbital of the third. Therefore, although the third shell has a capacity greater than eight, the ninth electron beyond the second shell goes to the fourth shell rather than the third. For potassium, atomic number 19, we have 2-8-8-1. Calcium is 2-8-8-2. The next electron goes into a $3d$ rather than a $4p$ orbital because the former is more stable. For scandium, atomic number 21, then, the structure is 2-8-9-2. Titanium is 2-8-10-2, vanadium 2-8-11-2, and chromium 2-8-13-1.

Why isn't chromium structure written 2-8-12-2? There is much evidence of a special stability associated with spherical symmetry about the nucleus. Individual p, d, and f orbitals are not spherically symmetrical about the nucleus but are directed along certain axes. Collectively, however, complete *sets* of these orbitals *are* spherically symmetrical. This means that if the orbitals are full or half full, the arrangement can be spherically symmetrical and appreciably more stable. In the example of chromium, the number 12 in the third shell implies that two electrons are in the s orbital, six in the p orbitals, and four in the d orbitals. This set of four electrons in five d orbitals has no special stability, because it is asymmetric with respect to the nucleus. But, if a fifth d electron could be acquired, each d orbital would have one. Then spherical symmetry with its increased stability would result. Here the $4s$ orbital is not very different in energy from the $3d$. If one of the $4s$ pair could leave the $4s$ orbital to take the fifth place in the $3d$ orbital set, a more stable arrangement evidently would result. Consequently the arrangement 2-8-13-1, which seems more stable than 2-8-12-2, is written for chromium.

Manganese already has one more electron than chromium. It therefore has enough electrons to make a half-full set of $3d$ orbitals without any contribution from the pair of 4s electrons: 2-8-13-2. Iron is 2-8-14-2, cobalt 2-8-15-2, nickel 2-8-16-2, and copper 2-8-18-1. Why isn't copper 2-8-17-2? This situation is similar to that of chromium. Here the number 17 means that the s and p orbitals are full and the five d orbitals contain only nine electrons, having room for one more. In this arrangement they are not symmetrical with respect to the nucleus, but the addition of one more electron to complete the 3d set would result in extra stability. This appears to happen by transfer of one of the 4s electron pair into the last remaining vacancy of 3d.

Zinc already has enough electrons to fill the 3d orbitals completely: 2-8-18-2. Furthermore, since the third shell is completely filled, additional electrons continue to fill the fourth shell in the p orbitals. Gallium is 2-8-18-3, germanium 2-8-18-4, arsenic 2-8-18-5, selenium 2-8-18-6, bromine 2-8-18-7, and krypton 2-8-18-8. The capacity of the fourth shell is 32, so 8 is nowhere near the limit. Nevertheless, the 37th electron finds the 5s orbital more stable than either the 4d or the 4f, so the structure of rubidium, atomic number 37, is 2-8-18-8-1. Strontium is 2-8-18-8-2.

Next we encounter a situation very similar to that of calcium, with atomic number 20. The filling of the fifth shell, just like the filling of the fourth shell, is interrupted while the underlying d orbitals are being filled. The ten elements from calcium to zinc constitute the interruption corresponding to the filling of 3d orbitals. The ten elements from strontium to cadmium correspond to the filling of 4d orbitals. When these have been filled, only then can the filling of the outermost shell, here the fifth, be continued. Electrons are added to the 5p orbitals from indium to xenon, with atomic number 54 and the electronic structure 2-8-18-18-8.

Again, the fifth shell is capable of accommodating many more electrons than eight, but the sixth shell offers its s orbital to the 55th electron as being more stable than a 5d or a 5f orbital. Cesium, with atomic number 55, has the structure 2-8-18-18-8-1, followed by barium, 2-8-18-18-8-2. Next the situation which occurred with calcium and strontium repeats itself. Instead of continuing the filling of the sixth shell, the next element, lanthanum, has an electron in the 5d orbitals. The two preceding interruptions in the filling of the outermost shell might lead us to expect beyond lanthanum another series of ten elements corresponding to the filling of the 5d orbitals.

But at this point still another complication arises. By the time the nuclear charge has been increased to 58, the 4f orbitals, previously left entirely vacant, become stable enough to receive electrons. Consequently there is an *interruption within an interruption*. Before the 6p orbitals can be filled, the 5d orbitals must be filled, but before they can be completely filled, the 4f orbitals must be filled. Since these are seven in number and can accommodate 14 electrons, there is a series of 14 elements interrupting the series of ten elements, which in turn interrupts the series of eight elements that would correspond to the filling of the outermost shell. When finally these 24 elements are inserted, the filling of the outermost shell resumes and continues until that shell holds eight electrons, at radon, with atomic number 86 and electronic configuration 2-8-18-32-18-8.

Beyond this point, the pattern is self-repeating. Electrons first fill the $7s$ orbitals, in francium and radium. There follows an interruption to fill the $6d$ orbitals, followed almost immediately before the d orbitals are filled by a second interruption to fill the $5f$ orbitals. At last, with element 104, these $5f$ orbitals have been filled. The filling of the $6d$ orbitals can now be resumed. However, no elements of higher atomic number are yet known. We can predict that the filling of $6d$ orbitals will be continued until complete, after which the filling of the seventh shell up to eight electrons, at atomic number 118, could be expected: 2-8-18-32-32-18-8.

THE PERIODIC LAW

Now let us examine the pattern of filling of the outermost shell as the chemical elements are built up one by one. In Figure 8.1, the number of outer-shell electrons is plotted against the atomic number. The important thing to notice is that this number of outer-shell electrons changes *periodically* with atomic number. There is a recurrent filling of outermost shells to eight electrons. No element has atoms with more than eight electrons in its outermost shell. Therefore, the following observation can be made: Atomic structure varies with atomic number in a periodic manner. Or, the **atomic structure is a periodic function of the atomic number.**

Figure 8.1. Periodicity of Outer-Shell Electrons.

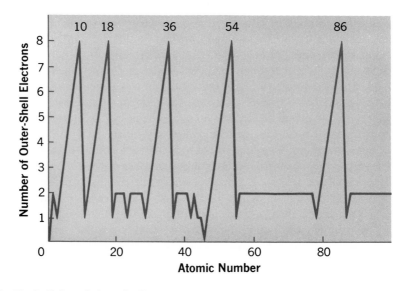

These are the fundamental statements of what is known as the **periodic law.** The periodic law was discovered in a different form over a century ago, long before anything was known about atomic structure. It is now recognized that the periodic law is firmly founded upon the fundamentals of the electronic configurations of the atoms. In its usual form, the periodic law states that the *properties* of the elements vary periodically with atomic number. The reason this is true is that the **properties depend on electronic configuration.**

PERIODIC TABLES

The periodic *law* is fundamental. Periodic *tables* are arbitrarily constructed to organize the facts based on the periodic law in the most useful manner. Since every chemist has his own personal opinion as to what kind of organization is most useful, many forms of the periodic table are known. They all have the same basic purpose: to organize the elements in chart form so that their similarities can be better recognized and their trends from one extreme to another presented in an orderly fashion. You will be able to appreciate the periodic table more fully after you have learned more about chemistry. For the present, it will be useful to become acquainted with it, in terms of what we have just learned about atomic structure.

In trying to learn what causes the apparent differences among the chemical elements, we should note that the underlying electronic configurations of the chemical elements are very nearly alike. The outer structure, on the other hand, is quite variable, and we should therefore look to this outer structure to explain the observable differences among the elements.

Because of the cyclic or periodic variation in the number of outer-shell electrons, certain outer-shell structures recur as the atomic number increases. For example, lithium (atomic number 3), sodium (11), potassium (19), rubidium (37), cesium (55), and francium (87) are all alike in having one outer-shell electron. Similarly, beryllium, magnesium, calcium, strontium, barium, and radium are alike in having two electrons in the outermost shell. Boron, aluminum, gallium, indium, and thallium all have three electrons in the outermost shell; the outermost shells of carbon, silicon, germanium, tin, and lead have four electrons; those of nitrogen, phosphorus, arsenic, antimony, and bismuth have five electrons; oxygen, sulfur, selenium, tellurium, and polonium have six electrons; fluorine, chlorine, bromine, iodine, and astatine have seven electrons; and neon, argon krypton, xenon, and radon have eight electrons. Those elements having similar external structure are recognized as families, or groups, having similar physical and chemical properties.

In addition, there is a series of elements from lithium to neon in which the number of outer-shell electrons increases progressively: Li 1, Be 2, B 3, C 4, N 5, O 6, F 7, Ne 8. A similar series is that from sodium to argon: Na 1, Mg 2, Al 3, Si 4, P 5, S 6, Cl 7, Ar 8. Another exists from potassium to krypton: K 1, Ca 2.....Zn 2, Ga 3, Ge 4, As 5, Se 6, Br 7, Kr 8. This series however is interrupted by the nine elements between calcium and zinc

Figure 8.2.   Periodic Arrangement of Major Group Elements

The table below lists the nontransitional elements by periods (horizontal rows) and groups (vertical columns). The symbol for each element is followed by its atomic number. The series of numbers on the next line represents the electronic configuration of an atom of the element.

Li 3 2–1	Be 4 2–2							
Na 11 2–8–1	Mg 12 2–8–2		Al 13 2–8–3	Si 14 2–8–4	P 15 2–8–5	S 16 2–8–6	Cl 17 2–8–7	Ar 18 2–8–8
			B 5 2–3	C 6 2–4	N 7 2–5	O 8 2–6	F 9 2–7	Ne 10 2–8
K 19 2–8–8–1	Ca 20 2–8–8–2	Zn 30 2–8–18–2	Ga 31 2–8–18–3	Ge 32 2–8–18–4	As 33 2–8–18–5	Se 34 2–8–18–6	Br 35 2–8–18–7	Kr 36 2–8–18–8
Rb 37 2–8–18– 8–1	Sr 38 2–8–18– 8–2	Cd 48 2–8–18– 18–2	In 49 2–8–18– 18–3	Sn 50 2–8–18– 18–4	Sb 51 2–8–18– 18–5	Te 52 2–8–18– 18–6	I 53 2–8–18– 18–7	Xe 54 2–8–18– 18–8
Cs 55 2–8–18– 18–8–1	Ba 56 2–8–18– 18–8–2	Hg 80 2–8–18– 32–18–2	Tl 81 2–8–18– 32–18–3	Pb 82 2–8–18– 32–18–4	Bi 83 2–8–18– 32–18–5	Po 84 2–8–18– 32–18–6	At 85 2–8–18– 32–18–7	Rn 86 2–8–18– 32–18–8

from scandium to copper, none of which has more than two outer-shell electrons. Another series exists from rubidium to xenon: Rb 1, Sr 2 . . . . . Cd 2, In 3, Sn 4, Sb 5, Te 6, I 7, Xe 8. This series is also interrupted, by nine elements between strontium and cadmium from yttrium to silver, none of which has more than two outermost electrons. Another series begins with cesium and ends with radon: Cs 1, Ba 2 . . . . . Hg 2, Tl 3, Pb 4, Bi 5, Po 6, At 7, Rn 8.

Each of these series begins with an element having one outer-shell electron, and ends with an element having eight outer-shell electrons. These series are generally called **periods** since they correspond to the periodicity of atomic structure. If these series are now placed one below another so that the beginning of each series forms a vertical column and the end of each series also forms a vertical column, the elements are thus arranged so that the eight families or groups listed above are together in vertical columns. Uniform trends, or corresponding parts of the separate periods are also together from left to right. This is the beginning of a periodic table, as shown in Figure 8.2.

In this most common form of periodic table, the elements have been placed vertically in groups and horizontally in periods. Notice that omitted for the present are those elements that constitute interruptions in the octet formation in the outermost shell. There is a fundamental reason for this omission, which we can understand much better after a study of those elements. Briefly, when the **penultimate** shell (immediately underlying the outermost shell) contains 2 or 8 or 18 electrons (except for copper, silver, and gold which are more or less in a class by themselves), the properties of the element depend mainly on the number of electrons in the outermost shell. But if the penultimate shell contains partially filled d orbitals, then the properties of the element depend on electrons of both the outermost shell and the penultimate shell. As a class, the properties of the elements that depend only on the outermost shell differ significantly from those of elements that depend on both outermost and penultimate shells. It is, therefore, most useful not only to discuss these classes separately, but also to place them separately in the periodic table.

The elements whose properties depend mainly on the number of outermost shell electrons are called **major group elements.** Those dependent on both outermost and penultimate shells are called **transitional elements** or **transitional group elements.** Most periodic tables, including the form most popular today, insert the transitional elements at the point of their interruption, between the major group elements. They are not consistent in this, however, because the f-orbital filling constitutes too long an interruption and would make the chart too awkward. This interruption within an interruption, called the **inner transitional elements,** is usually arranged below the major part of the table.

There is little or no advantage in splitting the major group elements apart by forcing the transitional elements between them, as is customarily done. We will arrange the transitional elements separately, indicating clearly where they would go in the periodic system. The inner transitional elements are arranged similarly.

Table 8.1. Old and New Periodic Table Group Numbers	Major Groups		Transitional Groups	
	Old	New	Old	New
	IA	M1	IB	T11
	IIA	M2	IIIB	T3
	IIB	M2′	IVB	T4
	IIIA	M3	VB	T5
	IVA	M4	VIB	T6
	VA	M5	VIIB	T7
	VIA	M6		T8
	VIIA	M7	VIII	T9
	O	M8		T10

The usual convention for distinguishing the different groups of the periodic table is to call the major group elements **A groups** (IA, IIA, etc.) and the transitional elements (or **subgroups**) **B groups** (IB, IIB, and so on). Unfortunately, however, this custom is not internationally standardized. A great deal of confusion exists in the world's chemical literature because chemists in one country cannot be sure which elements are meant by the group number assigned by chemists of a different country. There are other objections, too, to the A, B classification and the present numbering system. Therefore we will designate major groups by M plus number (M1, M2, and so on) and transitional groups by T plus number (T3, T4, and so on). Table 8.1 lists the presently accepted group numbers according to the usual American (but not British) convention, together with the new numbers proposed and used here in their place.

A special place had to be made for zinc, cadmium, and mercury, which differ from calcium, strontium, and barium, respectively, in having 18 instead of eight electrons in the penultimate shell, although they have two electrons in the outermost shell. These elements are usually included with the transitional elements but they have no business there at all. We shall place them with the major group elements where they certainly belong. Their group is labeled M2′ to distinguish it from M2.

In building a periodic table the electronic configurations of the transitional elements must be considered. They are all similar with respect to the outermost shell. With very few exceptions, such as chromium and copper, all have two outer-shell electrons. The distinguishing features of their electronic configurations are found in the penultimate shell. Here similarities exist among those elements having the same number of d electrons in their penultimate shells. For example, one d electron is in the penultimate shell of scandium, yttrium, and lanthanum. Titanium, zirconium, and hafnium have two d electrons. Vanadium, niobium and tantalum have three d electrons, and so on. Trends of increasing number of d electrons also occur periodically. The first series of transitional elements begins with scandium, Sc, with one d electron, and ends with copper, with 10 d electrons. A second series begins with yttrium, with one d electron, and ends with silver, with 10 d electrons. A third series

Figure 8.3.   Periodic Arrangement of Transitional Elements.

The table below lists the transitional elements by period and group. The information is laid out in the same manner as Fig. 8.2.

Sc 21	Ti 22	V 23	Cr 24	Mn 25	Fe 26	Co 27	Ni 28	Cu 29
2–8–9–2	2–8–10–2	2–8–11–2	2–8–13–1	2–8–13–2	2–8–14–2	2–18–15–2	2–8–16–2	2–8–18–1
Y 39	Zr 40	Nb 41	Mo 42	Tc 43	Ru 44	Rh 45	Pd 46	Ag 47
2–8–18–9–2	2–8–18–10–2	2–8–18–11–2	2–8–18–13–1	2–8–18–13–2	2–8–18–15–1	2–8–18–16–1	2–8–18–18–0	2–8–18–18–1
La 57	Hf 72	Ta 73	W 74	Re 75	Os 76	Ir 77	Pt 78	Au 79
2–8–18–18–9–2	2–8–18–32–10–2	2–8–18–32–11–2	2–8–18–32–12–2	2–8–18–32–13–2	2–8–18–32–14–2	2–8–18–32–15–2	2–8–18–32–17–1	2–8–18–32–18–1

begins with lanthanum, is interrupted immediately by an inner transitional series, and then continues to gold, with 10 d electrons. A fourth series begins with actinium, is immediately interrupted by an inner transitional series, and finally resumes at element 104. This last series is incomplete since no element above 104 is presently known.

By arranging the similar structures vertically and the trends or series horizontally, as before, a periodic table of transitional elements can be constructed as shown in Figure 8.3.

If Figures 8.2 and 8.3 are combined, and the inner transitional elements are added, the complete periodic system can be represented as in the periodic table of Figure 8.4. This form will be used throughout the rest of this book. It is an arbitrary arrangement. Many others have been proposed and several others are in common use. All are firmly based on the periodic law which, in turn, is based on atomic structure.

THE PERIODIC TABLE USED HERE

Figure 8.4 contains the table which is described below.

In this table, separate blocks are devoted to the major groups, the transitional groups, and the inner transitional elements because these three blocks of elements are customarily studied separately.

The major groups are designated by M and the transitional groups by T. For the major-group elements, M is followed by a number which equals the number of outer-shell electrons. For example, all elements of group M1 have one outer-shell electron. All elements of group M4 have four outer-shell electrons. All elements of group M7 have seven outer-shell electrons. The only exception is helium, which is placed in M8 because it resembles the rest of that group in properties, although its one shell limits it to two outer electrons.

For transitional groups, T is followed by a number equal, for the first two members only, to the number of electrons beyond an M8 element. For example, manganese in T7 has seven electrons more than argon, 18. Technetium has seven electrons more than krypton, 36. This does not hold for the third member of each group beyond T3, where 14 additional f electrons are also present. In other words, these elements have atomic numbers equal to 54 for xenon plus their group T number plus 14. Thus the atomic number of iridium in T9 is $54 + 14 + 9 = 77$.

The gap between M2 and M2′, which accommodates the transitional elements or, rather, indicates where they would go in order of atomic number, is shown physically by a separation in the chart. This separation extends not only vertically but also horizontally across the chart from zinc to bromine. This significant gap indicates that from M3 to M7, the elements within a group change downward fundamentally in electronic structure from an underlying shell of eight to an underlying shell of 18. Consequently, a smooth transition in properties down a major group from M3 to M7 cannot reasonably be ex-

Figure 8.4. Revised Form of Periodic Table.

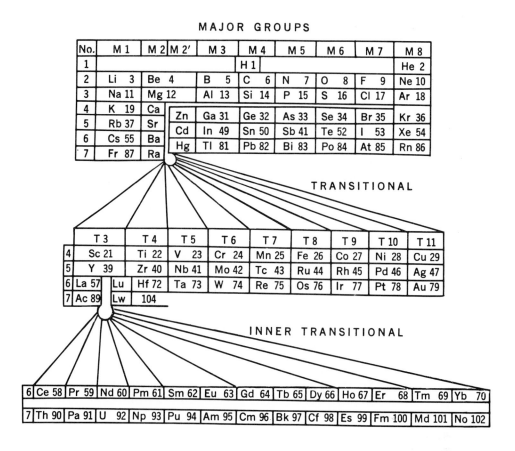

pected. Failure to show this clearly in older tables has led to serious and sometimes costly misinterpretations of the periodic table. Elements within each group, both M and T, increase in atomic number and atomic weight from top to bottom.

Hydrogen does not belong in any group but because its outer shell is half full, it more nearly resembles other elements (M4) having half-filled outer shells and is placed above and near M4.

Zinc, cadmium, and mercury are placed with the major group elements as M2′ to distinguish them from calcium, strontium, and barium as M2. In practically all other periodic tables they are included with the transitional elements. As we shall see, the M2′ elements always behave like major group elements and never like transitional elements. The placement with the major group elements as in Figure 8.4 is therefore long overdue.

As we will see in the rest of this book, certain similarities can be predicted among all the elements within any one group. Moderately uniform trends in properties are observed along each period from left to right, so that each element tends to be intermediate in properties between its horizontal neighbors. All transitional and inner transitional elements are metals. In the major groups, the trend is from metal at the left to nonmetal at the right, and from lesser to greater metallic properties from top to bottom within a group.

HISTORY OF THE PERIODIC LAW

As the discovery of new elements accelerated in the early 1800's, chemistry became more varied and more complex, and chemists began to wonder whether an unlimited number of elements might exist. Although certain similarities were noted among certain of the elements, the differences were even more conspicuous, and there seemed to be no obvious basis for organizing the elements in some systematic pattern. The first recorded observation which demonstrated any consistency was that of Johann Wolfgang Döbereiner (1780–1849), a professor at Jena, Germany. Döbereiner observed that certain triads of elements bore marked similarity to one another, and that the intermediate element had an atomic weight nearly the average of the other two. Among the fifty-five elements known in 1829, he observed that bromine seemed very similar to and intermediate between chlorine and iodine. Looking for more such groups of three, he also noticed the similarities of sulfur, selenium, and tellurium, and of calcium, strontium, and barium. But these three groups seemed to be all. No overall pattern emerged to include the remaining 46 elements, so Döbereiner's triads made relatively little impression.

During the following decades a dozen or more additional elements were discovered and the importance of atomic weights became recognized. But 33 years elapsed before further attempts to organize the elements in some systematic pattern. In 1862 a French geologist named Alexandre-Émile Béguyer de Chancourtois (1820–1886) arranged the known elements in order of increasing atomic weights and plotted them along a spiral graph which juxtaposed elements of similar nature. He commented on the apparent periodicity of properties and remarked that "the properties of substances are the properties of numbers." This attempt, like Döbereiner's, seemed to make little impression. The recognition of the importance of periodicity awaited a more favorable climate.

An English chemist named John A. R. Newlands (1837–1898) was next to present similar ideas. In 1864 he observed that when the elements were aligned in order of increasing atomic weight, every eighth element had similar properties. At that time there was no knowledge of atomic structure, and the concepts of atomic number or electronic configurations had not yet been developed. Furthermore, the M8 elements were not yet discovered, or Newlands would have said every ninth element. By analogy to the musical scale, Newlands called his observation the Law of Octaves. Unfortunately he didn't realize that only the early periods consist of eight elements, and in trying to recognize similarities where none existed, he weakened his arguments. When he presented these ideas at a scientific meeting they were received with ridicule, one scoffer asking him publicly whether he had tried aligning the elements alphabetically. When he tried to publish his paper he encountered difficulties with an editor who insisted the work was not worth publishing. Twenty-three years later the Royal Society awarded him their highest honor, the Davy medal, for his work, and the scoffer is remembered solely for his scoffing. What brought this change in attitude?

For one thing, other chemists were thinking along similar lines. A German chemist named Julius Lothar Meyer (1830–1895) studied the way in which the volume of a mole of atoms of each element changed with increasing atomic weight. He found that this "atomic volume" went through a cyclic pattern, with peaks at the alkali metals. Thus there were seven elements from peak to peak, just as Newlands had claimed, from lithium to sodium and from sodium to potassium. Beyond potassium, however, the distance to the next peak at rubidium was much greater, which showed where Newlands' Law of Octaves had encountered trouble. This gave Meyer an idea for arranging the elements in a periodic table, which he published in 1864 in incomplete form. In 1869 he extended this to include 56 elements arranged in groups and periods, but this work was not published until 1870.

Meanwhile, an imaginative Russian chemist named Dmitri Ivanovich Mendeleev (1834–1907) was similarly engaged. In 1869 he presented a now-famous paper entitled "The Relation of the Properties to the Atomic Weights of the Elements," including a periodic table which closely resembles those of today. He was not fooled into trying to force elements into positions to which their properties did not entitle them just because they were next in line among known atomic weights. Instead, he recognized gaps where elements remained to be discovered. For example, the next known element following zinc was arsenic. Zinc he recognized as resembling magnesium, but arsenic certainly did not resemble aluminum or silicon. Mendeleev, therefore, left two gaps following zinc and placed arsenic under phosphorus where it belongs. He boldly predicted that two new elements would one day be found to fill these gaps. One, under aluminum, he called "eka-aluminum," and the other, under silicon, he called "eka-silicon." He also left a blank after calcium which he called "eka-boron." Then he really stuck his neck out by predicting the atomic weights of these unknown elements and the properties of some of their compounds, and sat back to see what would happen. What did?

In 1875 an element corresponding to "eka-aluminum" was found and named gallium. In 1879 an element having the properties predicted for "eka-boron" was discovered. It was named scandium. In 1886 the element called germanium was discovered. It had the properties predicted for "eka-silicon." Mendeleev by this time had become a hero. He had stuck his neck out and it had paid off. In fact, in 1882 both he and Lothar Meyer were awarded the Davy medal. It took another five years for someone to say, "What about John Newlands?" Belatedly, another Davy medal came to him.

Thus, at least four men worked on very similar ideas during approximately the same period. But of these, Mendeleev receives major credit because of the phenomenal success of his predictions. He was bold enough to make them, smart enough to make them correctly, and lucky enough to have them verified by experiment within his own lifetime.

The periodic law is one of the great generalizations of all science. For us it will serve, through the periodic table, as a solid framework upon which to assemble and organize a vast variety of chemical information. The periodic table is the skeleton of chemistry, without which the whole body of chemical information would collapse into an unstructured, formless heap. But a skeleton is far from the most pleasant type of companion, so we will devote the rest of this book to building flesh onto the bones.

Test Your Memory

1. What is the order of decreasing stability of orbitals, within a given principal quantum level?
2. How is electronic configuration represented by spectral notation?
3. Why does the outer shell of an atom never have more than eight electrons?
4. In terms of structure, what is the periodic law? Explain.
5. What similarities justify the grouping of elements in the periodic system?
6. Define a *period*.
7. What is a *penultimate shell?*
8. What are *major group elements?*
9. What are *transitional elements?*
10. What are *inner transitional elements?* What is their electronic distinction?
11. Which group begins each period? Which group ends each period?
12. Beginning with hydrogen and helium as period I, how many elements are in each period?

Test Your Understanding

1. Which element is represented as $1s^2 2s^2 2p^6 3s^2 3p^6 3d^{10} 4s^2 4p^5$? In what group is it?
2. Write out the complete spectral notation for the structure 2-8-16-2.
3. How many p electrons are in a shell containing 14 electrons?

9

RADIOACTIVITY AND NUCLEAR ENERGY

NATURAL RADIOACTIVITY

Beginning in the late 1800's, the passage of electricity through an evacuated tube fitted with a metal lead called the cathode and another called the anode attracted great interest from physicists. In these vacuum tubes electricity appeared to jump the large gap between the electrodes or metallic leads in the form of *cathode rays*. Michael Faraday (1791–1867), an extremely talented experimentalist who had been trained as an assistant to Sir Humphrey Davy, had tried to force electricity through a vacuum but failed because the means of producing vacuums were inadequate in his day. The eventual production of better vacuums enabled the German physicist Julius Plücker (1801–1868) to begin investigating the passage of electricity through a tube in 1855.

The English physicist William Crookes (1832–1919) in 1875 improved the design of such a tube, called a Crookes tube in his honor. The nature of cathode rays gradually became evident through the work of Plücker, Crookes, and then the Englishman Joseph John Thomson (1856–1940), who finally established that a cathode ray was a stream of particles bearing a negative charge. At first it was possible only to measure the ratio of charge to mass in these particles, but then an American physicist, Robert Andrews Millikan (1868–1953), succeeded in measuring the charge itself. Using the charge-to-mass ratio and the charge, it was possible to calculate the mass of each particle as about 1/1840 that of the hydrogen atom. The particles were named **electrons** by the Irish physicist George J. Stoney (1826–1911).

X rays

This is a brief sketch of the background for the discovery of X rays. As the German physicist Wilhelm Konrad Roentgen (1845–1923) was studying the glow emitted when cathode rays struck certain chemical substances in a Crookes tube, he noticed a substance some distance outside the tube emitting light. This light appeared only when the current was on. Evidently some kind of radiation was escaping from the tube, passing through its glass wall and striking the substance outside. Roentgen discovered that even when he took this substance into the next room, it still glowed when the Crookes tube was turned on. The radiation apparently passed not only through the wall of the tube but also through the wall of the room. This was the discovery of the ultrahigh frequency electromagnetic radiation now known as X rays.

This discovery aroused great interest among scientists, one of whom was the Frenchman Antoine Henri Becquerel (1852–1908). In 1896 he was studying the phenomenon of *fluorescence,* the emission of light by a substance while it is irradiated by light from the sun or some other source. One of the substances that will glow when placed in sunlight is a uranium compound. Becquerel wondered if the light emitted by this sunlit compound included X rays. Knowing the penetrating power of X rays, he wrapped a photographic plate in heavy paper which sunlight could not penetrate, laid some crystals of the uranium compound on it, and exposed them to the sun. When he developed the plate, he found it had been fogged as though some kind of radiation had penetrated the protective layer of paper. He was naturally anxious to investigate further, but when he was all ready to perform another similar experiment, the sun disappeared into the clouds and failed to return for several days. Disgusted, he laid the protected photographic plate in a drawer with the crystals on it, to await better weather. But after several cloudy days he decided to develop the plate anyway. Much to his surprise, it was fogged even more than when the crystals had been exposed to the sun. He concluded that the rays which penetrated the paper need not have been induced by sunlight but might have come directly from the crystals. Further experiments confirmed this conclusion, and **radioactivity** had been discovered.

Working in Becquerel's laboratory was a young Polish graduate student, Marja Skłodowska Curie (1867–1934), who had recently married the French physicist Pierre Curie. Impressed with her ability, Becquerel told her about his new discovery and suggested that she try to find out which components of his uranium compounds and ores were responsible for their continuous radiation. This she did for her doctoral thesis, in collaboration with her husband. Their work led to the discovery that thorium as well as uranium was radioactive. They also discovered two new elements, radium and polonium, the latter named for Madame Curie's native Poland. For this work they, along with Becquerel, received the Nobel Prize in 1903.

The researches of Madame Curie and others, which were painstaking, laborious, and unexpectedly dangerous, shed much light on this new area of great and fundamental importance. Their work paved the way for an intensive study of the atomic nucleus, the understanding of which has permitted production of energy in quantities never before possible, and hazards of awesome magnitude for the human race.

Alpha, Beta, and Gamma Radiation

Three principal types of radiation from naturally occurring minerals have been recognized: **alpha, beta,** and **gamma** radiation. Alpha radiation consists of helium nuclei having mass 4 and a positive charge of 2, emitted from larger nuclei at high velocity. Beta radiation consists of electrons of high energy. Gamma radiation is high energy radiation similar to X rays, having neither charge nor mass.

A nucleus which suddenly emits an alpha particle discards two positive charges, reducing its atomic number by two. This process makes it an atom of a different element. The element is said to have **transmuted** itself to a different element. No ordinary chemical reaction can ever accomplish this. For centuries the alchemists had sought this kind of reaction: some way of changing mercury or lead into gold.

Electrons emitted as beta radiation originate in the nucleus, where there are no free electrons. Apparently these electrons originate from a neutron which thus becomes a proton. This additional proton in the nucleus increases the atomic number of the atom by one unit. Again, transmutation of the element has occurred, but in the opposite direction.

Several progressions of radioactive decay have been recognized. The most familiar is that of uranium, number 92, through radium, number 88, to lead, 82. Lead is not radioactive, so the series stops there. Each radioactive isotope of the intervening elements in the series has a different degree of radioactivity. There is absolutely no way of predicting when any given unstable nucleus will disintegrate. If the rate of radioactive decay is carefully studied for samples containing billions of radioactive atoms, a **half-life** can be established for each isotope. Beginning with a statistically large number of atoms, at the end of a certain period of time (the half-life of that particular kind of atom), half of these atoms will have disintegrated. At the end of the next equal period of time, half of the remainder will have disintegrated, and so on. Half-lives vary widely for different isotopes and different elements. Some radioactive isotopes have very long half-lives, measuring thousands or even millions of years. Others have extremely short half-lives, some as short as a fraction of a second.

ARTIFICIAL RADIOACTIVITY

Naturally occurring radioactive isotopes are chiefly those of elements high in atomic number. However, bombardment with nuclear particles such as neutrons can convert nuclei of elements of intermediate atomic number into radioactive isotopes. This was discovered in 1934 by the French physicists, Frederic Joliot-Curie and his wife Irene. When they bombarded aluminum with alpha particles, they discovered that once irradiated, the aluminum continued to give off radiation after the bombardment had ceased. The aluminum nucleus had been transformed from one of 13 protons and 14 neutrons to one of 15 protons and 15 neutrons, which made it no longer aluminum but phosphorus. Normally the phosphorus atom has 16 neutrons in its nucleus. With only 15 it is unstable and radioactive with a half-life of 14 days.

Since 1934 more than a thousand new isotopes of the different elements have been created, and they are all radioactive. These artificially produced **radioisotopes** have many uses. They behave chemically exactly like the normal isotope of the same element, yet they can be traced through a chemical reaction or physical movement (such as osmosis) by detection of the radiation which they emit. These radioactive tracer techniques permit chemical studies that would have been either extremely difficult or impossible by any other known methods. For example, a little radioactive phosphorus introduced into ordinary fertilizer may be followed closely in its progress through a corn plant—into the roots, up the stalk, into the leaves and tassels and so on—without destroying the plant or harming it in any way. Some radioisotopes have value primarily for the radiation they emit, for fighting malignancies or for sterilizing food.

Perhaps the best known of the detection devices used in radiation work is the Geiger counter, a gas tube which works on the principle that gas does not conduct electricity well unless it contains **ions,** which are atoms bearing

Figure 9.1. Geiger-Müller Radiation Counter.

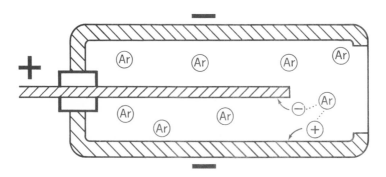

A particle or ray from a radioactive source strikes atoms of argon gas contained in the tube. Electrons are knocked off the argon atoms which become positively charged gaseous ions. The ionized argon gas is a conductor. A potential difference of about 1000 volts is maintained across the gas-filled tube, causing a detectable surge of current to flow each time a ray enters the tube and ionizes some argon atoms.

charge. If the space between two highly charged electrodes is occupied by a gas, as in a Geiger counter, no current will flow unless the gas becomes ionized. When radiation penetrates the gas tube, it knocks electrons off of hundreds of otherwise neutral molecules. The electrical resistance of the gas is broken down at once. A surge of electrons crosses from one electrode to the other. This surge can be electrically identified and counted, so each ray that enters the counter can be recorded. The intensity of the radiation is evaluated in terms of the number of counts per minute. Each count indicates the presence of a single atom whose nucleus has just disintegrated.

TRANSURANIUM ELEMENTS

For many years no element of higher atomic number than uranium, 92, was known. The brilliant Italian physicist, Enrico Fermi (1901–1954), postulated that elements of a higher atomic number could be prepared by bombarding uranium with neutrons. He tried this experiment in 1934 but was unable to determine whether such an element had been prepared. In 1940 the bombardment of uranium with neutrons was studied by two Americans, Edwin M. McMillan (1907–   ) and Philip H. Abelson (1913–   ), who identified a product of atomic number 93, which they named neptunium. Apparently, when uranium of mass 238 is bombarded by neutrons, it may absorb one neutron to become a uranium isotope of mass 239 which is unstable and emits a beta ray. The loss of an electron from the nucleus leaves a new proton, causing the nucleus to increase by one in atomic number. Thus neptunium is formed. By similar means artificial elements with atomic numbers up to 104 have been created, and additional ones are possible.

NUCLEAR ENERGY

Fission

The great physicist Albert Einstein (1879–1955) determined a relationship between mass and energy, $E = Mc^2$, where c is the speed of light. The square of the speed of light is such an enormous number [(9×10^{100}) cm^2/sec^2] that the conversion of a very small mass to energy must produce an extraordinary amount of energy. Although in theory this had been recognized for many years, most scientists believed that the actual process might never be accomplished. But following the work of Fermi on neutron bombardment of uranium, two German chemists, Otto Hahn and Lise Meitner, continued the work of trying to identify the products. They became convinced that one of the products was a radioactive isotope of element 56, barium.

No previously observed nuclear transmutation had involved a change in atomic number greater than one or two. If Hahn and Meitner were correct, the bombardment of uranium by neutrons was producing an element 36 units lower in atomic number. The uranium nucleus was apparently splitting apart, undergoing what is termed **fission.** Since atoms of lower atomic number need fewer neutrons per proton for stability of their nuclei, such fission would be expected to release surplus neutrons, each of which might cause another fission in a chain reaction. The energy released by a nuclear reaction was known to be much greater than for an ordinary chemical reaction, so this new process presented the possibility of releasing enormous amounts of energy by the conversion of only a little mass.

Fearful lest their enemies develop practical methods of obtaining such energy first, the Americans began a crash program, the Manhattan Project to accomplish this. Many illustrious American scientists, aided by Fermi, who had fled from Mussolini's Italy, succeeded in developing the nuclear fission for use in an atomic bomb.

The uranium isotope with mass 235, which occurs only as a very small fraction of natural uranium, was found to be much more fissionable by neutron bombardment than the common isotope of mass 238. There are enough stray neutrons in the atmosphere resulting from cosmic radiation to initiate the

Figure 9.2. Nuclear Fission.

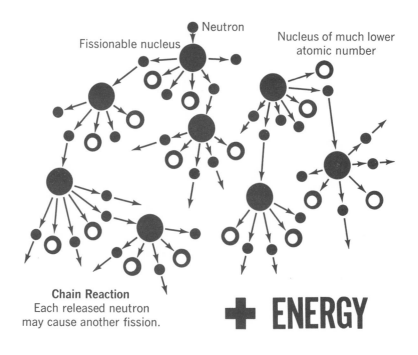

Neutron

Fissionable nucleus

Nucleus of much lower atomic number

Chain Reaction
Each released neutron may cause another fission.

+ ENERGY

fission of uranium 235. However, a chain reaction of explosive proportions does not occur unless at least a certain minimum mass of the isotope, called the **critical mass,** is present. The bomb can be a device in which two portions of uranium 235, each smaller than the critical mass, can be driven together by a small explosion. With the critical mass exceeded, the chain reaction accelerates out of control and a tremendous detonation occurs.

Production of nuclear energy can be controlled by moderating the chain reaction, inserting cadmium rods into the fissionable material. These absorb neutrons readily, preventing them from building to an excessive concentration. Another moderator, graphite, slows down the neutrons released by fission so that they can cause additional fission, which they do not do if they are moving too fast.

Most of the mass of the uranium remains unchanged in a nuclear fission reaction. If the total mass could be converted to energy, one gram could produce as much energy as is obtained by the burning of 3,000 tons of coal.

Fallout

One of the principal hazards associated with nuclear weapons, outside the immediate vicinity of their explosion, is the highly radioactive products of fission. Among these is an isotope of strontium with a mass of 90, which has a long half-life (over 27 years) yet is dangerously radioactive. The chemical similarity between calcium and strontium, arising from their electronic similarity (see Chapter 8), permits strontium, whether ordinary or radioactive, to find its way into the bones of living animals, where radioactivity can cause leukemia and other damaging diseases. Thus although most of the elements in the fission products which constitute **radioactive fallout** have an intense radioactivity that is "burned out" within a few days, strontium-90 is an exception.

Fusion

The total atomic mass of an element is never quite as large as the sum of the masses of the nucleons (i.e., protons and neutrons) which presumably compose it. For instance, the mass of the neutron is 1.00866 amu, and that of the proton, 1.00732 amu. The sum of the masses of two neutrons and two protons, corresponding to the helium nucleus, is 4.03196 amu. Yet the atomic mass of helium is only 4.002. The difference, plus the mass of the electrons, is believed to represent the mass converted to the nuclear **binding energy** when the individual nucleons joined together to form the helium nucleus. The average binding energy per nucleon, considered for all the elements, increases with increasing atomic weights up to the neighborhood of 50 to 80 amu and then goes down again. This suggests that the most stable nuclei are those of elements near iron, and that the breakdown of heavier nuclei to such elements is only one way by which energy might be produced from nuclear transformations.

The other way is by the build-up of the intermediate elements from lighter nuclei. Even building up light elements from still lighter elements should produce energy. The production of nuclear energy by combining lighter nuclei to form heavier ones is called **fusion.** It is the source of energy of the

Figure 9.3. Nuclear Fusion.

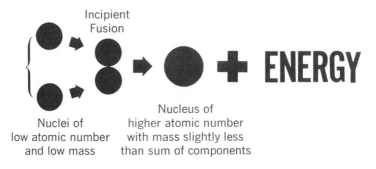

Incipient Fusion

Nuclei of
low atomic number
and low mass

Nucleus of
higher atomic number
with mass slightly less
than sum of components

hydrogen bomb and is believed to be the source of energy in the sun, where hydrogen atoms appear to be fusing to form helium atoms.

Whereas nuclear fission can be brought about fairly readily if the appropriate isotopes are available, such isotopes are in limited supply. Much greater quantities of lighter elements are available. If hydrogen could be caused to form helium or some similar fusion could be brought about under controlled conditions on earth, an indefinitely large supply of useful energy would become available. At present, it seems necessary to initiate a fusion reaction by heating substances to temperatures on the order of a million degrees. Such temperatures so far can be produced only by nuclear fission. Consequently, a hydrogen bomb has to be exploded by means of an atomic bomb of the fission type. No practical way of initiating or controlling the reaction has yet been discovered although the problem is being widely studied.

Although recent work has shown a number of interesting interactions between outer electrons and atomic nuclei that shed light on the nature of chemical bonding, for practical purposes it will be satisfactory to regard the atomic nucleus as merely a positive charge at the center of the atom. The chemical and physical properties of the elements, unrelated to the stability of their nuclei, are also essentially unrelated to the particular structure of their nuclei.

Test Your Memory

1. What is *radioactivity?*
2. Define *alpha, beta,* and *gamma* radiation. From what part of the atom do they emanate?
3. What does emission of an alpha particle do to the atomic number?
4. How can an element transmute to one of higher atomic number?
5. What is meant by *artificial radioactivity?* Of what use is it?
6. What is the origin of transuranium elements? Why are they so named?
7. What is *fission?* What is *fusion?*
8. What are three qualities of strontium-90 that make it especially hazardous to man?

Test Your Understanding

1. If a single atom of a radioactive isotope having a half-life of one year could be observed, how long would it remain intact?
2. What kind of radiation might be expected from an atom of nuclear charge 104 as it goes to 105?
3. Why is nuclear fusion difficult to produce in the laboratory, when hydrogen is so abundant?
4. How does absorption of the product neutrons serve to moderate a fission reaction so that it does not occur explosively fast?
5. Why does a hydrogen-bomb explosion involve dangerous fallout?

Part 2

Chemical Bonding and Physical Properties

10

CHEMICAL BONDING IN METALS

METALS AND NONMETALS

You are already familiar with the special qualities that distinguish certain substances as metallic and others as nonmetallic. Metallic substances with a smooth, polished surface have a very high reflecting power called **metallic lustre.** This gives them an appearance different from that of nonmetallic substances. Metallic substances feel cold to the touch, indicating that they conduct heat away from the fingers much more rapidly than do nonmetallic substances. Most substances that are not metallic are electrical insulators rather than conductors whereas all metals are electrical conductors. Metals are not the only conducting substances but at ordinary temperatures they are the best conductors known.

Most of the chemical elements are metallic, including all of the transitional and inner transitional elements, as well as about two thirds of the major group elements. No sharp distinction is possible between metals and nonmetals because a number of elements, sometimes called **metalloids,** have some of the qualities of both. But in the periodic table of Figure 8.2, an approximate dividing line can be established in the form of a stair step downward to the right from the line between beryllium and boron. Except in the first very short period which contains only hydrogen and helium, the change from metal to nonmetal within a period, moving from left to right, occurs after the element which has the same number of outer-shell electrons as the period number.

For example, the period beginning with lithium is period two. Beryllium with two outer electrons is the last metal, with boron a nonmetal (metalloid). The period beginning with sodium is period three. Aluminum with three outer electrons is the third element and the last metal, the metalloid silicon coming next. The period beginning with potassium is period four. The element having four outer electrons, germanium, is taken as the last metal although it is more like a metalloid. The nonmetal or metalloid arsenic follows. Period five begins with rubidium, and here metallic properties are observed through the element antimony, which has five outer electrons. Usually the first element following the last metal in the period also has some metallic qualities, as does even the second sometimes.

Usually a metallic element is distinguished electronically by having more outer-shell vacancies than electrons. All nonmetallic elements except boron have a number of outer-shell electrons equal to or greater than the number of vacancies. As we shall see, the distinctive class differences in properties arise from this difference in electronic configuration.

Figure 10.1.   Metallic, Nonmetallic, and Metalloid Elements.

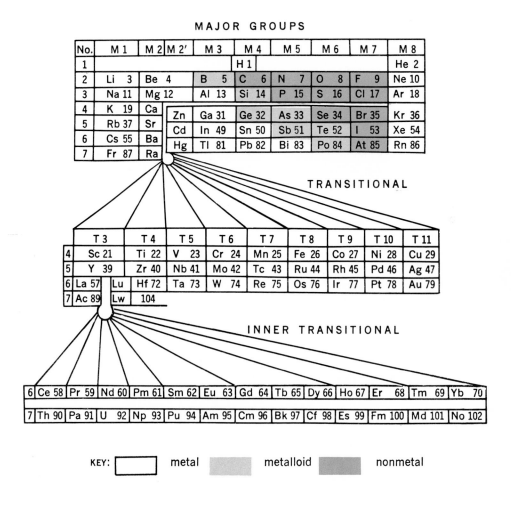

INTERACTIONS OF METAL ATOMS

Let us consider the nature of atoms that have fewer outer-shell electrons than vacancies. A low-energy vacancy in an outer shell represents a potential set of four quantum numbers for an electron in that atom. All atoms are electrically neutral because the number of negative charges in the electronic cloud equals the number of positive charges in the nucleus. This electroneutrality is apparent only from a distance, however. At points near the surface of the atom, at the fringes of the electronic cloud, the atom may appear to bear a positive charge. Indeed it is the positive charge of the nucleus that holds the electrons together in the cloud. Otherwise their mutual repulsion would force them to fly apart toward infinity. So although at some distance the effects of the negative field of the electrons and the positive field of the nucleus cancel one another, close to the atom, an outside electron is attracted by a positive charge from the nucleus. Nowhere is this effective positive charge nearly as great as actually exists on the nucleus; a large part of the nuclear charge is screened by the intervening electrons. Nevertheless, an outer-shell vacancy may be regarded as a region within which any electron could sense a substantial part of the nuclear charge, and be attracted to it.

When energy differences are small between outer-shell orbitals that are occupied by electrons and those that remain vacant, it is not difficult for an electron to move from its orbital to a vacant one of similar energy on the same atom. The low-energy orbital vacancies in the outermost shell of a metal therefore give an electron greater freedom of movement.

Imagine what may happen if two or more metal atoms come near one another. Filled outer orbitals of one will repel filled outer orbitals of the others. However, if filled outer orbitals or single electrons of one atom happen to enter a region corresponding to empty orbitals of another atom, no such repulsion will occur. Instead, the electrons of the first atom will find themselves attracted to the nucleus of the second atom. Since these same electrons are now attracted to both atomic nuclei, this attraction acts as a force holding the two atoms together.

The electrons which can be mutually shared with other atoms of a metal are called **valence electrons.** (The word "valence" refers to bonding between atoms.) If one or more electrons is removed from or added to a neutral atom, the atom acquires a net positive or negative charge. Such an atom, bearing an electrical charge, is called an **ion.** A positive ion, formed by the removal of electrons from a neutral atom, is called a **cation.** A negative ion, formed by the acquisition of electrons by a neutral atom, is called an **anion.** For a useful but crude illustration of bonding in metals, consider the metal to be composed of the metal cations embedded in a cloud of relatively free valence electrons. The electrons serve as the glue to hold the cations together. In other words, the metal atoms are not thought of as being attached directly to one another at all. Rather, the cations remain near to one another because of their common attraction to the electron cement in which they are embedded. Because there are more vacancies than electrons to fill them, the electrons are

Figure 10.2.   Representation of Metallic Bonding.

Each metal atom can be thought of as a cation

surrounded by its valence electrons, like this:

Each metal atom has more outer shell vacancies than electrons. Through these vacancies each atom attracts the valence electrons of other atoms. The valence electrons
are distributed throughout all available orbitals and are not localized between specific

pairs of atoms. The atoms do not attract one another as such, but rather the cations
are held together by their mutual attraction for the negative "glue" of valence electrons occupying the space among the cations.

able to move rather freely among the cations and are called **delocalized electrons.** Consequently this type of bonding in metals is called **delocalized bonding,** indicating that no atom in the metal is *directly* attached to a *specific*
neighbor by sharing specific electrons. **Metallic bonding** is the result of mutual
attraction between the nuclei of all the atoms in the crystal and all the valence
electrons.

When metal atoms converge, they become bound together in a closely
packed array. In most metals this packing is the closest possible for spheres
of the same size. Each interior atom has twelve neighboring atoms in direct
contact with it. Two types of such packing are **hexagonal closest packing**

Figure 10.3.   Hexagonal Closest Packing.

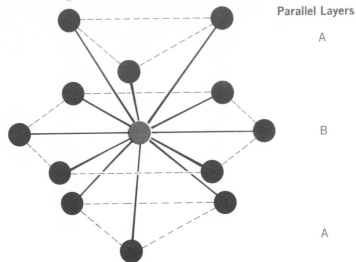

Parallel Layers

A

B

A

This alternating sequence of layers characterizes hexagonal closest packing. Only one central atom with its twelve closest neighbors is shown. All interior atoms are similar in environment to the central atom drawn. The triangles above and below the hexagon are identically oriented. Compare with Fig. 10.4.

Figure 10.4.   Cubic Closest Packing, or Face-Centered Cubic Packing.

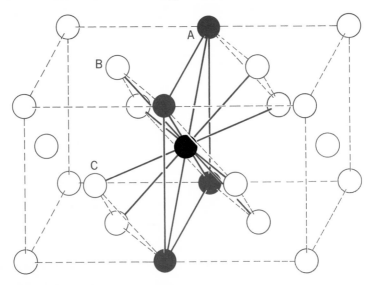

Notice that the atom at the center of a cube face has four neighbors at the corners of a face, and eight more at the centers of the eight adjoining cube faces—12 closest neighbors in all. Compare carefully with Fig. 10.3. Notice the similar hexagon of neighbors, with a triangle above and below, but here the triangles are reversed, not oriented alike. Therefore these layers are not in A-B-A-B sequence as in hexagonal packing, but rather, A-B-C.

and **cubic closest packing** (or **face-centered cubic**). Another common metal structure, **body-centered cubic,** has each interior atom surrounded by eight atoms in direct contact with it at the corners of a surrounding cube and six more a little farther away at the centers of the six adjacent cubes.

Figure 10.5.   Body-Centered Cubic Packing.

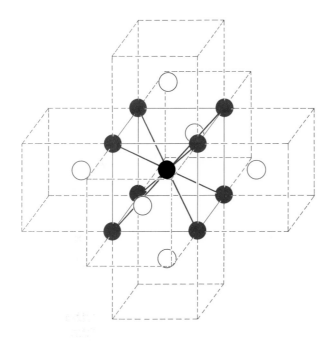

Each central atom has eight adjacent neighbors at the corners of a surrounding cube. Six more are farther away, at the centers of the six adjoining cubes. Although this is not the closest possible packing of spheres of equal size, it is a common structure for metals, including, for example, the alkali metals.

EXPLANATION OF METALLIC PROPERTIES

The modern theory of metals is highly mathematical and extremely complex. The picture presented above is only a very simple approximation. Nevertheless it is useful for it helps us to understand the properties that distinguish metals from nonmetals. We know for example that many metals are malleable and ductile: when placed under stress they tend to flow rather than break. Under a sharp stress like the blow of a hammer, they are more likely to flatten out than to crumble. When an attempt is made to break them, they are more likely to bend. If you try to visualize this on an atomic basis, you will appreciate that it would be impossible to change the shape of any substance without changing the relative positions of its atoms. If specific attachments between neighboring atoms existed these would have to be broken in order to change their relative positions, and once broken, the bonds might not readily be replaced by new bonds. Thus, the substance would probably be brittle. But in the delocalizing bonding of metals, one layer of atoms can slide over another without breaking specific bonds. When the change in position is complete, the atoms are just as securely bound as they were initially. An understanding of metallic bonding thus helps explain the pliability of metals, usually called **malleability** and **ductility.**

The conduction of heat and of electricity both depend on the mobility of outer-shell electrons. Usually it is necessary to promote the valence electrons to higher vacant orbitals in order to permit them to move freely as a current of electricity, which is just a flow of electrons through a conductor. In a conductor these vacant orbitals are only a little higher in energy than the occupied

Figure 10.6.   Electron Energy Levels in Metals, Semiconductors, and Insulators.

In order for electricity to flow through a metallic conductor, electrons must occupy a band of energy levels known as a conduction band.

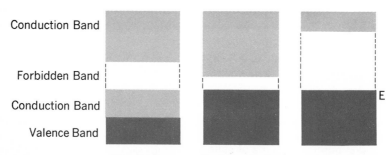

Conduction Band

Forbidden Band

Conduction Band

Valence Band

Conductor   Semiconductor   Insulator

E

In a conductor (i.e., metal) the valence band and the conduction band in effect coincide or overlap. It is easy for valence electrons to move to a slightly higher energy level to become current by moving through the crystal.

In a semiconductor, a narrow forbidden band separates the filled valence band from the conduction band. A relatively small increase in energy, achieved, for example, by heating, allows electrons to jump the energy gap and thus become conducting electrons.

In an insulator (i.e., nonmetal or compound) the forbidden band is too broad. Except under extraordinary conditions electrons cannot jump to the conduction band. Therefore no current can flow.

ones and are easily reached by the electrons. In a nonconductor a large jump in energy is required. Ordinarily the voltage available is not enough to promote the valence electrons to such high energy levels. Therefore, they have no way of moving through the nonconductor or **insulator.**

The simple picture presented here also provides a reasonable explanation of the special qualities of metals in contrast to nonmetals. This will become clearer when we study more about nonmetals in the next chapter.

DIFFERENCES AMONG METALS

Even though it is useful to group metals as a class, to compare them with other kinds of substances, metals may differ significantly from one another, both in bonding strength and in physical and chemical properties. The bonding strength tends to increase as the number of valence electrons available per atom increases. Where *d* orbitals are available for bonding, the bonding strength is greater. As a class the transitional metals are much more tightly held together, and therefore physically stronger, than the major group metals. Much more will be said about the strength of bonds later when we consider the relationships between atomic structure and the physical properties of substances.

Test Your Memory

1. Name some distinctive qualities of metals.
2. What is a *metalloid?*
3. What electronic distinction can be made between metals and nonmetals?
4. What are *valence electrons?*
5. Define *ion, cation,* and *anion.*
6. Describe a simple picture of a metallic crystal.
7. What causes metallic bonding (that is, what is the origin of metallic bonding forces)?
8. What is meant by *delocalized electrons?*
9. How does an electrical conductor differ fundamentally from an insulator?
10. Explain *malleability* and *ductility* of metals.

Test Your Understanding

1. When sodium vapor is cooled, some Na_2 gas molecules form but on further cooling these condense to metallic sodium. What would you infer about the total bonding energy per mole of Na atoms in the metal compared to that in the Na_2 molecules?
2. What difference between metals and nonmetals allows metals to conduct electricity?
3. Why does a piece of metal tend to bend or flatten out under mechanical stress?

11

COVALENCE

CHEMICAL BONDING BY NONMETALS

We have just seen that metallic bonding can be explained as the result of mutual attraction of the nuclei of different atoms for the same shared electrons. *All chemical bonding* is essentially the consequence of the *attraction* of *positively* charged nuclei for *negatively* charged electrons.

The importance of vacant, low-energy, outer orbitals was stressed when we discussed the bonding between metallic atoms. Each outer orbital vacancy represents a region capable of attracting an electron from outside the atom by exposing it to the nuclear charge. In nonmetal atoms, outer orbital vacancies have similar significance. However, here there are as many or more outer-shell electrons as vacancies. All nonmetal atoms except hydrogen, helium, and boron have at least four of the possible eight electrons in the outer shell. A nonmetal differs from a metal in having no extra vacancies of energy low enough for shared electrons to spread out. Consequently, the shared electrons in nonmetal bonding do not become delocalized to the extent that those in metallic bonding do, but they remain localized, usually in the vicinity of only two nuclei. This kind of bonding, called **covalent bonding,** is the most important type in chemistry.

In 1916, the American chemist, G. N. Lewis (1875–1946), first proposed the idea that a chemical bond consists of a sharing of two electrons by two atoms. His Nobel prize-winning contemporary, Irving Langmuir (1881–1957), called this the covalent bond. Lewis and Langmuir observed that in most compounds, if one considered the shared electrons to belong to each atom, sharing of electron pairs seemed to result in completing the octet of outer-shell electrons for both atoms involved. For instance, carbon atoms have four electrons in their outermost shell, which could hold eight, and chlorine atoms have seven electrons in their outermost shell, which could hold eight. Each chlorine atom, by taking one electron from carbon into its outermost shell, can acquire an octet. The carbon, by taking one electron from each of four chlorine atoms into its outermost shell, can also acquire an octet. By mutual sharing of two electrons between each chlorine and the carbon, all five atoms in effect fill their outermost shells to the octet limit.

Maintaining an octet of electrons in each outer shell has since been found to be unnecessary although it is extremely common. But the idea of an electron pair forming the bond remains a fundamental concept in modern bonding theory. Most of the investigation of bonding since 1916 has been directed toward discovering how the two-electron bond works. Although we still do not know exactly, much progress toward understanding has been made.

CHARACTERISTICS OF COVALENT BONDING

Consider what may occur when two hydrogen atoms come together. (Remember that each hydrogen atom consists of a proton, as its nucleus, surrounded by one electron.) The two nuclei must repel one another because of their like charges. The two electrons must repel one another for similar reasons. But each nucleus must attract not only its own electron but also the electron of the other hydrogen atom. Can these attractions exceed the total repulsions? If they can, the atoms can hold one another together; if they cannot, the atoms will merely repel one another and move apart. It is found that, if the electron spins are opposed, each atom can accommodate the electron of the other in its own *s* orbital. If this happens, the two electrons moving in the region of

What principle requires the spins to be opposed?

both nuclei hold the two atoms together as an H_2 molecule, by a *covalent bond*. The strength, or **energy,** of this bond for the hydrogen molecule is experimentally measured as 104.2 kcal per mole. In other words, this is the quantity of energy needed to pull apart the diatomic molecules (H_2) to form the separate atoms (H) again. Since this is a very substantial amount of energy for this kind of interaction, we describe the bond as strong and the molecule as stable.

To explain why two neutral atoms find one another so mutually attractive, we must recognize, as we did for metallic atoms, that electroneutrality of an atom from a distance does not necessarily mean a neutral effect at close range. The outer-shell vacancy on each hydrogen atom corresponds to a region around its nucleus in which the positive charge of the nucleus is not effectively screened by the other electron. Consequently the electron from each atom can occupy a region around the nucleus of the other, as well as its own, in which it is strongly attracted. This mutual attraction of the two different nuclei for the same two electrons is the determining factor in forming the bond. The repulsion between the two nuclei and the repulsion between the two electrons

Figure 11.1. Schematic Representation of H and H₂.

Let us picture an atom with a vacant orbital in its outermost shell as a circle with a double well:

Next, let us imagine an electron to be represented by a black bar:

We can then represent an atom of hydrogen like this:

When two hydrogen atoms meet, the electron of each can be accommodated by the vacancy of the other:

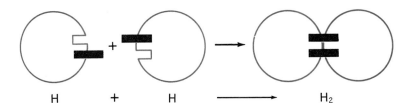

| H | + | H | ⟶ | H₂ |

This is the simplest example of a covalent bond. To form such a bond, each atom must furnish

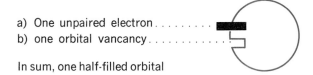

    a) One unpaired electron . . . .
    b) one orbital vancancy . . . .

    In sum, one half-filled orbital

The atoms are held together by the attraction of each nucleus for the shared valence electrons.

modify this attraction, but they are inadequate to overcome it. The net result of all the forces is attraction.

The most favorable condition for the bonding of two atoms exists when the two nuclei are a specific, optimum distance apart. If they are forced still closer together, the forces of repulsion begin to dominate. In hydrogen this repulsion would result primarily from pushing the two proton nuclei closer together. If the nuclei are farther apart than the optimum distance, then the net attractive force is weaker because coulombic forces diminish with increasing distance. The optimum distance between the two nuclei of atoms combined by a covalent bond is called the **bond length.** Several experimental procedures have been developed for accurately determining the bond length. Probably the two most important properties of a covalent bond are the closely related properties of its *energy* and its *length*.

A **covalent bond** between any two atoms is the net attraction that occurs when each atom supplies one unpaired electron to be shared with the other and one vacancy to accommodate the electron of the other, so that the two valence electrons are attracted by both nuclei. In other words, each atom must supply one outer-shell, half-filled orbital, in which the electron and the vacancy are of equal importance in forming the bond. The bond length and the bond energy are the consequence of the balance of repulsive and attractive forces among *all* the component particles of the two atoms, not just those between the bonding electrons and the nuclei. Both length and energy can usually be determined experimentally. The nature of the interactions is so extremely complex, however, as to defy quantitative theoretical calculation except in the simplest molecules.

Consideration of helium, atomic number 2, can be helpful in understanding covalent bonding. The helium atom has its $1s$ orbital completely filled with two electrons surrounding a nucleus of $+2$ charge. When two helium atoms come together, the same kinds of attractions and repulsions are possible as for hydrogen with one highly important exception: neither atom possesses any low-energy, stable, vacant orbital which might accommodate electrons of the other atom. In other words, there is no region at all where an electron from one atom might become sufficiently exposed to the nuclear charge of the other to produce a net attraction between the two atoms. Consequently the repulsions are dominant and the atoms only bounce apart. An atom of helium is incapable of forming a covalent bond. It lacks both the requisites exhibited by

Figure 11.2. Why Helium Atoms Form No Bonds.

By the method shown in Figure 11.1, an atom of helium would be represented as:

If two helium atoms meet, neither can provide an unpaired electron or an orbital vacancy:

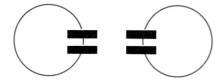

So, **no bond**

hydrogen: it has no single, unpaired electron available to be shared with another atom, and it has no vacancy capable of accommodating an electron from another atom. The pair of electrons around the helium nucleus is much more effective at blocking the nuclear charge than is the single electron around the hydrogen nucleus.

An additional question about hydrogen may shed more light on the nature of covalence. Why does hydrogen stop at H_2 molecules? Why not H_3, H_4, or H_n, where n is any number of atoms? No doubt you can anticipate the answer by considering the characteristics of the hydrogen molecule, H_2. All the electrons of both atoms are occupied in the covalent bond that holds the two atoms together. Both the atomic orbitals are effectively utilized by the two valence electrons. No other electrons are available. No other orbitals are available. Consequently no other bonds can be formed. A diatomic hydrogen molecule (H_2) is incapable of forming chemical bonds to anything. The reasons are very similar to those given for the nonbonding of helium. And this leads us to a consideration of another important aspect of covalence. Although hydrogen atoms can form but one bond each and helium atoms none, many chemical compounds consist of atoms capable of forming more than one bond. How do they do this? What determines the number of covalent bonds an atom can form?

Valence or Combining Power

The word **valence** is not very precisely defined but, in general, it refers to the combining power of an atom. To state the valence of an atom as a number is to state the number of covalent bonds which it can form. From the discussion above, we can state that the valence of hydrogen is one, and the valence of helium is zero. But oxygen is known to have a valence of two, aluminum three, and carbon four. What causes the difference, and how can one predict what valence an element will show? Ability to predict valence is very important. If we know how many bonds each of two different kinds of atoms can form, we can predict the relative numbers of each atom that will react with the other to form a compound.

Let us start at the right-hand side of the periodic table, with element number 10, neon, and work to the left. The outer shell of neon atoms is the second principal quantum level, which has a capacity of eight electrons. In neon atoms, the first shell contains its quota of two electrons and the second shell eight, making the total of ten. This means that the outermost shell is filled completely. There are no extra vacancies for an outside electron or an electron from another atom. The third principal quantum level is empty but with a nuclear charge of only $+10$ it is far too unstable to accommodate an outside electron adequately. Lacking this requisite for forming covalent bonds, neon has a valence of zero. It cannot combine with itself, with hydrogen, or with any other elements.

Moving left one atomic number to fluorine, number 9, we find an element with an electronic distribution represented by 2-7. With only seven electrons in a shell capable of holding eight, fluorine clearly must have one vacancy that might accommodate an electron from elsewhere. Furthermore, with seven electrons in only four outermost orbitals, one, and only one, electron must be unpaired, available to be shared with another atom under favorable circumstances. In other words, fluorine atoms possess the two requisites for forming one covalent bond each. These two requisites can be described together as a "half-filled orbital" which implies both the single electron and the vacancy. If two fluorine atoms come together, the presence of a half-filled outer orbital on each insures that the net force will be one of attraction. One covalent bond can form. Each atom provides one of the two valence electrons. The atoms are held together by the fact that the dominant interaction is the attraction of the two nuclei for the two shared electrons. The result is a fluorine molecule, F_2. Again, when the bond has been formed, no additional bonding is possible; no additional vacancies exist. Fluorine molecules are incapable of forming additional covalent bonds.

Fluorine atoms, on the other hand, have a valence of one. When a fluorine atom meets a hydrogen atom, they combine on a one-to-one basis to form the molecule HF, called hydrogen fluoride. There is no question of why the formula is not HF_2, or HF_3, or H_2F, or H_3F. When HF has been formed, the normal bonding abilities of both atoms are fully utilized and no further covalent bonds are possible.

Oxygen (2-6) has its outermost shell containing only four electrons in the $2p$ orbitals which could hold six.

Where are the other four electrons located?

Remember the scene in the atomic theater when electrons were choosing their seats? They would condescend to sit with one another only if the seat afforded a better view of the nuclear stage. If the view was the same, they preferred to sit alone. A natural consequence of the repulsion between like charges, **Hund's rule of maximum multiplicity,** requires that:

> When a set of like orbitals is available to electrons, they will always occupy these orbitals singly until there is no longer any choice but to pair with another electron.

Therefore, the four electrons in the three $2p$ orbitals of oxygen will be located two in one p orbital and one in each of the other two p orbitals. Thus they spread out as far as possible. The *two* half-filled orbitals provide the requisites for forming *two* covalent bonds. Therefore, with hydrogen atoms, which can form only one covalent bond each, oxygen joins on a one-to-one basis to form water (H_2O). Similarly, oxygen joins fluorine to form oxygen difluoride (OF_2). Oxygen has a valence of two and is **divalent.**

Nitrogen has five outer-shell electrons. These fill the $2s$ orbital and singly occupy each of the $2p$ orbitals. Clearly such an arrangement shows the capacity to form three covalent bonds. Nitrogen and hydrogen therefore form ammonia (NH_3). Nitrogen and fluorine form nitrogen trifluoride (NF_3).

Nitrogen and oxygen, on the other hand, do not follow the simple rules we have been using. We shall postpone dealing with their compounds for the present, except for the one with the formula N_2O_3. This formula is accounted for by considering the number of bonds formed by oxygen to equal the number of bonds formed by nitrogen. If nitrogen atoms form three bonds apiece and oxygen atoms two bonds apiece, then two nitrogen atoms could join to three oxygen atoms by the equivalent of six bonds.

A carbon atom (2-4) has four outer-shell electrons. In the ground state (the most stable state) these are located two in the $2s$ orbital and one in each of two $2p$ orbitals, with the third $2p$ orbital vacant. This would mean two half-filled orbitals, and we would predict that a carbon atom could form just two covalent bonds. This would be wrong.

The cause of our mistake is our failure to consider two other facts which have become well known in chemistry although we have not discussed them previously in this book. First, major group atoms tend to form all the covalent bonds of which they are capable, making maximum possible use of all available electrons and orbital vacancies. Second, the s orbital is more stable than the p orbitals of the same principal quantum level, but not by much. Under favorable circumstances an electron can be promoted from the s to a vacant p orbital. The possibility of forming additional bonds is such a favorable circumstance. When bonding is possible, one of the s-orbital electrons of the outer shell of a carbon atom is readily promoted into the otherwise vacant p orbital. This leaves the s orbital half filled and makes each of the p orbitals half filled. The carbon atom now has the capacity to form four covalent bonds instead of only two. Doubling the number of bonds more than compensates for the energy needed for promotion. Carbon unites with hydrogen to form methane (CH_4) and with fluorine to form carbon tetrafluoride (CF_4). Carbon has a valence of four and is **tetravalent.**

In boron we recognize a somewhat similar situation. With three outermost electrons, a boron atom (2-3) has a filled $2s$ orbital and a single $2p$ electron. We might have predicted that boron would have a valence of one. But having observed creation of the valence state in carbon, we can see that boron, with two vacant p orbitals in the outer shell, can also undergo promotion of one of the s electrons. This provides three half-filled orbitals for covalent bond formation. Boron forms boron trifluoride (BF_3), boric oxide (B_2O_3), and boron nitride (BN), all predictable on the basis of its recognized trivalence.

A beryllium atom has two outer-shell electrons, both in the $2s$ orbital. The $2p$ orbitals lie vacant. Although beryllium has two outer-shell electrons it does not resemble helium because helium has no low-energy vacant orbitals whereas beryllium has three. It is relatively easy under bonding conditions for one electron from the $2s$ orbital of beryllium to be promoted to one of the vacant p orbitals, resulting in two half-filled orbitals and the capacity to form two covalent bonds. The valence of beryllium is two. In the outermost shell of helium there are no p orbitals. An electron of helium has no place of great enough stability to which to be promoted. Therefore, it must remain paired, and helium has a valence of zero.

Finally, a lithium atom (2-1), has only one electron in the outermost shell. Therefore there is one half-filled orbital and only one covalent bond is possible. Lithium has a valence of one. It can form LiH and LiF.

> What would be the formulas of compounds of lithium with oxygen and with nitrogen?

Valence State

In general, for Groups M2, M2′, M3, and M4 of the periodic table, a distinction must be made between the ground state and the valence state of atoms. In each of these elements, the outermost shell contains both a pair of s electrons and at least one vacant p orbital. This combination always presents

Figure 11.3.   Distinction Between Ground and Valence States of Atoms.

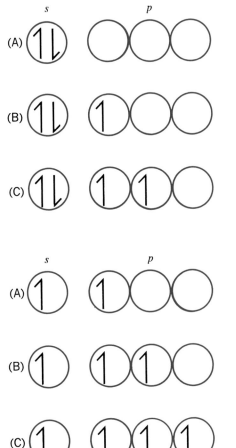

Each circle represents an orbital and each arrow an electron. The arrow direction represents the spin magnetic quantum number of the electron: up $= +\frac{1}{2}$, down $= -\frac{1}{2}$.

Ground states differ from valence states when there are two, three, or four outermost electrons in the configuration shown.

Valence states result when one electron of a pair in an s orbital is promoted to an otherwise vacant p orbital.

Such promotion increases by two the number of half-filled orbitals available for the formation of covalent bonds. This promotion is normally accompanied by hybridization of the s and p orbitals.

the possibility of promotion of one of the *s* electrons to the vacant *p* orbital, creating two half-filled orbitals capable of covalent bonding. These elements are practically never in the ground state and they practically always behave chemically as if one of their outer *s* electrons were already promoted to a vacant *p* orbital. In other words, they almost always behave as if in the valence state, demonstrating the electronic configuration necessary for full bonding. The distinction between ground state and valence state exists only for the groups of the periodic table mentioned above. It is shown graphically in Figure 11.3. For purposes of predicting valence, we need only consider the valence state. In other words, an atom can form as many covalent bonds as it has half-filled outer shell orbitals in the valence state.

Predict chemical formulas for each of the following combinations: H and Na, H and Cl, H and S, H and P, Li and P, Li and S, Li and Cl, B and Cl, Be and O, Be and H, Be and S, Be and Cl.

Hybridization

Up to now we have paid no attention to the fact that some bonds are formed by half-filled *s* orbitals and some by half-filled *p* orbitals. Remember that *s* orbitals occupy regions of shape different from *p* orbitals. The *s* orbital occupies a sphere with the nucleus at its center, but *p* orbitals are directed primarily along a straight line through the nucleus. Does this make some difference in the nature of the bonds they form? For example, if one of the outer-shell electrons of beryllium is promoted to an outer *p* orbital, putting beryllium in the valence state, then one of the half-filled orbitals is *s* and the other is *p*. Since the *p* orbital does not hold electrons as tightly as the *s* orbital does, how can the bonds be equal?

When beryllium atoms form two bonds with atoms of the same element, it is found experimentally that they are exactly equal in strength and in length. Therefore we are forced to conclude that the orbitals forming the two bonds have somehow become identical.

The term describing this equalization of valence orbitals is **hybridization.** The *s* and the *p* orbitals are said to have averaged with one another to form two new "hybrid" orbitals. More specifically, they are called *sp* hybrids, to indicate the kind and number of orbitals from which they were formed.

Similarly, the three covalent bonds formed by boron to three like atoms other than boron are identical. The orbitals involved are the *s* and two of the *p* orbitals. If instead of two bonds being alike and one different, all three are alike, then hybridization must also have occurred here. The bonds formed by boron are described as sp^2 hybrids, again showing the kind and number of simple orbitals from which they originated. The sp^2 means that one *s* orbital has hybridized with two *p* orbitals.

In carbon atoms, promotion of an *s* electron to the one *p* orbital that was vacant in the ground state gives three *p* orbitals and one *s* orbital for the four covalent bonds. Again, all evidence indicates that these bonds are identical.

Therefore they are called sp^3 hybrids, indicating that they are the average of one s and three p orbitals and that the four hybrid orbitals are exactly alike.

The concept of hybridization is most useful for application to atoms in which the valence state differs from the ground state. However, it is also applied sometimes to other elements such as nitrogen. Instead of picturing the three bonds in ammonia (NH_3) as utilizing the three p orbitals of the nitrogen, the pair of s electrons even though unpromoted can be considered to enter into the hybridization. The bonds in ammonia are then described as sp^3 hybrid bonds, as in carbon compounds, rather than straight p orbital bonds. The nonbonding electron pair occupies the fourth sp^3 orbital.

Nonmetal to Metal Bonds

Metal atoms do not behave in combination with nonmetal atoms as they do with other metal atoms. The electron pair forming a bond between a metal atom and a nonmetal atom remains relatively localized between the two atoms because the nonmetal atom has no low-energy vacancies into which the electrons might spread out. Therefore, predictions of valence from the number of half-filled, outer-shell orbitals per atom is just as valid for combinations of metal atoms with nonmetal atoms as it is for nonmetal-nonmetal combinations.

For the major group elements, the number of possible half-filled orbitals per atom is equal to the number of outer-shell electrons for Groups M1 through M3. From Groups M4 through M7, the number of possible half-filled orbitals per atom is equal to the number of outer-shell vacancies. In other words, when the number of vacancies in the outer shell exceeds the number of electrons, the possible number of covalent bonds is limited by the number of outer-shell electrons. When the number of electrons in the outer shell equals or exceeds the number of vacancies, then the possible number of covalent bonds is limited by the number of outer-shell vacancies. Thus the valence of a major group element is equal to the group number up to M3, and equal to 8 minus the group number from M4 on. Thus, even if you cannot remember the exact electronic configuration of a given element, you can predict its valence from the periodic table if it belongs in a major group.

As yet, there is no simple, general method for predicting the valence shown by metallic elements in their compounds with other metals. The composition of such intermetallic compounds, hundreds of which are known, certainly cannot be predicted directly from the outer-shell electronic configurations. However, except for these intermetallic compounds, which are relatively unimportant in general chemistry, you can predict with reasonable confidence the formulas of dozens of binary (two-element) compounds. These compounds include both metal-nonmetal and nonmetal-nonmetal combinations. Although not all known compounds of these types can be predicted this simply, enough of them can to build our confidence that chemistry can be a reasonable science. To the extent that we can understand what atoms are like, we can also begin to understand why they form bonds in the way they do. Eventually we

Figure 11.4. Valence Structures of Major Group Elements.

Except for H and He, all major group elements can be represented, according to the scheme of Fig. 11.1, as having four outermost shell orbitals, like this:

Each pair of "wells" or vacancies represents a vacant orbital.

The outermost shell electrons may then be added one to an orbital until pairing is necessary:

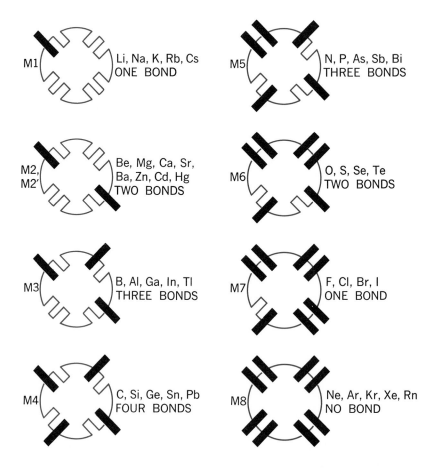

M1   Li, Na, K, Rb, Cs
     ONE BOND

M2, M2'   Be, Mg, Ca, Sr, Ba, Zn, Cd, Hg
          TWO BONDS

M3   B, Al, Ga, In, Tl
     THREE BONDS

M4   C, Si, Ge, Sn, Pb
     FOUR BONDS

M5   N, P, As, Sb, Bi
     THREE BONDS

M6   O, S, Se, Te
     TWO BONDS

M7   F, Cl, Br, I
     ONE BOND

M8   Ne, Ar, Kr, Xe, Rn
     NO BOND

The number of covalent bonds an atom can form is equal to the number of half-filled orbitals in its outer shell.

126 Covalence

Figure 11.5. Predicting Formulas of Binary Compounds of Major Group Elements.

In binary compounds, like atoms are usually not directly attached to one another. Each atom is attached only to an atom or atoms of the other kind. When this is so, the total number of bonds formed by one element must exactly equal the total number of bonds formed by the other. Therefore, the empirical formula of the compound will contain the minimum number of each kind of atom needed to form an equal number of bonds. For example, suppose the elements are from Groups M3 and M6:

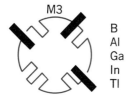

M3

B
Al
Ga
In
Tl

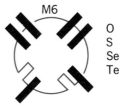

M6

O
S
Se
Te

Each atom can form three bonds.
2 atoms × 3 bonds/atom = 6 bonds.

Each atom can form two bonds.
3 atoms × 2 bonds/atom = 6 bonds.

Therefore it is reasonable to predict formulas of the type $(M3)_2 (M6)_3$:

B_2O_3	Al_2O_3	Ga_2O_3	In_2O_3	Tl_2O_3
B_2S_3	Al_2S_3	Ga_2S_3	In_2S_3	Tl_2S_3
B_2Se_3	Al_2Se_3	Ga_2Se_3	In_2Se_3	Tl_2Se_3
B_2Te_3	Al_2Te_3	Ga_2Te_3	In_2Te_3	Tl_2Te_3

can develop an appreciation of how bond formation is related logically to the physical and chemical properties of all chemical substances.

Covalent Bonds to Transitional Elements

The major electronic distinction between major group and subgroup or transitional elements is that underlying d orbitals are partially occupied in the latter but either absent, completely vacant, or completely filled in the former. This difference produces a very important distinction in bonding. Major group elements use only their outer-shell orbitals in bonding. Transitional elements may use both outer-shell orbitals and underlying d orbitals in bonding.

None of the transitional elements has more than two outer-shell electrons.

Characteristics of Covalent Bonding **127**

Figure 11.6. Representation of Valence Structure of Transitional Elements.

Atoms of transitional elements can be represented schematically as double circles with orbital wells:

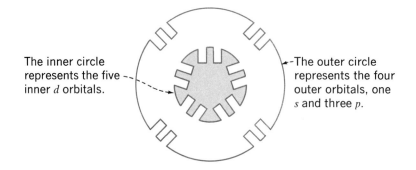

The inner circle represents the five inner *d* orbitals.

The outer circle represents the four outer orbitals, one *s* and three *p*.

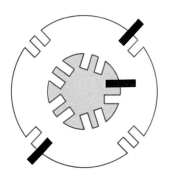

For example, the T3 elements, Sc, Y, and La, show only an oxidation state of +3. Each atom can form three covalent bonds.

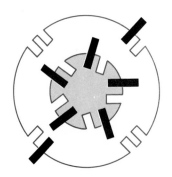

The T7 elements, Mn, Tc, and Re, can show an oxidation state of +7, corresponding to the seven half-filled orbitals shown here. However, they also can form fewer than seven bonds. Manganese most commonly forms only two, leaving the relatively stable d^5 arrangement intact.

Consequently all the transitional elements are metals. Their predictable covalent bonds are therefore with nonmetals. Here we find a variability to valence that is much more typical of transitional metals than of major group metals. We can predict an upper limit to the number of covalent bonds a transitional element atom can form, but we cannot predict with assurance which of several possible valences it will exhibit under all possible conditions.

The maximum theoretical number of covalent bonds that can be formed by a transitional element atom is equal to the number of half-filled orbitals in both its outer and next-to-outer shells. For instance, scandium, in Group T3, has two outer-shell electrons and one underlying d electron. With these it can have three half-filled orbitals and form three covalent bonds. The maximum valence of scandium is three. In this case, lower valences are not known. Titanium (T4) has two outer-shell electrons and two underlying d electrons. These can supply four half-filled orbitals. Titanium therefore has a valence of four. However, compounds in which titanium forms only three bonds or two bonds are also known. Similarly, vanadium (T5) can form five covalent bonds but is known also to form four, three, and two. Chromium (T6) can form a maximum of six covalent bonds but is known more commonly to form fewer, down to two. Likewise manganese (T7) can form a maximum of seven covalent bonds, but in most of its compounds it forms fewer.

Manganese is an element in which each of the five underlying d orbitals contains one electron. Beyond manganese the elements have more d-orbital electrons than vacancies. Consequently the number of half-filled orbitals possible begins to be limited by the number of vacancies rather than electrons. In practically all compounds of T8, T9, and T10 the number of covalent bonds is smaller than the theoretical maximum, so we would be wise not to try to predict their valence at this stage in our study. For transitional groups T3 through T7, however, we can predict with confidence that the maximum number of covalent bonds possible is given by the group number. Fewer than the maximum are commonly observed. Based on this knowledge we can make predictions of reasonable upper limits to the composition of binary compounds of these elements. For instance, zirconium (T4) can be predicted to unite with not more than four fluorine atoms, forming ZrF_4.

> Predict possible formulas for combinations of the following pairs of elements: Y and Cl, Y and O, Ti and S, Ti and O, Ti and Br, Mn and O, Cr and O, Mo and F, V and O, W and S, Ta and Cl, Sc and S, Hf and I, La and I, Re and O.

MULTIPLE BONDS AND RESONANCE

In some atoms, notably those of carbon, nitrogen, and oxygen, the formation of a covalent bond brings other orbitals close to one another. In such circumstances, double and triple bonds can form, in which each atom supplies two or three half-filled orbitals. Such bonds are called **double** and **triple bonds.**

In a double bond, four electrons are mutually shared by the two nuclei. In a triple bond, six electrons are so shared. For example, carbon burns in oxygen or air to form the compound carbon dioxide (CO_2). Since carbon can form four covalent bonds and oxygen can form two, the carbon unites with oxygen by double bonds. The carbon shares four electrons with each oxygen atom. In the nitrogen molecule (N_2) each nitrogen atom shares three of its outer electrons with the other, giving a six electron bond that is extremely strong. In fact, it is almost the strongest known chemical bond.

There are also many compounds in which the bonding is more than single but not exactly double or triple. Such compounds form, for example, from nitrogen and oxygen. In addition to the N_2O_3 predicted earlier on the basis of simple logic, compounds are known which have formulas NO, N_2O, NO_2, and N_2O_5. In each of these the bonds are multiple but not integrally multiple. That is, they cannot be classified as double or triple; they are intermediate. To describe situations that cannot be treated adequately as involving either one, or two, or three covalent bonds, the word **resonance** is used. Whenever a molecule cannot be accurately represented as having only single, double, or triple bonds, it is said to possess resonance. Since an intermediate bonding condition is usually more stable than any structures that might be drawn using whole numbers of covalent bonds, chemists also frequently use the term **resonance stabilization** to denote the extra stability of the intermediate condition.

The chief principle in resonance is that wherever a molecule might as well have a double bond in more than one equivalent location but does not have enough electrons for all the possible double bonds, the electrons tend to spread out among all possible locations rather than concentrate as electron pairs. For example, the most common form of carbon is graphite, which consists of planes of carbon atoms in condensed, six-member rings (Fig. 11.8), each carbon atom forming a covalent bond to each of three neighbors. Its fourth half-filled orbital could equally well form a double bond with each of its neighbors but certainly not with all three at once. Instead of forming a double bond with one neighbor to the exclusion of the others, carbon shares

Figure 11.7. Schematic Representation of Double Bonds.

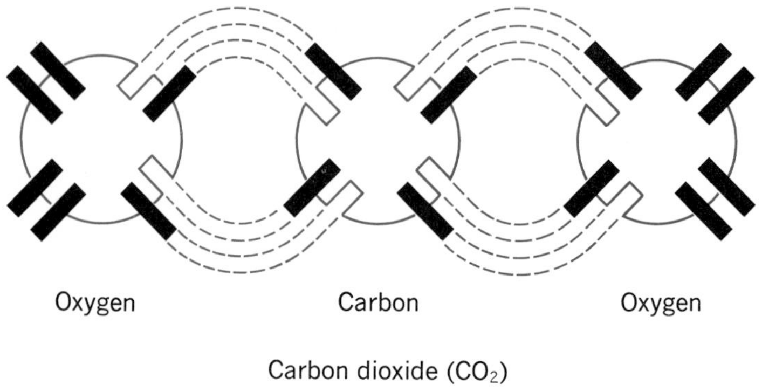

Oxygen   Carbon   Oxygen

Carbon dioxide (CO_2)

Figure 11.8. Representation of a Fragment of a Layer of Graphite.

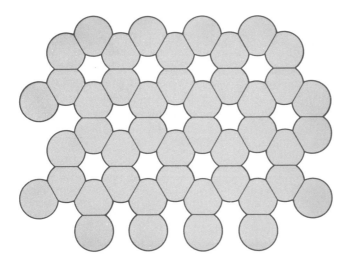

Each carbon atom is bonded to only three other carbon atoms. Each atom forms $1\frac{1}{3}$ bond to each of its neighbors. This equal division of the fourth half-filled orbital of each carbon atom among all three of its neighbors is an example of resonance.

its fourth half-filled orbital with all three neighbors simultaneously. Each carbon-carbon bond is thus equivalent to one-and-one-third covalent bonds. Graphite cannot be described accurately in terms of bonds having whole numbers of electron pairs, but it is more stable because the "extra" electrons spread out as much as possible.

Multiple bonds are always shorter and stronger than single bonds.

COORDINATE COVALENCE

The requisites for the formation of a covalent bond have been listed as one half-filled orbital to be supplied by each atom for mutual sharing of an electron pair. Yet often when atoms have united by covalence to form molecules, making the fullest possible use of their half-filled orbitals, they may then go on to form additional bonds to other substances. This was at first a very mysterious phenomenon. It still is, in the sense that we do not know nearly as much about bonding as we sometimes think we do, or wish we did. But in most of such examples the additional bonding can be explained as a covalent bond in which one atom supplies both of the paired electrons to be shared. The other atom supplies a completely vacant orbital to accommodate that electron pair. Once the bond is formed, it is said to be indistinguishable from an ordinary covalent bond involving sharing of two electrons, one furnished by each atom.

This supplementary type of bond is called the **coordinate covalent bond.**

Figure 11.9.   Schematic Representation of Coordinate Covalence.

Outer orbitals indicated only

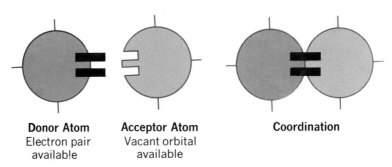

Donor Atom	Acceptor Atom	Coordination
Electron pair available	Vacant orbital available	

Caution: Not all outer electron pairs are available for sharing. M8 atoms are never donors. Usually the donor must have an excess of negative charge. The donor atom may possess negative charge as the result of being an anion, being part of an anion, or being attached to less electronegative atoms.

It is relatively uncommon for an atom to unite through coordinate covalence until it has already formed all the ordinary covalent bonds possible. The compounds that form between atoms that are already part of molecules of other compounds are in a sense "compounds of higher order." More frequently, they are called **coordination compounds.** Since they are formed by combination of simpler molecules, they are more complex, and are also labeled **complex compounds,** or **coordination complexes.** A compound formed by one *molecule* adding to another by coordination is called an **addition** compound.

The atom, ion, or molecule containing the atom, that provides the pair of electrons for coordinate covalence is called the **donor,** the **electron donor,** or the **ligand.** The atom, ion, or molecule containing the atom, that provides the vacant orbital for coordinate covalence is called the **acceptor,** the **electron acceptor,** or the **central atom.** Coordinate covalence is often referred to as **donor-acceptor interaction,** or **donor-acceptor bonding.** The British often call it **dative bonding.**

Almost every anion, and certainly every simple, monatomic anion, possesses at least one outer-shell pair of electrons that might be shared with some atom having a vacant orbital. In addition, many neutral molecules contain at least one atom, always a nonmetallic atom, that has at least one, sometimes more, pairs of electrons that might be donated to another acceptor atom. A large number of species are therefore capable of acting as ligands. A few examples are H_2O, which has two lone pairs (as the extra electron pairs are often called) on its oxygen atom; NH_3, which has one lone pair on the nitrogen; and the fluoride ion, F^-, which has four lone pairs in its outer shell.

Every simple cation, as an atom that has lost at least one electron, must have at least one outer-shell vacant orbital capable of accommodating an electron pair from some donor or ligand. Furthermore, every simple molecule that contains a metal atom must have vacant orbitals remaining on the metal

Figure 11.10. Formation of an Addition Compound.

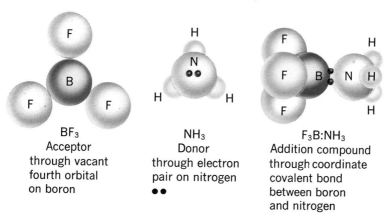

BF₃
Acceptor
through vacant
fourth orbital
on boron

NH₃
Donor
through electron
pair on nitrogen
●●

F₃B:NH₃
Addition compound
through coordinate
covalent bond
between boron
and nitrogen

atom since they were there in the first place, before the metal combined. Therefore, a large number of species also are capable of acting as electron acceptors in the formation of coordination bonds. The number of possible coordination compounds, or complex ions, or coordination complexes, is practically without limit.

For example, if a hydrogen atom loses one electron it becomes H^+, the hydrogen ion. This has a vacant $1s$ orbital and can therefore act as an acceptor. When a hydrogen ion encounters an ammonia molecule (NH_3), the proton H^+ (note that a hydrogen ion is only a proton) at once attaches itself to the lone pair of electrons left on the nitrogen after the three other hydrogen atoms have combined. The ammonium ion, NH_4^+, that results from this coordinate covalent bond formation is one of the simplest examples of a complex

Figure 11.11. Formation of a Complex Ion.

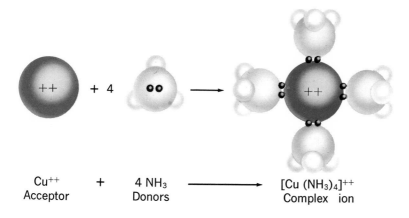

Cu^{++}
Acceptor

$+$

$4 NH_3$
Donors

⟶

$[Cu (NH_3)_4]^{++}$
Complex ion

ion. If instead of using the hydrogen ion to accept the electron pair from the nitrogen, we allowed ammonia to come in contact with gaseous hydrogen chloride (HCl), the two gases would unite to form a visible white smoke consisting of minute crystals of ammonium chloride (NH_4Cl):

$$NH_3 + HCl \rightarrow NH_4Cl$$

This reaction is very similar to the first. The proton leaves the chloride ion behind as the hydrogen chloride loses its hydrogen nucleus, joining the ammonia molecule to form the complex ammonium ion. Then the ammonium ion, being positive, becomes attached to the negative chloride ion, forming the solid salt. (This involves also a kind of bonding to be discussed in Chapter 13. All that is intended to be illustrated here is the coordinate covalence.) Once the ammonia has acquired the extra proton, its bonds become equalized, and all four hydrogens are held equally. There is no way of telling which of the hydrogen-nitrogen bonds is the original coordinate covalent bond and which the normal covalent bonds.

As another example, boron unites with fluorine to form boron trifluoride (BF_3). This makes use of all three of the outer-shell electrons of boron. The fourth orbital remains available as an acceptor. When a BF_3 molecule encounters a fluoride ion (F^-), as it might in a solution of sodium fluoride (NaF) for example, it can accept an electron pair from the fluoride ion, thus forming the complex ion fluoroborate (BF_4^-). Notice that this ion bears a negative charge because it acquires an extra electron by taking on the negatively charged fluoride ion.

When a chromium salt like chromium chloride ($CrCl_3$) dissolves in water, the lone pairs on the oxygen of the water are attracted to the vacant orbitals on the Cr^{+++} ion, forming the complex ion $Cr(H_2O)_6^{+++}$. By evaporation of the water of the remaining solvent, the complex salt $Cr(H_2O)_6Cl_3$ would be isolated as a residue.

WAVE MECHANICAL DESCRIPTIONS OF COVALENCE

Let us reexamine the interactions involved in the formation and existence of a molecule of hydrogen. The fundamental particles are two protons and two electrons. Six interactions among charges are therefore involved: (1) Each electron repels the other; (2) each proton repels the other; (3) and (4) each proton attracts its own electron; and (5) and (6) each proton attracts the electron of the other atom. This is the very simplest molecule known, yet to calculate the complete interactions quantitatively to determine the bond energy and length is so formidable a job that it requires a high-speed computer solving a fifty-term mathematical equation to find the values relatively easily determined by experimental methods. Immensely complicated calculations have recently been performed for a few other small molecules with reasonably good success. But in general, the greater the number of particles (electrons and nuclei) involved, the more nearly impossible the task becomes.

Nevertheless, many chemists are interested in developing greater theoretical understanding of bonding by applying the methods of wave mechanics to such problems. Such methods have shed much light on somewhat lesser problems associated with atomic structure and molecular properties. Although the quantum or wave mechanical approach to theoretical chemistry requires complex mathematics far beyond the scope of this elementary treatment, it is useful to understand some of the qualitative concepts of bonding which result from this treatment.

Two principal ways of describing a covalent bond have been developed. One, called **valence bond** theory or **atomic orbital** theory, considers the two atoms as relatively independent but with orbitals that overlap one another (Fig. 11.12). The electrons of the bond thus may occupy a region in common between the two nuclei. The other, called **molecular orbital** (**MO**) theory, considers that the two orbitals involved in the bonding, one from each atom, interact to form two new molecular orbitals. A molecular orbital is like an atomic orbital except that instead of being a region surrounding one nucleus it surrounds two or more nuclei. One of the molecular orbitals (Fig. 11.13) is of higher energy than the original separate atomic orbitals, because it represents a region which concentrates the two electrons away from the region between the two nuclei. This orbital is called an **antibonding** molecular orbital. The other is of lower energy than the original separate atomic orbitals, because it concentrates the electrons in the region between the two nuclei. This orbital is called a **bonding** molecular orbital. Each molecular orbital, like an atomic orbital, is capable of accommodating two electrons of opposite spin. Accord-

Figure 11.12. Orbital Overlap in Covalence.

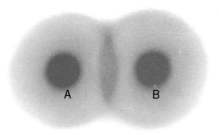

Atomic orbital or valence bond concept: one type of representation of a covalent bond between atoms A and B is drawn. The valence electrons tend to concentrate within this region of orbital overlap. Overlap of s orbitals is shown here.

Figure 11.13.   Molecular Orbitals in the Hydrogen Molecule.

(sigma)   σ   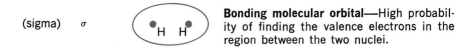   **Bonding molecular orbital**—High probability of finding the valence electrons in the region between the two nuclei.

(sigma starred)   σ*   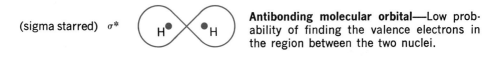   **Antibonding molecular orbital**—Low probability of finding the valence electrons in the region between the two nuclei.

ing to molecular orbital theory, every electron in a bonding orbital has its bonding effect cancelled by an electron in an antibonding orbital. The number of bonds between two atoms is taken as half the difference between the number of bonding electrons and the number of antibonding electrons.

To illustrate, there are only two electrons and two molecular orbitals in a hydrogen molecule. When the electrons are fed into the molecular orbitals, they will prefer the more stable bonding orbital. They therefore become paired in this orbital, leaving the antibonding orbital unoccupied. The net number of bonding electrons is two, and the bond is a single bond. The molecular orbital explanation of the nonexistence of helium molecules is that the two $1s$ orbitals interact to form the antibonding and the bonding orbitals as in the hydrogen molecule. However, here each atom furnishes two electrons: the first two enter the bonding orbital but the second two must go into the antibonding orbital, where they cancel the effect of the first two, resulting in no bond.

Advanced theoretical chemistry currently places greater emphasis on molecular orbitals. Neither concept should be considered "correct" because both have certain advantages. Neither one, unfortunately, is successful in revealing the complete truth in a clearly understandable way. It is important to remember that a given bond is exactly the same no matter how one chooses to describe it. To the extent that different descriptions are correct, they must be different ways of saying equivalent things. This is true of valence bond and molecular orbital theories. It will be true of any other concept that is consistent with experimental fact.

The plain fact is that chemical bonds are not simple. They may seem simple to the extent that we can find a useful viewpoint from which to examine them, to recognize some principles that help us toward a practical understanding of them. Probably it would be fair to say that if an explanation of any scientific phenomenon is simple enough for humans to understand, it is too simple to be complete, or completely accurate. If then we must choose between

Figure 11.14. Molecular Orbital Engery Diagram for the Hydrogen Molecule.

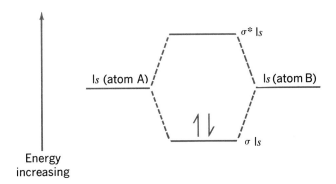

σ^* molecular orbital: antibonding

σ molecular orbital: bonding

In a molecular orbital the electrons occupy a region around two or more atomic nuclei instead of just one as in an atomic orbital. The molecular orbital (MO) is called *poly-nuclear* because more than one nucleus is involved. Notice that both electrons of H_2 occupy the bonding orbital, leaving the antibonding orbital vacant.

idealistic ignorance and practical understanding, by all means let our choice be practical understanding. Let us always keep in mind, however, that by making such a choice we can never eliminate the possible existence of other explanations. In science, as in other areas, we must always remain aware of the limits of our knowledge and understanding.

Test Your Memory

1. What is a *covalent bond?*
2. Name the requisites for forming a single covalent bond.
3. How does the *valence bond theory* differ from the *molecular orbital theory* of bonding?
4. Why does hydrogen have a valence of one?
5. Why does helium not form covalent bonds?
6. Why is fluorine limited to one covalent bond per atom?
7. Explain the formula of water.
8. How can boron form three covalent bonds?
9. What is meant by *hybridization?*
10. What is meant by an *sp³* hybrid orbital?
11. Distinguish between the ground and valence states.
12. Why are valence electrons localized in covalent bonds between atoms of nonmetals?
13. What is a *multiple bond?* Give examples.

Wave Mechanical Descriptions of Covalence **137**

14. What is meant by *coordinate covalence?*
15. What is a *ligand?*
16. What is necessary for an atom to act as acceptor?
17. Illustrate by an equation the formation of a coordinate covalent bond.

Test Your Understanding

1. Predict the probable formulas of compounds of the following pairs of elements: (a) hydrogen and phosphorus, (b) hydrogen and magnesium, (c) chlorine and silicon, (d) oxygen and gallium, (e) sulfur and calcium, (f) rubidium and bromine, (g) potassium and phosphorus, (h) zinc and oxygen, (i) germanium and iodine, (j) lithium and oxygen, (k) aluminum and arsenic.
2. What feature of the structure of oxygen gives to water the possibility of acting as ligand?
3. Distinguish between the ground and valence states of magnesium.
4. What feature of the structure of boron gives BF_3 the possibility of acting as an acceptor?

12

MOLECULAR STRUCTURE AND FORMULAS

BOND ANGLES

Two Bonds

When the same atom forms two or more covalent bonds, these bonds form specific angles with respect to one another. These angles determine the overall distribution of atoms in space (i.e., the geometry of the molecule). The arrangement of the atoms of a molecule in space and with respect to one another is called the **molecular structure** of the compound or element. Molecular structure has a dominant influence on the physical properties of a substance and may also influence its chemical properties. Therefore it is important to know the molecular structure of any substance that interests us.

Practically all bond angles can be predicted approximately by seeking the structure which minimizes the electrostatic repulsion among the electrons. Let us consider each lone pair of electrons as occupying a specific location on the surface of an atom. Each bond—whether single, double, or triple, or somewhere in between—will also be considered as occupying a specific location on the surface of the atom. Since electrostatic repulsion decreases with increasing distance between the charges, electrons on an atom are expected to separate as far as possible to minimize the repulsive forces among them.

Consider an atom in which all the electrons on the surface, whether or not they are engaged in bonding to other atoms, are found in just two positions. What will these positions be? If only one of the positions has a bond, there is no bond angle to determine. If both positions have bonds, then the angle between these bonds is easy to reason out. On the surface of a sphere, the distance between two points is greatest when they are on opposite ends of an axis, as with the poles of the earth. Thus, the bonds are in the same straight line, forming a bond angle of 180°. In hydrogen cyanide (HCN), carbon forms a single covalent bond to hydrogen and a triple covalent bond to nitrogen. All four valence electrons of the carbon are involved in these two bonds so there are none left over. In other words, all the valence electrons of carbon are tied up in just two locations. Therefore, the bond angle must be 180°, and HCN is **linear.**

In carbon dioxide (CO_2), the carbon atom is joined to each oxygen atom by a double bond. Again this uses all four of the valence electrons of the carbon, two for each bond. Since there are only two electron locations on the carbon atom in CO_2, these are as far apart as possible. The oxygen atoms are therefore at opposite sides of the carbon, giving an O-C-O angle of 180°.

When magnesium chloride is vaporized, the solid salt separates into individual molecules of formula $MgCl_2$. Since magnesium atoms have only two outer-shell electrons, the two chlorines use both of these in forming two covalent bonds. There are no electrons left over on the magnesium to prevent a linear structure with a 180° bond angle.

Predict the structures of CS_2 and $HgCl_2$.

If, however, the formation of two bonds would still leave one or two pairs of electrons in the outer shell of the central atom which are not involved in bonding, the bonds cannot be linear because of the repulsion between them and the lone pairs of electrons. For example, a sulfur atom has two more electrons in its outer shell than does a carbon atom. When sulfur combines with oxygen to form sulfur dioxide (SO_2), these two extra electrons are still on the sulfur, uninvolved in the bonding. For this reason sulfur dioxide is not linear like carbon dioxide, but **bent.** The farthest apart three locations can be on the surface of a sphere is at the corners of an equilateral triangle with the sphere center in its plane. The angles are each 120°, which is close to the observed bond angle in SO_2.

When two hydrogen atoms join an oxygen atom to form water (H_2O), two lone pairs of electrons on the oxygen atom remain uninvolved. These prevent water from being linear, causing the O-H bonds to come nearer together to one another to minimize the repulsion of the lone pairs. Four equally spaced locations as far apart as possible on a sphere form a regular tetrahedron. Bonds to the corners of such a tetrahedron form 109°28′. However, a lone pair would be expected to have a little greater repulsive power or occupy more space on the surface of the sphere than a pair that must be shared with a hydrogen atom. The two hydrogen atoms are thus forced a little closer together than 109°, the observed bond angle being 104.5° in water.

Predict the structures of H_2S and Cl_2O.

When an atom forms three covalent bonds, the angle between two of them will depend on whether or not there are any nonbonding electrons on the atomic surface. If all the outer-shell electrons of the atom are involved in the bonds, then there are only three locations. The farthest apart they can be results in bond angles of $120°$ as indicated in the discussion of SO_2. For example, boron trifluoride (BF_3), has all the boron outer-shell electrons in three locations, so the bond angles are $120°$. The molecule is therefore a triangle and planar. But if there is also an electron pair present that is not involved in the three covalent bonds, the bond angles become more nearly tetrahedral ($109°28'$) with the electron pair at one corner of the tetrahedron. For instance, after nitrogen has bonded with three hydrogens, it still has a lone pair. We cannot expect a planar molecule, like that of BF_3, because this lone pair will repel the three bonds out of the plane of the nucleus. The observed bond angle in ammonia is about $107°$, close to that for a tetrahedral arrangement. One may imagine the ammonia molecule to be a tetrahedron with hydrogen atoms at three corners and a lone pair of electrons at the fourth. In effect this gives ammonia the structure of a low pyramid with the nitrogen atom sitting over a triangle of hydrogen atoms.

Predict the structures of PCl_3 and $InCl_3$.

Four Bonds and More

When an atom forms four covalent bonds the structure will be tetrahedral if all its valence electrons are used. If there are still one or more electron pairs left over, then a different structure will be predicted. We have not yet considered covalence in which more than four bonds are formed by the same

Predict the structures of $SiCl_4$ and GeH_4.

atom. There are some we shall look at later that form five and six bonds. In the case of five bonds, or four bonds and one lone pair, or three bonds and two lone pairs, you just cannot find five equal positions on the surface of a sphere. The best that can be done, apparently, is to form a triangle for three locations, with a fourth location above it and the fifth below it. This geometric figure is called a **trigonal bipyramid.** Trigonal means having three sides, and a bypyramid consists of two opposing pyramids having a common base. The bond angles of course cannot be all alike. Six locations make a very symmetrical arrangement on the surface of a sphere, a regular octahedron, with angles to adjacent bonds $90°$ and to opposite bonds $180°$.

These relatively few geometric structures cover most of molecular chemistry.

Figure 12.1.   Molecular Structures and Bond Angles.

No. bonds		Bond angle	Examples
2	 Bent	90-114°	H_2O, H_2S, Cl_2O, OF_2, SCl_2, SO_2, O_3
		120° if only one lone pair	

| 2 | 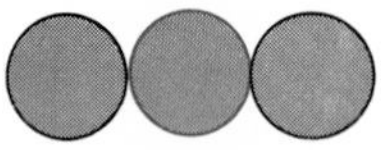 Linear | 180° | $HgCl_2$, BeF_2, CO_2, $MgBr_2$, $ZnCl_2$ |

This is as far apart as two locations can be.

| 3 | Planar triangle | 120° | BF_3, BCl_3, $AlCl_3$, $AlBr_3$, GaI_3, SO_3 |

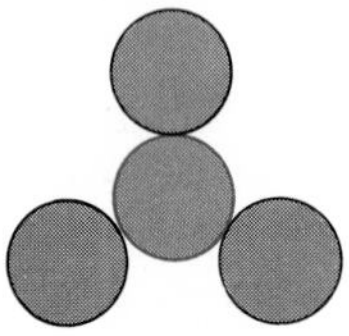

This is as far apart as three locations can be.

| 3 | Pyramidal | 90-114° if one lone pair | NH_3, PCl_3, $AsBr_3$, SbI_3 |

This gives the best separation of three bonds and a lone pair.

| 4 | 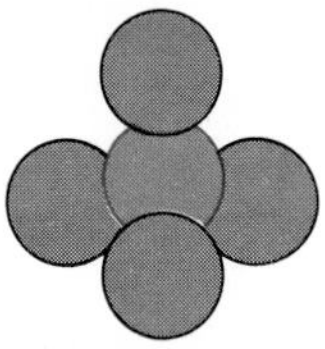 Tetrahedral | 107-114° (ideally, 109°28′) | CH_4, SiH_4, CCl_4, SiF_4, $GeBr_4$ |

This is as far apart as four locations can be.

| 5 | Trigonal bipyramid | 90° and 120° | PCl_5, $SbCl_5$, PBr_5, AsF_5 |

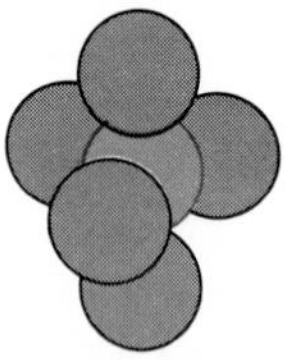

Five atoms cannot be equally spaced around a sphere.

| 6 | 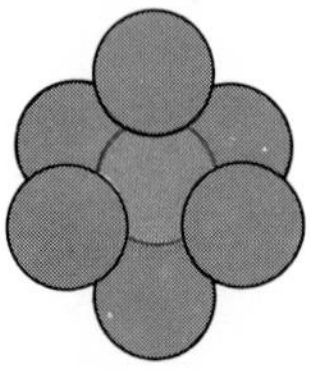 Regular octahedron | 90° | SF_6, PCl_6^-, SeF_6, WF_6, $[Co(NH_3)_6^{3+}]$ |

This is as far apart as six locations can be.

142 Molecular Structure and Formulas

Since molecules are three-dimensional and paper is two-dimensional, it is difficult to indicate molecular structure clearly on paper. Figure 12.1 attempts to do this for the types of structures we have just considered. But it is important to indicate as much as we can symbolically in describing a compound. If the exact bond angles cannot be shown, at least diagrams can be drawn showing which atoms are attached to which. Such diagrams are called **structural diagrams** or **structural formulas.** A number of examples are given in Figure 12.2. In these a single covalent bond is indicated by a straight line between the two symbols representing the atoms joined. A double bond is represented by a double straight line, and a triple bond by a triple straight line.

The ways of representing molecules that cannot be described except in terms of resonance are more complicated and will not be considered here. For example, a carbonate ion consists of a carbon atom joined equally to three oxygen atoms, with the help of two extra electrons which give it a double minus charge: $CO_3^=$. The carbon electrons are fully occupied in forming the three bonds so the structure is planar and triangular and the bond angles are $120°$. But if we indicate the bonds as single we fail to take into account the

Figure 12.2.   Some Structural Formulas.

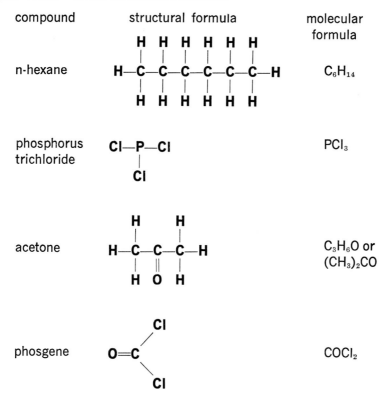

compound	structural formula	molecular formula
n-hexane		C_6H_{14}
phosphorus trichloride		PCl_3
acetone		C_3H_6O or $(CH_3)_2CO$
phosgene		$COCl_2$

fact that carbon has four electrons to use in such bonding. If we try to indicate the bonds as double bonds we are expecting carbon to furnish six orbitals when we know it has only four to contribute. If we indicate two single bonds and one double bond we make appropriate use of carbon's bonding ability, but then we must face the experimental fact that all the bonds are exactly equal and there is no evidence that one is double and the other two single. A double bond is always considerably shorter than a single bond, and these three are of equal length. So any ordinary structural formula for the carbonate ion would prove misleading or erroneous, except to indicate a triangle of oxygen atoms around carbon.

ELECTRONIC FORMULAS

Another type of representation of molecules that is often useful is the **electronic formula.** This can be a combination of structural and electronic formulas or merely electronic. If it is merely electronic, the representation of a single covalent bond is a pair of dots between the two atomic symbols instead of the straight line as in the structural formula bond. A double pair of dots represents

Figure 12.3. Some Electronic and Electronic-Structural Formulas.

compound	electronic-structural formula	molecular formula
n-hexane	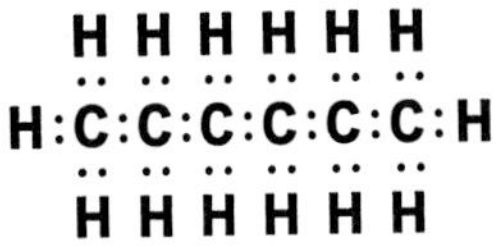 H:C:C:C:C:C:C:H (with H above and below each C)	C_6H_{14}
phosphorus trichloride	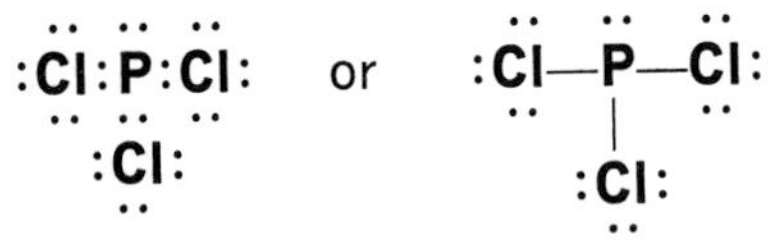 :Cl:P:Cl: with :Cl: below, or :Cl—P—Cl: with :Cl: below	PCl_3
acetone	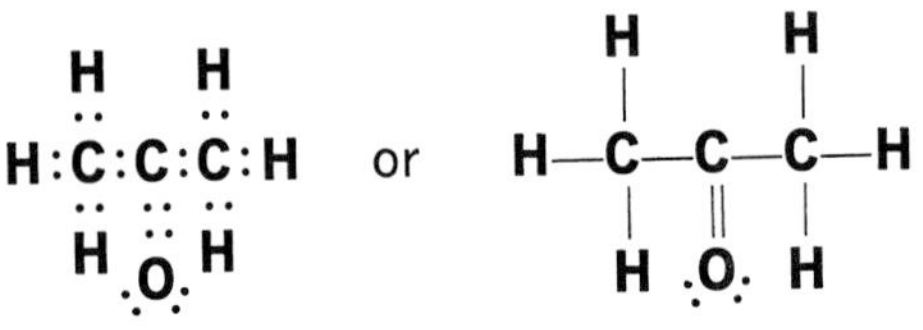 H:C:C:C:H with H above and H:O:H below, or H—C—C—C—H with H and .O. and H below	$(CH_3)_2CO$
phosgene	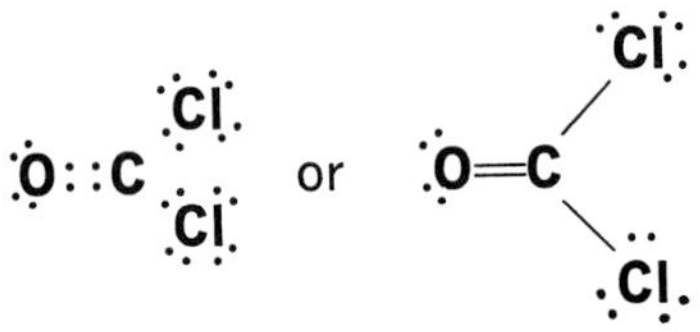 O::C with Cl above and Cl below, or O=C with Cl above and Cl below	$COCl_2$

144 Molecular Structure and Formulas

a double bond. Three pairs of dots represent a triple bond. The lone pairs are also indicated as pairs of dots next to the symbol for the atom. Examples of this kind of representation are shown in Figure 12.3. Since the straight lines are easier to draw than the pairs of dots, a combination of structural and electronic formula is often used. In such a combination the bonds are represented by lines and the lone pairs by dots. Examples of this combination are also shown in Figure 12.3.

Write electronic formulas representing N_2, Cl_2, CO_2, CH_4, HCl, BF_3, and PF_3.

ISOMERS

The molecular structure is especially important in indicating which atoms are attached to which other atoms. In many combinations of atoms the order of

Figure 12.4.   Examples of Isomers, Showing Structural Differences.

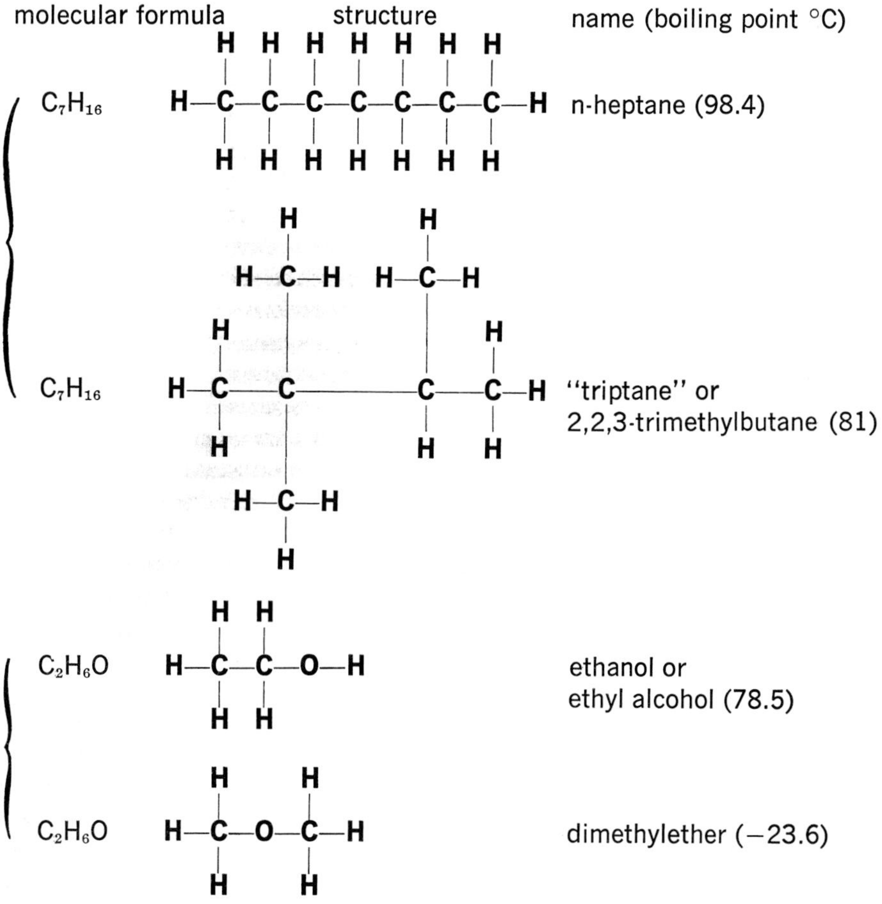

molecular formula   structure   name (boiling point °C)

C_7H_{16} n-heptane (98.4)

C_7H_{16} "triptane" or 2,2,3-trimethylbutane (81)

C_2H_6O ethanol or ethyl alcohol (78.5)

C_2H_6O dimethylether (−23.6)

attachment is variable. If the order of attachment is not the same, the molecule is not the same either. Even though it may be composed of exactly the same number of atoms of each of the same elements, it represents a different compound, with different properties throughout. Different compounds having identical molecular formulas but different structural arrangements of the component atoms are called **isomers.** Some examples of isomers are shown by structural formulas in Figure 12.4. Do not conclude that a mere difference in arrangement should make only a small difference in properties, for this is not necessarily so. Look for instance at the formula given for dimethyl ether and that for ethyl alcohol in Figure 12.4. With identical empirical and molecular formulas, dimethyl ether is an anaesthetic gas, whereas ethyl alcohol is an intoxicating liquid. Look also at the empirical and molecular formulas C_7H_{16}. The one called **normal heptane** is one of the worst knocking fuels you could put into your gas tank. It is so bad that it serves as the standard for zero in the octane rating system used to evaluate motor fuels. The one called **triptane** is the best hydrocarbon known, from the viewpoint of burning smoothly in an internal-combustion engine.

SUMMARY

So far we have seen that matter consists of atoms of different basic substances called chemical elements. From a knowledge of the arrangement of electrons in the cloud surrounding the nucleus, we can predict how different atoms will combine with one another when they come together. We can understand how the different structures originate, and how the arrangement of atoms is important. But the subject of chemical bonding is not a simple one. We will need to keep on reexamining and refining it as our study of chemistry proceeds.

Indeed, before we go any farther, we must take into account one more property of atoms that up to now we have not considered. The next chapter is devoted to this property, called **electronegativity.**

Test Your Memory

1. What is the expected bond angle when all outer-shell electrons of an atom are involved in only two bonds?
2. In what respect are HCN and CO_2 similar and why?
3. Why is a water molecule bent?
4. If three bonds are formed by an atom which also has an outer non-bonding electron pair, what bond angles are predicted?
5. What is meant by *isomer?*

Test Your Understanding

1. Predict formulas and structures of molecules formed from the following pairs of elements: (a) hydrogen and sulfur, (b) tin and chlorine, (c) carbon and fluorine, (d) antimony and bromine, (e) boron and chlorine,

(f) mercury and iodine, (g) two carbon atoms and four hydrogen atoms, (h) sulfur and chlorine.

2. Represent each of the above compounds by each of the three types of formula described in this chapter.

3. Draw as many isomeric structures as you can for C_5H_{12}, remembering that each carbon atom must form four single bonds and each hydrogen, one.

13

ELECTRONEGATIVITY AND BOND POLARITY

BOND POLARITY

When two like atoms are joined together by a covalent bond, as in H_2 or F_2 or Cl_2, the electron pair forming the bond is evenly shared by both atoms, since both have exactly equal attraction for them. The electrons on a time-average basis spend as much time closely associated with one nucleus as they do with the other. Such a covalent bond is called a **nonpolar** covalent bond. Its distribution of electrons is symmetrical with respect to both nuclei. Suppose the two bonded atoms were not exactly alike in their attraction for the bonding electrons. Then one would expect these electrons to spend more than half the time more closely associated with the atom that attracted them more, and less than half the time more closely associated with the atom that attracted them less. Since the atoms were both initially neutral, this unevenness of sharing would produce the effect of placing a partial negative charge (δ^-) on one atom, leaving an equivalent partial positive charge (δ^+) on the other atom. (A partial charge is a fraction of the charge on the electron, the smallest known unit of charge.) The electron distribution in the bond would thus be unequal, unsymmetrical, and **polar.** Polar covalence differs from nonpolar covalence in significant respects.

Before going into more explanation of polarity in bonds, let us be sure that we understand thoroughly the general meaning of polarity. Imagine any portion of matter, such as a pencil, as consisting of neutral atoms and therefore an equal number of negative and positive charges. We could balance that pencil on a finger, thus locating a point at the center which could be defined as the center of gravity of the pencil. This would mean that at that particular point, the total downward pull of gravity on one end of the pencil is exactly equal to the total downward pull of gravity on the other end of the pencil. If

Figure 13.1. Polar and Nonpolar Particles.

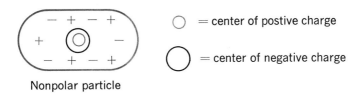

Nonpolar particle

◯ = center of postive charge

◯ = center of negative charge

If the *center* of positive charge coincides with the *center* of negative charge, the particle is *nonpolar.* Its *dipole moment* is zero because it has no dipole (separation of poles).

If the *center* of positive charge does not coincide with the *center* of negative charge, the electric poles are separate, and the particle is *polar.* Being polar, it has a measurable tendency to become oriented in an electrical field, as shown. This tendency is measured as the *dipole moment.* The **dipole moment** is the product of the charge and the distance of separation.

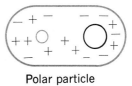

Polar particle

A particle lacking a dipole would be unaffected by an electrical field.

A *covalent bond* is polar if the valence electrons are unevenly shared, and nonpolar if the valence electrons are evenly shared. If a molecule has no dipole moment, either all its bonds are nonpolar, as in H_2, or the bond moments cancel one another, as in CO_2 where the two bonds are polar but in opposite directions in a linear molecule. A molecule such as HCl is certain to be polar because of the higher electronegativity of chlorine. Therefore it has a measurable dipole moment, with H the positive end and Cl the negative end of the dipole.

Bond Polarity 149

the pencil weighs 30 g, and we balance it at its center of gravity, then the total of 30 g bears down on our finger just as though all the atoms were actually directly above the finger which of course they are not. In a similar way, electrical charge that is distributed throughout a region may be regarded as possessing a "center of gravity" of charge, or a center of charge. At this point the total charge may be regarded as if somehow all the charges could be concentrated physically at that one point.

There must be one point in the region occupied by that pencil, then, at which we could regard the total negative charge of all its electrons as being concentrated. In actuality we know they are spread throughout the pencil. This point we call the **center of negative charge.** There must also be one point in the region occupied by that pencil at which the total positive charge of all the atomic nuclei may be similarly regarded as being concentrated, the **center of positive charge.** If, as would normally be the case in a pencil, the centers of negative and positive charge exactly *coincide,* then the pencil, or the charge distribution within the pencil, is *nonpolar.* A *separation* of these centers is called a **dipole.** If some disturbance or inequality should cause the center of negative charge to be at a point in space different from that of the center of positive charge, then the pencil, or the charge distribution within the pencil, would amount to a dipole. The pencil would be called polar. A **polar covalent bond** is one in which an electrical dissymmetry has been created because the shared electrons are not evenly shared.

ELECTRONEGATIVITY

Atoms of the different elements differ in their ability to attract the shared electrons in a covalent bond. The atoms of some elements, such as fluorine, oxygen, and chlorine, attract such electrons very strongly. The atoms of certain other elements, such as sodium and potassium, attract such electrons very weakly. The atoms of still other elements, such as carbon and hydrogen, are intermediate in their attraction for electrons. This attraction that is characteristic of each element is called **electronegativity,** the relative ability of an element to acquire a negative electrical charge. Note that this is *not* the same as the quality of *possessing* a negative charge. In fact, they are opposite qualities, as we shall soon see. Therefore, the choice of the word electronegativity is somewhat unfortunate, but since it is so widely used, we will continue to use it.

Electronegativity can be estimated in a wide variety of ways. It is an elusive quantity, difficult to define precisely. Up to the present time at least, it has been impossible to measure directly and quantitatively. However, several very different methods of estimation have led to results which generally agree. We may be reasonably confident that we know the approximately correct relative electronegativity values for most of the major group elements. Values for most of the transitional elements are known with considerably less certainty. A set of values on the most widely accepted arbitrary scale is given in Table 13.1.

Table 13.1. Electronegativities of Some of the Elements

					H		
					2.3		

Li	Be		B	C	N	O	F
0.9	1.6		1.9	2.5	2.9	3.5	3.9
Na	Mg		Al	Si	P	S	Cl
0.8	1.4		1.5	1.9	2.2	2.7	3.3
K	Ca	Zn	Ga	Ge	As	Se	Br
0.7	1.1	1.9	2.1	2.3	2.5	2.8	3.0
Rb	Sr	Cd	In	Sn	Sb	Te	I
0.7	1.0	1.7	1.9	2.0	2.2	2.3	2.5
Cs	Ba	Hg	Tl	Pb	Bi		
0.7	0.9	1.9	2.0	2.0	2.1		

Effective Nuclear Charge

Perhaps we can acquire some feeling for the nature and causes of electro-negativity by considering the results of increasing the atomic number while adding electrons to the outermost shell. We have already considered in Chapter 10 the fact that although atoms are electrically neutral as observed from a distance, the nuclear charge is recognized at the surface of the atom. This means that the electrons are incapable of completely blocking off the positive charge of the nucleus at the surface of the atom. Indeed, no chemical bonds would form between any atoms if it were not possible for the electrons of each atom to sense the presence of, and be attracted to, the nucleus of the other. In other words, although the full strength of the nuclear positive charge is greatly diluted by the intervening electronic cloud, there is at the surface of an atom an **effective nuclear charge.** This is the difference between the actual nuclear charge and the shielding effect, or charge cancellation, by the inter-vening electrons.

Estimates have been made of the effect of each electron on reducing the actual nuclear charge that is sensed at the surface of an atom. Roughly, each interior-shell electron reduces the effective positive charge by one. Each penultimate (next to outermost shell) electron reduces the positive charge only by about 0.85, and each outer-shell electron by only about 0.35. In other words, because of the special qualities of their position and motion about the nucleus, the outer-shell electrons are only about one-third effective in blocking off nuclear charge from each other. As each period of the periodic table be-gins, by starting the filling of a new outer shell, the effective nuclear charge is quite low because the underlying electrons do a fairly thorough screening job.

With each increase in atomic number, the nuclear charge goes up by one, but the new electron only blocks off about one third of this. This means that the net gain in effective nuclear charge is about two thirds of a positive charge for each increase in the number of outer-shell electrons.

In sodium, atomic number 11, the effective nuclear charge sensed by an electron from another atom is about +2. In other words, the foreign electron is prevented, by the underlying 10 electrons of the sodium atom, from sensing the presence of as large a nuclear charge as the actual +11. It does sense a positive charge of about +2. In magnesium, atomic number 12, this effective nuclear charge has grown by about two thirds to +2.67. In aluminum, atomic number 13, the effective nuclear charge is +3.33. By the time chlorine is reached, in this period, with the addition of four more outer-shell electrons and four more protons to the nucleus, the effective nuclear charge has grown by an additional 8/3, or to about +6.

Consequences of Effective Nuclear Charge

We may expect this progressive increase in the effective nuclear charge to have certain very important effects on the nature of the atoms of these elements. One is an effect on atomic size. We have been talking rather loosely about conditions "at the atomic surface" as though atoms have definite surfaces. In fact, the electronic clouds are so nebulous that the probability of finding electrons decreases only slowly as the distance from the nucleus increases. It is difficult to define exactly where an atom ends or begins. However, if two like atoms unite by a single covalent bond, the distance between their nuclei can be measured experimentally. This is called the **bond length.** It is reasonable to define a **covalent radius** as one half the single bond length between like atoms.

As the effective nuclear charge increases, this results in stronger forces holding the electrons near the nucleus. Consequently, since the "size" of an atom represents a balance between the interelectronic repulsions and the nuclear attraction, the size must decrease as the effective nuclear charge increases. As shown in Figure 13.2, the covalent radii of the elements decrease as the number of outer-shell electrons increases.

Figure 13.2. Schematic Representation of Atoms Showing Radius and Relative Electronegativity.

Radius can be shown by the size of the circle. Relative electronegativity can be represented by the depth of the electron well:

Sodium has large atoms of low electronegativity.

Chlorine has small atoms of high electronegativity.

Figure 13.3. Variation in Some Atomic Properties Across a Period.

Atomic number	element	Atom	Effective nuclear charge	Radius, Å	Electro-negativity
11	Na	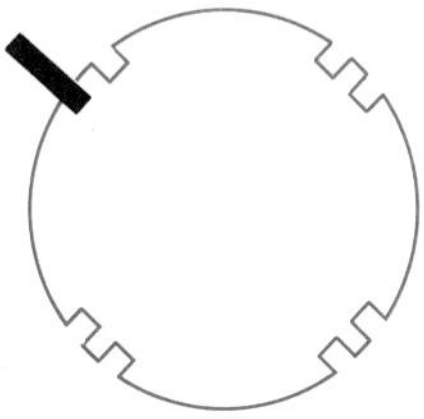	1.87	1.54	0.8
12	Mg		2.54	1.36	1.4
13	Al		3.21	1.18	1.5
14	Si		3.88	1.11	1.9
15	P		4.55	1.06	2.2
16	S		5.22	1.02	2.7
17	Cl		5.89	0.99	3.3

The other effect of increasing effective nuclear charge is an increase in the electronegativity. In fact, electronegativity is a measure of the attraction that an atom exerts on the electrons shared with another atom. This attraction is the result of an effective nuclear charge. Electronegativity and the effective nuclear charge at a point separated from the nucleus by the covalent radius are nearly the same thing. As shown in Figure 13.2, electronegativity increases as the number of outer-shell electrons increases. It tends to decrease as the atomic radius increases, for the distance through which the electrostatic attraction of the nucleus must operate becomes greater.

Electronegativity Equalization

In a qualitative way it can be said that the greater the electronegativity difference between the two atoms, the greater the unevenness of sharing that causes bond polarity. But we would like to know *how* polar a given bond is, and how it compares with another polar bond. We would also like to know how the polarity of one bond formed by a certain atom may be influenced by the other bonds to that same atom. Let us picture two atoms, initially different in electronegativity, uniting through formation of a covalent bond. Because of the difference in initial attraction for the shared electrons, the atom that was higher in electronegativity must acquire more than half share of the valence electrons, thus becoming partially negative. This must leave the other atom partially positive. Before we can know *how* negative and *how* positive, we must have some idea of what goes on in this merged electronic cloud about two nuclei.

If an atom having a certain radius acquires an extra electron, this upsets the balance between interelectronic repulsion and nuclear attraction: the nuclear charge remains unchanged; the amount of screening of it increases; and the repulsion among electrons becomes greater with more electrons present. This leads to a reduced effective nuclear charge as well as to an increased radius. Both of these effects weaken the attraction the atom has for additional electrons. On the other hand, if an electron is removed from a neutral atom, this also upsets the balance between electronic repulsions and nuclear attractions. It does so by reducing the interelectronic repulsions and thus permitting the effective nuclear charge to increase, which decreases the radius. A **negative ion** is always larger than the neutral atom and attracts electrons far less strongly. A **positive ion** is always smaller than the neutral atom and attracts electrons more strongly.

Let us apply these facts to the condition of *partially* charged atoms. The same kind of effects should be observed. The atom which initially is more electronegative expands and becomes *less* so as it succeeds in acquiring partial negative charge. The atom which initially is less electronegative contracts and becomes *more* so as it becomes partially positive. It seems reasonable to suppose that these adjustments in the electronic clouds of each atom must cease at that point at which they reach the *same* electronegativity.

This postulate is known as the **principle of electronegativity equalization.** In one sense, it is equivalent to observing that two electrons can hardly be shared by two atoms having orbitals different in energies, for this would seem to require the electrons to be continually transferring from higher to lower energy orbitals and back again. The principle of electronegativity equalization may be considered to be a statement of **equalization of orbital energies** when covalent bonds are formed.

Figure 13.4.   Equalization of Electronegativities.

Assume that atom A is relatively large, not compact, and low in electro-negativity.

Assume that atom B is relatively small, compact, and highly electronegative.

When they form AB by a covalent bond,

atom A, now having less than half of the valence electrons, becomes partially positive, smaller, and more electro-negative.

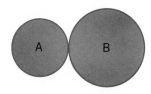

Atom B acquires more than half of the valence elec-trons, becoming partially negative, larger, and less electronegative.

In the molecule AB, the electronegativities have become equal: the bonding electrons in effect become equally attracted to both nuclei by spending more of their time around the nucleus that originally attracted them more, and less time around the other nucleus.

Let us go through polar bond formation once more, using a specific ex-ample. Sodium atoms are initially low in electronegativity. Chlorine atoms are initially high in electronegativity. A sodium atom has one outer-shell electron. It therefore has the capacity to form one single covalent bond. A chlorine atom has seven outer-shell electrons with but one vacancy. It also has the capacity to form one single covalent bond. When a sodium atom comes in contact with a chlorine atom, they can form a covalent bond by sharing a pair of electrons. But since the chlorine was initially much higher in electro-negativity, it tends to attract the electron pair more strongly than does the sodium. As the valence electrons begin to spend more than half of their time more closely associated with the chlorine nucleus than with the sodium nucleus, they increase the electron population about the chlorine atom. This causes it to expand and become less electronegative. As the sodium tends to lose to the chlorine the only outer-shell electron it has, it acquires (together with a partial positive charge) a higher effective nuclear charge. This draws the remaining electrons closer in around the nucleus and increases the electronegativity. When the decreasing electronegativity of the partially negative chlorine atom equals the increasing electronegativity of the partially positive sodium atom, this adjustment stops. The shared electron pair is now equally attracted to both nuclei, but only because it spends more than half its time more closely associated with the chlorine nucleus. In effect, the **equalization of valence orbital energies** is made possible by the uneven sharing of electrons.

In many books, bond polarity is discussed as though it depended solely on the electronegativity difference between the two atoms forming the bond. Other attachments the same atoms may also have are not taken into account. This is misleading. Ample experimental evidence suggests that every bond in a molecule affects the nature of all the other bonds in that molecule. Therefore we should consider bond polarity to be based squarely on electronegativity difference only for diatomic molecules. The principle of electronegativity equalization provides a method of accounting for all the bonds in the molecule. **When two** *or more* **atoms form a compound, they become adjusted to the same intermediate electronegativity.**

What is the intermediate electronegativity reached by the equalization process? The assumption is made that it is given by the geometric mean of the electronegativities of all the atoms in the formula before they formed the compound. Whereas the arithmetic mean is found by adding a series of numbers and dividing the sum by the number of figures added, the geometric mean is found by multiplying together all the numbers in the series and taking the nth root of this product, where n is the total number of figures multiplied. For instance, to obtain the intermediate electronegativity of water, the electronegativity of hydrogen is multiplied by the electronegativity of hydrogen times the electronegativity of oxygen. The cube root of the product gives the geometric mean, the intermediate electronegativity.

Partial Charge

What values should be assigned to the partial charges that result from electronegativity equalization? By a rather straightforward process which will not be detailed here, one can determine how much the electronegativity of any element would change if the atom acquired a unit charge. That is, we can determine the electronegativity of its cation or anion. The **partial charge** on any atom of that element in any compound is then defined as a ratio. It is the ratio of the change in electronegativity that the atom underwent in forming that compound, to the change in electronegativity it would have undergone had it succeeded in acquiring or losing an electron completely. It is not very

Figure 13.5. Color Scale to Represent Relative Partial Charge.

To represent compounds having bond polarity, it is helpful to show *partial charges* on the atoms in illustrations in this book. Within the practical limits of the two-color printing used here, the following graduated color scale is used:

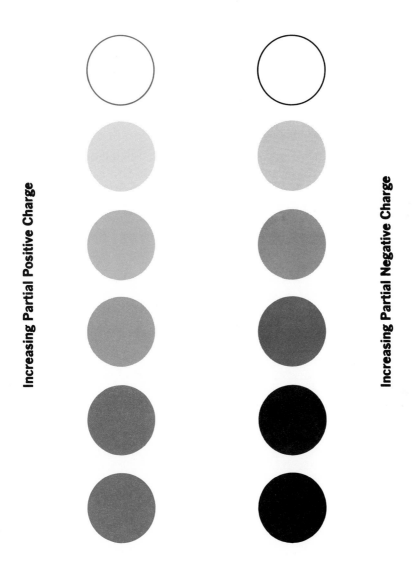

difficult to calculate the partial charge on each atom in any compound for which the formula is known. Quantities such as these, which cannot be measured directly by conventional experimental methods, can only be considered estimates of the actual physical situation. Values of partial charge given in this book were calculated by the method just outlined.

Test Your Memory

1. What is *polarity?*
2. Distinguish between a polar and a nonpolar covalent bond.
3. Define *electronegativity.*
4. (a) What is *effective nuclear charge?*
   (b) Why does it increase from left to right across a period?
   (c) What effect does this have on atomic radius?
   (d) What effect does it have on electronegativity, and why?
5. (a) State the principle of electronegativity equalization.
   (b) How is equalization of electronegativity accomplished?
6. What is the origin of *partial charge?*

Test Your Understanding

1. Considering the structure of CO_2 and the fact that both bonds are polar, would you predict that the molecule as a whole would be polar or not? Why?
2. Fluorine is more electronegative than oxygen. What would be the direction of bond polarity, if any, in OF_2?
3. Why is a fluoride ion less electronegative than a fluorine atom?
4. What should be the sum of all the partial charges in a molecule?

14

IONIC BONDING AND CRYSTAL STRUCTURE

THE IONIC MODEL OF NONMOLECULAR SOLIDS

Only a few years before G. N. Lewis' suggestion in 1916 that a chemical bond consists of a sharing of electrons, the German chemist Richard Abegg (1869–1910) proposed a theory that the bonding in many solid salts arises from the electrostatic attraction between ions of opposite charge. As he, and later, physicist Walter Kossel (1888–1956), pointed out, nonmetal atoms tend to acquire electrons, forming negative ions isoelectronic with (having the same number of electrons as) the next higher "inert gas" (M8 element). Metal atoms tend to lose their outer-shell electrons, leaving behind positive ions that are isoelectronic with the next lower M8 element.

For example, by acquiring one electron, the fluorine atom (2-7) becomes the fluoride ion F^- (2-8), which like neon has 10 electrons. Similarly the chloride ion Cl^- (2-8-8) is isoelectronic with argon, having 18 electrons. The bromide ion Br^- (2-8-18-8) is isoelectronic with krypton, atomic number 36. Through gaining one electron, iodine, atomic number 53, becomes the iodine ion I^-, with 54 electrons like xenon. The elements of group M6—oxygen, sulfur, selenium, and tellurium—all lack two electrons of a filled octet, like an M8 element, in their outermost shells. The doubly negative ions—$O^=$, $S^=$, $Se^=$, and $Te^=$—are isoelectronic with neon, argon, krypton, and xenon, respectively.

On the other hand, sodium, atomic number 11, has but one electron in its outermost shell surrounding a core of 10 electrons. The Na^+ ion is therefore isoelectronic with neon. Potassium, atomic number 19 (2-8-8-1), can lose one electron and then have 18 electrons left, making the K^+ ion like argon. The rubidium ion, Rb^+, is similarly isoelectronic with the krypton atom, as is the cesium ion, Cs^+, with xenon. Magnesium, atomic number 12 (2-8-2), can become isoelectronic with neon by losing the two electrons of its outermost shell to become the Mg^{++} ion. By losing its three outermost electrons to become the Al^{+++} ion, aluminum (2-8-3) can do likewise. These are just a few of the many possible examples.

The M8 elements had been found to be incapable of forming chemical bonds. (Even today, when we know that krypton and xenon can form certain bonds to fluorine and oxygen, the relative inertness of these elements is still their most striking characteristic.) Therefore, it was easy to conclude that something very special about the atomic numbers 2 (He), 10 (Ne), 18 (Ar), 36 (Kr), 54 (Xe), and 86 (Rn), prevented the atoms having these numbers from forming chemical bonds. This inertness was ascribed to a unique stability of their particular electronic configurations. Consequently, it was very attractive and appealing to assume that other elements seek greater stability by acquiring these favored configurations through gain or loss of electrons. In a typical metal-nonmetal reaction, the nonmetal atom would become isoelectronic with an M8 element by taking away the valence electrons of the metal. This would leave the metal ion isoelectronic with an M8 element also. Then, once the ions were formed, their opposite charges would attract and hold them together tightly in the solid crystalline form called a salt.

Figure 14.1. The Ionic Model of Sodium Chloride Crystal.

A chlorine atom, by taking an electron from a sodium atom, completes its octet and becomes a Cl- ion, which is larger and isoelectronic with argon.

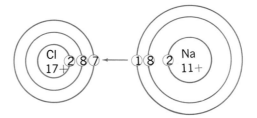

A sodium atom, by losing an electron to a chlorine atom, becomes a Na+ ion, which is smaller and isoelectronic with neon.

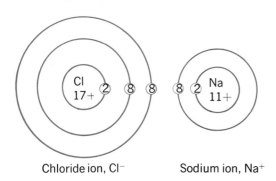

Chloride ion, Cl⁻   Sodium ion, Na+

Electrostatic attractions between oppositely charged ions hold the crystal together. The bonding is called *ionic* or *electrovalent*.

For example, a sodium atom, atomic number 11 (2-8-1), has one outer-shell electron. Loss of this electron leaves the sodium ion Na^+ with the electronic configuration of neon, atomic number 10. A chlorine atom, atomic number 17 (2-8-7), has one outer-shell vacancy. By filling this vacancy it can acquire a completed octet in the outer shell to become the chloride ion Cl^-, isoelectronic with the argon atom. When sodium and chlorine atoms meet, each chlorine atom takes an electron from a sodium atom, simultaneously forming Na^+ ions and Cl^- ions. Being mutually attracted to one another, these pack together in such a way as to minimize repulsions among like charges while maximizing attractions among unlike charges. In this particular substance, each sodium ion is surrounded by and in direct contact with six chloride ions, and each chloride ion is surrounded by and in direct contact with six sodium ions. The compound is very stable as evidenced by the evolution of a large amount of heat during its formation from the elements. The crystal is tightly held together as evidenced by the fact that it doesn't melt until heated to 808°C.

This idea of the solid salts as formed by the combination of metallic elements with nonmetallic elements was further developed through the work of Sir William Bragg (1862–1942) and his son, Sir William Lawrence Bragg (1890–   ), Englishmen who pioneered in investigating the structure of crystals by the use of X rays. Their results showed that no individual molecules could be recognized in the crystal and that the arrangement was just what might be expected for the packing of oppositely charged particles. This *ionic model* was also consistent with the observation that many of these salts dissolve in water in the form of the separate ions. As we shall see in a later chapter it served to explain the action of an electric current on molten salts, as studied by the famous English scientist Sir Humphrey Davy in the early 1800's. The ionic model gives a simple and reasonable explanation of the valences of metals and nonmetals and the formulas of their salts. Small wonder, then, that the concept of ionic bonding, or electrovalence as it is sometimes called, has been an attractive part of chemical theory.

Two other experimental quantities are very pertinent to the theory of ionic bonding and deserve careful consideration. These are ionization energies and electron affinities.

Ionization Energy

When the vapor of an element is subjected to electron bombardment, no effect is observed as the energy of these bombarding electrons is increased, until a minimum electron-accelerating voltage is reached. At this potential, called the **ionization potential,** positive ions of the element begin to form. Converted to units more directly useful in chemistry, the ionization potential becomes **ionization energy** and is given in kilocalories per mole of atoms. The ionization energy is one of the very few properties of an atom that can be measured experimentally, directly, and usually quite accurately. It is the en-

Figure 14.2. First Ionization Energies of Gaseous Atoms, kcal/mole, 25°C.

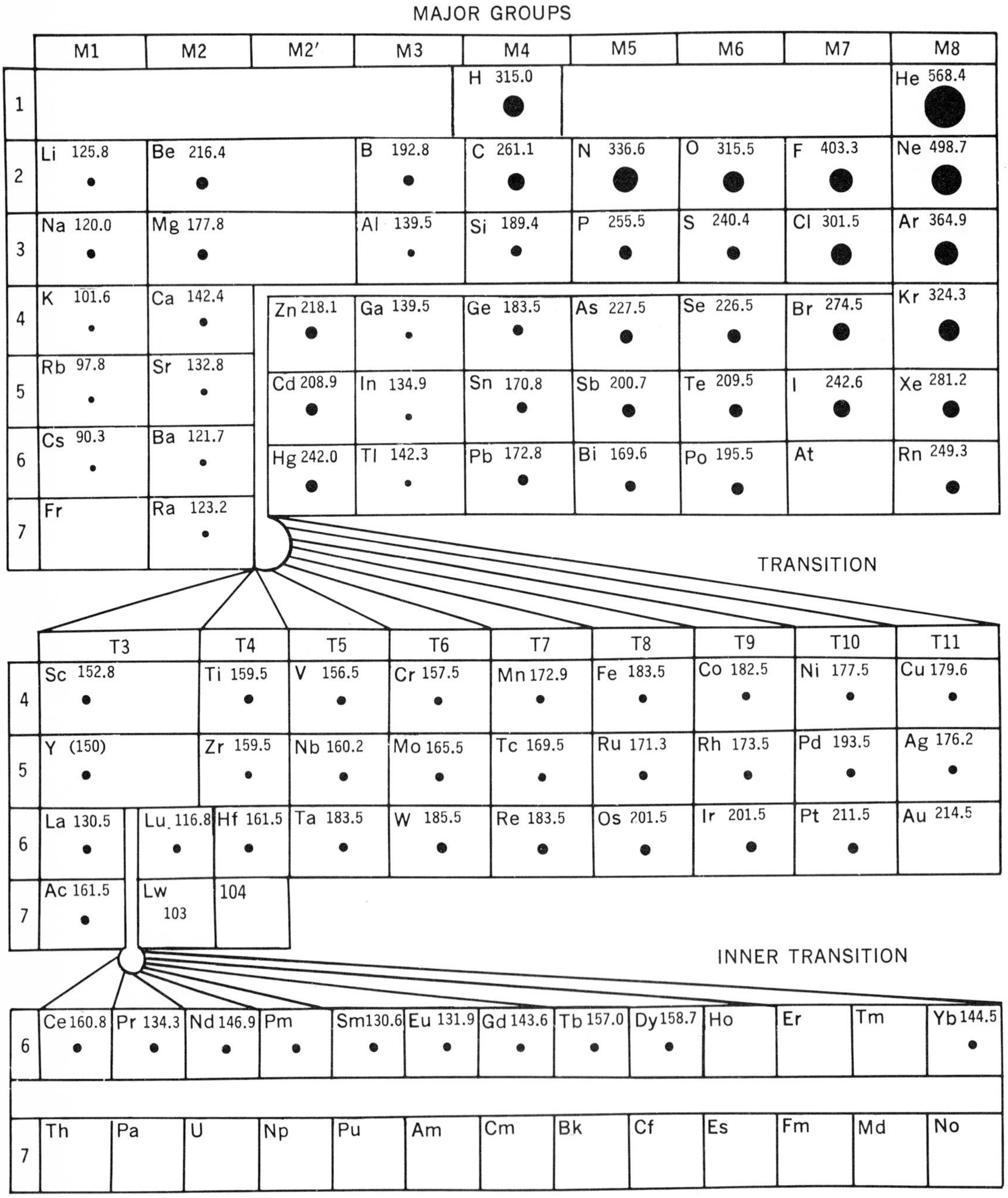

MAJOR GROUPS

	M1	M2	M2′	M3	M4	M5	M6	M7	M8
1					H 315.0				He 568.4
2	Li 125.8	Be 216.4		B 192.8	C 261.1	N 336.6	O 315.5	F 403.3	Ne 498.7
3	Na 120.0	Mg 177.8		Al 139.5	Si 189.4	P 255.5	S 240.4	Cl 301.5	Ar 364.9
4	K 101.6	Ca 142.4	Zn 218.1	Ga 139.5	Ge 183.5	As 227.5	Se 226.5	Br 274.5	Kr 324.3
5	Rb 97.8	Sr 132.8	Cd 208.9	In 134.9	Sn 170.8	Sb 200.7	Te 209.5	I 242.6	Xe 281.2
6	Cs 90.3	Ba 121.7	Hg 242.0	Tl 142.3	Pb 172.8	Bi 169.6	Po 195.5	At	Rn 249.3
7	Fr	Ra 123.2							

TRANSITION

	T3	T4	T5	T6	T7	T8	T9	T10	T11
4	Sc 152.8	Ti 159.5	V 156.5	Cr 157.5	Mn 172.9	Fe 183.5	Co 182.5	Ni 177.5	Cu 179.6
5	Y (150)	Zr 159.5	Nb 160.2	Mo 165.5	Tc 169.5	Ru 171.3	Rh 173.5	Pd 193.5	Ag 176.2
6	La 130.5 / Lu 116.8	Hf 161.5	Ta 183.5	W 185.5	Re 183.5	Os 201.5	Ir 201.5	Pt 211.5	Au 214.5
7	Ac 161.5	Lw 103	104						

INNER TRANSITION

6	Ce 160.8	Pr 134.3	Nd 146.9	Pm	Sm 130.6	Eu 131.9	Gd 143.6	Tb 157.0	Dy 158.7	Ho	Er	Tm	Yb 144.5
7	Th	Pa	U	Np	Pu	Am	Cm	Bk	Cf	Es	Fm	Md	No

ergy required to remove to infinity one electron from a neutral isolated or gaseous atom:

$$A(g) + \text{ionization energy} \rightarrow A^+(g) + e^-$$

Where A represents an atom of any element, and (g) denotes that it is in the gaseous state.

When the energy of the bombardment has been elevated far enough, it can knock off a second electron. The energy required is called the **second ionization energy.** Similarly, electrons can be knocked out of the atomic clouds one by one until nothing is left but the bare nucleus. Each successive electron requires greater energy. The energies are called the **third ionization energy,** the fourth, and so on. It is noteworthy that although each successive electron removal always requires more energy, the increase in energy required becomes exceedingly large when the outer-shell electrons have been removed and the next electron must come from an underlying shell of two (for the $n = 1$ shell) or eight electrons. This fact attests to the great stability of the outer octet (and the outer pair in helium). It helps to explain why no ordinary chemical reaction can provide enough energy to break into the underlying closed shells for electrons. For example, it requires 120 kilocalories per mole of atoms to remove the outermost electron from sodium atoms forming sodium ions, Na^+, but to take away a second electron to form Na^{++} would require 1192 kilocalories per mole.

The first ionization energies for the chemical elements vary with atomic number in the expected periodic manner. Lowest values are observed for the M1 elements which have only one outer-shell electron. The M8 elements, in keeping with the stability of their electronic clouds, have the highest ionization energy in each period. The trend in between M1 and M8 is somewhat erratic but generally upward. As atoms within a group grow larger, from top to bottom of the periodic table, the ionization energy tends to decrease slightly, showing that an outermost electron in a shell farther out from the nucleus is not held quite so tightly even though the nuclear charge is greater. The trend in ionization energies roughly parallels the trend in electronegativities. This should not be surprising since an atom that strongly resists the removal of one of its own electrons might well be expected to attract strongly an outside electron provided an orbital vacancy is available. Similarly, an atom that cannot hold its own electron very tightly cannot be expected to attract outside electrons strongly.

For our present purposes, the ionization energies are significant because they give us a quantitative measure of how feasible the formation of positive ions really is. For example, is a certain atom likely to form a $+4$ ion if the total ionization energy necessary is more than 3000 kilocalories per mole? Bond and reaction energies are normally much lower than this, so we could predict in this instance that such an ion would not be formed for lack of an adequate energy source. Ionization energies also suggest how strongly a positive ion may attract an outside electron, since the same amount of energy required to remove an electron should be released when the positive ion regains an electron.

Electron Affinity

Electron affinity is much more difficult to determine than ionization potential but is in some ways equally interesting. This is the energy released when a gaseous atom acquires an extra electron, becoming a gaseous negative ion. Accurate or reliable values are now known for many of the elements, the most reliable being those for the halogens:

$$X(g) + e^- \rightarrow X^-(g) + \text{electron affinity}$$

The highest known value is that of chlorine, about -85 kilocalories per mole of atoms. (Remember the convention that heat evolved is given a minus sign.) It is quite significant that the formation of a doubly negative ion, such as $O^=$ or $S^=$, is endothermic—the electron affinity is positive. An atom of oxygen will take on one electron with the release of energy, but much greater energy must be expended to force it to take on a second electron.

Limitations of the Ionic Model

Let us now consider the formation of sodium chloride once more. Older chemistry textbooks sometimes say that sodium tries to get rid of its valence electron because it "wants to" become like neon. They also say that chlorine tries to gain an extra electron because it then becomes like argon. The first statement is completely wrong, as the experimental ionization energy of 120 kcal per mole proves. The truth is that a sodium ion, rather than remain "like neon," will attract an outside electron strongly and acquire it with the evolution of 120 kcal per mole. If we overlook the obvious fact that a chloride ion actually bears little or no resemblance to an argon atom except in the number of electrons in its cloud, the second statement is true in that chlorine atoms do acquire extra electrons with the evolution of 85 kcal of energy per mole. Notice, however, the disparity of values. The gain in energy through formation of a chloride ion is not nearly enough to offset the expenditure of energy to form a sodium ion. Why should an electron jump from a sodium atom to a chlorine atom if it costs 35 kcal $(120 - 85)$ per mole? This could not occur without an additional source of energy.

A rational answer to this problem lies in the electrostatic energy created by the pair of oppositely charged ions being close to one another. This energy is calculable by Coulomb's law for energy, using the factor 332 to convert to kcal per mole (assuming the charges to be centered at the nuclei):

$$\text{electrostatic energy} = 332 \times 1 \times -1/R$$

Here 1 and -1 are the charges on the ions and R is the bond length, or distance between the nuclei. In the single gaseous molecule of NaCl, the bond length is 2.36 Å. If we consider this molecule to consist of a pair of ions, the energy is $-332/2.36$ or -141 kcal per mole. Since this is more than adequate to supply the 35 kcal that must be expended to transfer one electron from an atom of sodium to an atom of chlorine, the existence of the molecule as an ion-pair seems quite reasonable. Then if we consider the additional electrostatic energy to be released by bringing these NaCl units together into the packed form of the crystalline solid, the stability of the ionic model seems quite well established. In fact, the calculated crystal energy is in good agreement with the value arrived at experimentally, not only for this compound but for all the alkali halides.

The ionic bonding model provides such a beautifully simple picture of so very many crystalline salts that it has become widely accepted and used. Unfortunately, like most simple models in science, it is too simple. Most chemists now agree that most chemical bonding is intermediate between the extremes of nonpolar covalence and complete electrovalence, and that even the most ionic of compounds probably have some degree of **covalent character.** Although a full discussion would be beyond the scope of this book, this discussion would be misleading unless some of the more practical aspects of the problem are considered briefly.

It is interesting that in most salts the distance between nuclei is nearly the same as it would be if the bonds were completely nonpolar covalent. We can distinguish between the ionic and covalent models by defining a completely ionic bond as one in which the bonding electrons penetrate only toward the nucleus of the anion and never toward the nucleus of the cation. Any degree of covalence means that at least a part of the time these electrons also penetrate toward the nucleus of the cation. Except for this difference, the bonding electrons must occupy practically the same region whether the bonding is purely ionic or purely covalent. This situation is far different from removing electrons to an infinite distance for which the ionization potential measures the energy necessary.

Perhaps the most cogent objection to the ionic model is that it fails to recognize the properties inherent in the electronic structure of cations and anions. Remember that every simple anion is a positive nucleus surrounded by a cloud of electrons bearing excess negative charge and having lone pairs of electrons in the outermost orbitals. Because of the excess of negative charge, these lone pairs are not held too tightly by the nucleus and can be donated to an appropriate acceptor. In other words, all simple anions are potential electron donors. Furthermore, every simple cation originated as a metal atom having vacant outer-shell orbitals, and the loss of the valence electrons to form the cation created still more vacancies. By decreasing the shielding of the nucleus, the loss of electrons increases the effective nuclear charge potentially felt in these vacant orbitals, giving the cation the power to act as an electron-pair acceptor. Every simple cation is a potential electron acceptor.

When an "ionic" crystal lattice is constructed, each cation becomes surrounded by anions in direct contact with it. Each anion becomes similarly surrounded by cations in direct contact with it. Attributing the cohesive energy of the crystal solely to the electrostatic attractions between oppositely charged ions completely ignores the inevitable donor-acceptor interaction between

Figure 14.3.   An Objection to the Ionic Model.

All simple anions have excess negative charge and lone pairs of electrons in the outer shell. Therefore, all such anions are **potential electron donors.**

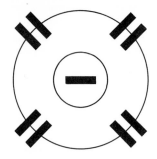

All simple cations have excess positive charge and vacant orbitals in their outermost shell.

Therefore, all such cations are **potential electron-pair acceptors.**

How can one type of ion be closely surrounded by the other type without the occurrence of **donor-acceptor interaction?**

cations and anions. How could electron donors be packed around each acceptor and electron acceptors be packed around each donor without donor-acceptor interaction occurring? Or, we may look at it this way: Since the centers of both anions and cations are positive nuclei, is the attraction between them really between the centers of charge at these nuclei or between the nucleus of the cation and the *electrons* of the anion?

THE COORDINATED POLYMERIC MODEL

Let us examine a model which, without abandoning its advantages, improves on the ionic model by taking this donor-acceptor interaction into account; for the donor-acceptor interaction amounts to partial covalence of the bonding. Indeed, it is possible to calculate the total bonding energy quantitatively by assuming that the crystal can be described *as though* it were made of ions part of the time and neutral atoms covalently bound for the rest of the time. For example, when the partial charges in sodium chloride are calculated by electronegativity equalization as described in Chapter 13, the charge on sodium is found to be 0.67 of an electron charge and the charge on chlorine -0.67 of an electron charge. Calculating what the energy would be if sodium chloride were completely ionic 67 per cent of the time and completely covalent 33 per cent of the time predicts an ionic energy of 122 kcal per mole and a covalent energy of 30 kcal per mole. The total bonding energy of 152 kcal per mole is in excellent agreement with the experimental value of 153. Notice that the 67 per cent electrovalence contributes 80 per cent of the total energy. Thus in terms of bond energy it is not unreasonable to call sodium chloride an ionic compound.

This model does *not* imply that the atoms in the crystal are actually changing back and forth from ionic to covalent forms. Rather, this model allows the total energy to be calculated correctly by dividing up the ionic and covalent contributions in this manner. Note that no binary salts are completely ionic and most are considerably farther from completely ionic than the 67 per cent calculated for NaCl when determined by calculation of partial charges through application of the principle of electronegativity equalization. Nevertheless the correct *total* bonding energies are calculated for these salts when such partial charges are used to apportion the ionic and covalent contributions.

Table 14.1 Calculated and Experimental Bond Energies in Some Nonmolecular Solids

(kcal/mole)

Compound	Per cent ionicity	Calculated			Energy determined experimentally
		Covalent energy	Ionic energy	Total energy	
KF	85	13	164	177	174
NaCl	67	30	122	152	153
CaF_2	47	84	290	374	370
$CaCl_2$	40	84	203	287	290
MnF_2	33	84	211	295	294
$MgCl_2$	28	103	147	250	247
AgBr	25	76	45	121	119
MgO	21	119	120	239	239
TiO_2	20	110	346	456	456
$CdBr_2$	17	81	76	157	155

This new model is called the **coordinated polymeric** model of nonmolecular solids. Its chief advantage over the ionic model, in addition to seeming more realistic as a physical picture, is that it serves to explain the bond energy quantitatively in a wide range of metal-nonmetal compounds and over a wide range of bond polarity. The ionic model is really not very satisfactory for compounds less ionic than the alkali metal halides, which are the most ionic of all. Furthermore, with only minor modifications, the same methods used for interpreting and calculating bond energies in the most highly polar *nonmolecular* solids can be used for slightly polar *molecular* compounds. Therefore, instead of following the established practice of talking loosely about "covalent compounds" and "ionic compounds" as though they were two distinct classes, we will treat them together as representing a complete range of bond polarity. By this view, "ionic" bonding is the extreme upper limit of bond polarity in the covalent bond. When the valence electrons are so unevenly shared that they are completely monopolized by the more electronegative atom, then true ions exist and the ionic model is most satisfactory. In actual binary compounds, however, this extreme is probably never reached and only approached closely in the alkali halides.

To visualize the nature of nonmolecular solids as described by the coordinated polymeric model, consider an atom of sodium reacting with an atom of chlorine. The electron of the sodium is not completely removed by the chlorine atom but only partially so. In other words, since each atom can form one single covalent bond, an NaCl molecule forms. Since the two elements differ greatly in electronegativity, the electrons are so unevenly shared that the bond is highly polar. Now, even before the sodium and chlorine reacted, the sodium atom had outer-shell vacant orbitals. The chlorine atom had outer-shell lone pairs of electrons. The process of electronegativity equalization, by giving the chlorine atom an abundance of negative charge, greatly improved its ability to donate these lone pairs of electrons. Thus, although the initial reaction product was described as molecules of NaCl, such molecules would have a strong tendency to condense further into larger and larger aggregates, with the chlorine of one molecule acting as donor to the sodium of another. Whether we say the negative chlorine attracts the positive sodium or that the chlorine donates to the acceptor sodium, our conclusion is the same. This explains the well-known fact that NaCl is not molecular but a crystalline aggregate in which no specific molecules can be identified.

When a sodium atom is surrounded by six chlorine atoms equally spaced and at equal distance from it, as in sodium chloride, there is no reason why a specific covalent bond to one of the chlorine atoms would be any more stable than to any other of the chlorine atoms. Similarly, when a chlorine atom is surrounded by six sodium atoms, evenly spaced and at the same distance, as in sodium chloride, there is no reason why one bond should differ from the others. Therefore, whether we start with polar molecules of NaCl or with sodium ions and chloride ions brought together from the gaseous state, the product is the same; it cannot be changed one bit by changing its description.

It is important not to become unduly disturbed by such uncertainties and failures of general agreement in chemical theory. This is the very essence of science. Nature is as it is and man can never change it. But man's interpretations should change frequently as he seeks and finds new insights and new experimental evidence to support, modify, or alter his thinking. Any model, such as the ionic model, should be used to the extent that it is useful, but there is nothing sacred about it. If other ideas are suggested, let us give them a fair hearing. One of man's great weaknesses as a scientist is his unconscious wish for some kind of stability of thought and belief. This makes him uncomfortable when faced with ideas different from those first learned. It makes it very difficult for him to view them with the objective impartiality that is essential to scientific methods. So, if you are learning chemistry as a complete and established set of facts, rules, principles, and theories, you are learning it wrong. That simply is not the way it is.

SALTS OF COMPLEX IONS

Many common substances, such as carbonates, sulfates, nitrates, phosphates, and many others, are similar to the binary compounds just discussed. All form solids in which no individual molecules are detectable. Here again we might argue about whether they are best described as "ionic" (the usual description) or "coordinated polymeric." Either description might be used. Calcium carbonate, for example, is usually thought of as consisting of discrete calcium ions (Ca^{++}) and carbonate ions ($CO_3^{=}$). In fact, in the crystalline solid each calcium atom is surrounded equally by six oxygen atoms, each from a different carbonate group. Each oxygen atom of a carbonate group is next to two calcium atoms. It would seem at least equally reasonable to describe this solid as a coordinated polymeric compound. Each oxygen acts as donor to two calcium atoms. Each calcium atom acts as acceptor to six oxygen atoms.

CRYSTAL STRUCTURE

In a crystalline compound composed of molecules, the structure is determined by the shape, polarity, and other qualities of the individual molecules. The structure of a molecular solid is difficult to discuss in a general way. One may note that very symmetrical arrangements are characteristic of the crystals formed from any set of component particles—whether molecules, atoms, or ions—that are all alike.

In a nonmolecular compound, crystal structure involves the arrangement of the individual atoms or ions rather than of molecules. Again, symmetry is its outstanding characteristic. Here the term *coordination number* becomes very useful. It signifies the number of neighbors that appear to be attached to each interior atom of the crystal. Sodium chloride has been described as having a crystalline form in which each atom is surrounded by six of the other kind of atom. The coordination number of the sodium is six and the coordination number of the chlorine is six. Sodium chloride crystal involves 6:6 coordination. This particular structure is called **cubic** or **rocksalt** since it is the structure of sodium chloride. Many other compounds, including most of the

All alkali (M1) halides except CsCl, CsBr, and CsI			**Table 14.2. Some Compounds Having Rocksalt (NaCl) Structure.** (6:6 coordination)
All alkali (M1) hydrides			
MgO	CdO	CaS	
CaO	FeO	SrS	
SrO	NiO	BaS	
BaO	MgS	PbS	

Figure 14.4. The Structure of Rock Salt (NaCl).

In a 6:6 coordination crystal, each atom is surrounded by atoms of the other element at the 6 corners of a regular octahedron.

binary compounds of M1 elements with M7 elements, have the rocksalt structure.

Some of the univalent atoms of extra-large size tend to form crystals in which the coordination is 8:8. This is the characteristic structure of cesium chloride (CsCl) and is called the **cesium chloride structure.** In it, each cesium atom is at the center of a cube with chlorine atoms at each corner, and each chlorine atom is at the center of a cube with cesium atoms at each corner. We do not really understand why some compounds assume the rocksalt structure and some the cesium chloride structure. We cannot understand these things without gaining a greater knowledge of the solid state than is now available.

When atoms combine in a 1:1 ratio, they do not necessarily organize in an 8:8 or 6:6 coordination. If it is 6:6 it is not necessarily the same as rocksalt. For example, a number of compounds such as nickel arsenide (NiAs) crystallize in a form in which each atom is surrounded by six of the other kind. Instead of being at the center of an octahedral arrangement as in sodium chloride, half the atoms are inside trigonal prisms of the other kind. Quite a number of 1:1 compounds crystallize in one of two forms of 4:4 coordination.

	Zinc blende form	Wurtzite form
	CuCl	BeO
	CuBr	ZnO
	CuI	ZnS
Table 14.3. Some Compounds	AgI	AgI
Having Zinc Sulfide (ZnS)	BeO	CdS
Structures (4:4 coordination)	BeS	MnS
	ZnS	
	CdS	
	HgS	

Figure 14.5. The Structure of Cesium Chloride (CsCl).

In an 8:8 coordination crystal, each atom of one element is surrounded by atoms of the other element located at the 8 corners of a cube.

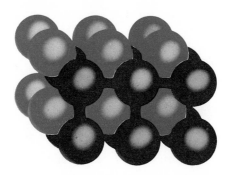

In each of these, every interior atom is surrounded by four of the other kind at the corners of a regular tetrahedron. Why these differences occur is not known, nor do we know how to predict the crystalline structure of compounds in general.

CaF_2	PbF_2	Li_2S	**Table 14.4. Some Compounds Having Fluorite (CaF_2) Structure** (8:4 coordination)
SrF_2	Li_2O	Na_2S	
BaF_2	Na_2O	K_2S	
CdF_2	K_2O	Cu_2S	

When the atomic ratio in a solid compound is 1:2 or 2:1, the coordination is usually 8:4 (4:8), or 6:3 (3:6). The most common structure involving the former is that of calcium fluoride (CaF_2). In mineral form calcium fluoride is known as **fluorite.** Here each calcium atom is surrounded at the corners of a cube by eight fluorine atoms, and each fluorine atom is surrounded at the corners of a regular tetrahedron by four calcium atoms. Two

TiO_2	FeF_2	SnO_2	**Table 14.5. Some Compounds Having Rutile (TiO_2) Structure** (6.3 coordination)
ZnF_2	CoF_2	PbO_2	
MgF_2	NiF_2	MnO_2	

principal types of structure involve the 6:3 coordination. One is that of the mineral **rutile,** which is titanium dioxide (TiO_2). Here each titanium atom is surrounded by six oxygen atoms at the corners of a regular octahedron. Each oxygen is coordinated to three titanium atoms. This crystalline form extends symmetrically in all directions.

A different crystalline form, of which there are several modifications, is called the **layer lattice,** such as shown by cadmium chloride ($CdCl_2$). Here

Crystal Structure **171**

each cadmium atom is at the center of an octahedron of chlorine atoms. Each chlorine is coordinated to three cadmium atoms, but layers are formed. Each layer consists of a sandwich of cadmium atoms between chlorine slices. Adjacent layers come in contact with one another through chlorine atoms.

Test Your Memory

1. What is meant by *ionic bonding?*
2. a) What is *ionization energy?*
   b) What is *electron affinity?*
   c) How does the ionization energy of any metal compare with the electron affinity of any nonmetal?
3. What is meant by *coordinated polymeric* model?
4. Define the *coordination number* of an atom.
5. Describe the crystal structure of sodium chloride.
6. What is meant by *6:3 coordination?*

Test Your Understanding

1. What, if anything, is wrong with saying that magnesium, atomic number 12, tends to get rid of two electrons so it can be like neon, atomic number 10?
2. On what basis is it stated that no individual molecules are present in an ionic salt?
3. Why would simple molecules of a metal-nonmetal salt tend to condense to higher states of aggregation?
4. What does a simple nonmetal anion possess that would make it a potential electron donor?
5. What are the characteristics of a metal atom that give its cation the ability to act as an electron-pair acceptor?

15

OTHER TYPES OF ATTRACTION

The older term for **protonic bridge,** which is still more widely used, is **hydrogen bond.** The reason for using the term *protonic bridge* is that the kind of bonding called hydrogen bonding is known only where the hydrogen atom involved bears partial *positive* charge. The word *protonic* describes this condition of the hydrogen. The hydrogen atom "partakes of the nature of the proton" by being positively charged.

Protonic bridging is the joining together of molecules by interaction of the positive hydrogen on one molecule with a pair of electrons on the other. In a sense, it is hydrogen acting as though it were divalent, even though it has but one orbital available for bonding. Ordinary single covalent bonds usually cannot be broken without absorption of at least forty and often more than 100 kilocalories per mole of bonds. Protonic bridges, in contrast, have energies of only 5-10 kilocalories per mole. Nevertheless these interactions are strong enough to have very significant effects on the physical properties of compounds whose molecules can become interconnected through protonic bridging.

Only those compounds in which hydrogen is appreciably positive can form protonic bridges. In other words, the hydrogen, which itself is a little above average in electronegativity, must be attached to a more electronegative atom. Usually this is nitrogen, oxygen, or fluorine. A second requirement for protonic bridge formation is that the atom of the other molecule, to which the positive hydrogen is attracted, must have an electron pair in its outer shell that can attract the hydrogen strongly enough to form the bridge. This means *first* that the other atom must bear a partial negative charge to enhance the availability of its electron pair. *Second,* it seems essential that this other atom be of small size. This requirement probably arises from the fact that hydrogen atoms are very small. If an electron pair is on a large atom, there is more room for it to be spread out. In this condition it appears to be relatively unavailable to the hydrogen. But if the electron pair is on a small atom, repulsion by the other electron pairs on this atom forces a relatively high concentration of charge in one direction, making this pair available for interaction with the positive hydrogen of the other molecule. Nitrogen, oxygen, and fluorine appear to be the elements best suited to serve as providers of electron pairs for protonic bridging. Their atoms are small enough to force concentration of the electron pair. They are also usually quite negative in their compounds because of the initially high electronegativity of these elements compared to any others.

The exact nature of protonic bridging is still being actively studied. Simple electrostatic explanations appear reasonably effective but not wholly satisfactory. The hydrogen atom ordinarily remains closer to the atom to which it is originally attached than to the atom of the other molecule which furnishes the electron pair. Nevertheless it is possible that the hydrogen orbital may be somewhat involved in the protonic bridging as well as in the covalent bond that holds it to its own molecule. In any case, it does appear reasonable to describe protonic bridging as a **force of attraction** between a partially positive hydrogen atom of one molecule and a pair of electrons on a negatively charged small atom of another molecule.

Notable examples of protonic bridging are found in ammonia, water, and hydrogen fluoride. Although under ordinary conditions ammonia is a gas, it can be liquefied rather easily. In the liquid state the lone pair on the nitrogen can become bridged to another ammonia molecule through the positive hydrogen. Larger and less negative atoms fail to become so bridged; PH_3, AsH_3, and SbH_3 (all in the same family with ammonia) are all gases much harder to liquefy than ammonia. Water molecules are capable of forming protonic bridges through both their two positive hydrogen atoms and their two lone pairs of electrons on the negatively charged oxygen. No such bridges are formed by H_2S, H_2Se, or H_2Te, all gases. Hydrogen fluoride molecules become associated through interaction of their positive hydrogen atoms with lone pairs on the negative fluorine of other molecules. Even hydrogen chloride (HCl), in which the hydrogen is quite positive, fails to form protonic bridges with itself at ordinary temperatures, presumably because the chlorine, although negative, is too large.

Which do you think would be more volatile, CH_3Cl or CH_3OH? Why? Look up their boiling points.

Many other compounds, especially those containing oxygen or nitrogen, are capable of forming protonic bridges not only with like molecules, but with molecules of different compounds as well. Later we shall discuss more experimental information demonstrating the significance of protonic bridging in chemistry.

Figure 15.1.   Protonic Bridging in Liquid and Solid Water.

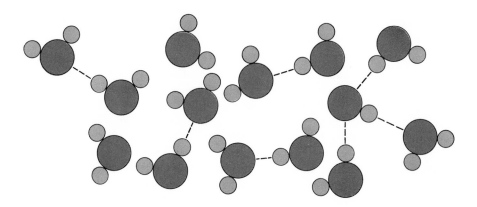

Liquid water has a highly dynamic structure in which individual protonic bridges continuously break and reform in other positions. All the water molecules continuously change their relative positions in the liquid. Above is a two-dimensional representation of a three-dimensional phenomenon.

Note especially the positive charge on hydrogen, the negative charge on oxygen, and the linear nature of the protonic bridge. Remember that each oxygen atom has two lone pairs of electrons, each capable of attracting a protonic hydrogen from another water molecule.

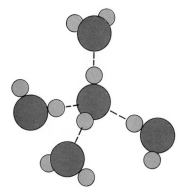

This means that if enough of the thermal energy is removed by cooling, each water molecule can form four protonic bridges. Two form through its hydrogen atoms and two through its lone pairs. Each water molecule thus becomes surrounded tetrahedrally by four other water molecules. When the bulk of the water becomes bridged like this, it changes to the crystalline form known as ice.

Van der Waals forces are nondirectional, attractive interactions that exist in addition to the bonding forces we have already discussed whenever atoms or molecules or other aggregates come close enough to one another. Strictly speaking, they are not considered to be chemical bonds, since the term *bond* is usually reserved for application to stronger types of attachment. Nevertheless, they are forces that cannot be ignored if a reasonably thorough understanding of the nature of matter is to be attained. Even among atoms that can form no bonds, or between molecules in which each atom has formed all the bonds of which it is capable, van der Waals forces occur. We want to know why.

These forces are named after the Dutch physicist Johannes van der Waals (1837–1923), who studied their effects largely on the properties of gases. Although in some respects their origin is very complex, perhaps we can approach an understanding by looking closely at the nature of all atoms and molecules. All such particles are electrical systems in which electrons are in extremely rapid motion. As long as the particle is isolated from all other matter, the motion of its electrons is influenced only locally, by the nuclear charge and by the other electrons. But it would be impossible to bring together two such electrical systems without causing an interaction between them, because of the repulsions and attractions of the charges. At first thought, we might decide that their approach could only produce repulsion as their electron clouds come together. But we know that a net attraction occurs.

Remember that electrons can move without the need of moving the whole particle of which they are components. Their individual motion is adjustable, according to the conditions and circumstances. When two particles come near one another, the electrons of each tend to *correlate* their motions with those of the other, in such a way as to minimize the repulsions. For example, the electron on particle *A* will try to be on the opposite side of *A* when an electron on particle *B* approaches. It will tend not to come toward *B* until *B*'s electron is retreating. Similarly, the electron on particle *B* will adjust its motion to avoid proximity to the electron on particle *A*. An electron cannot shield its nucleus from the electron of another particle while it is on the opposite side of the nucleus from that particle. The result of electron correlation is therefore a rapidly oscillating electrical dissymmetry. This causes a net attractive force to be exerted between the two particles. In other words, dipoles are induced by the interaction of the two particles. On the average their ends of opposite charge are closer together than their ends of like charge. Figure 15.2 depicts the origin of these forces.

Van der Waals forces are very weak compared to chemical bonds. However, the more electrons a given particle has, the greater the possibilities for electron correlation, and therefore the greater the net attractive forces that can be produced. Furthermore, van der Waals forces tend to be greater the more nuclei there are to share the electrons, because this also enhances the possibility of electron correlation. Also, molecular geometries allowing closer

Figure 15.2. Representation of the Origin of van der Waals Forces.

In an isolated atom, the center of positive and negative charges may be regarded as coincident at the nucleus.

However, when two or more atoms come near one another, the electron clouds tend to repel one another. To minimize these repulsions,

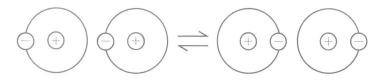

electrons of one atom tend to synchronize or correlate their motions with those of the other(s).

The effect is to induce a very rapidly oscillating dipole in each.

The net force of attraction created between opposite ends of these atomic dipoles is the major contributor to van der Waals forces.

intermolecular approach promote stronger attractions. Between very large molecules these forces may become very appreciable.

Some of the most interesting consequences of both van der Waals forces and chemical bonds will be discussed in following chapters.

Test Your Memory

1. What is a *protonic bridge?*
2. What is a *hydrogen bond?*
3. How does a protonic bridge compare in strength with an average co-valent bond?
4. What molecules exhibit protonic bridging to the greatest extent?
5. What is meant by *electron correlation?*
6. What is an *induced dipole?*
7. How do van der Waals forces among ordinary molecules compare in strength with the covalent bonds?

Test Your Understanding

1. In protonic bridge formation, what is the importance of the size of the atom that bridges to hydrogen?
2. On what basis is it assumed that the hydrogen atom in protonic bridging is not simply forming two covalent bonds?
3. How could induced dipoles provide an interatomic attraction?
4. Consider these isomeric molecules:

$$CH_3—CH_2—CH_2—CH_2—CH_3 \qquad \text{(normal pentane)}$$

$$\begin{array}{c} CH_3 \\ | \\ CH_3—CH_2—CH_3 \\ | \\ CH_3 \end{array} \qquad \text{(neopentane)}$$

Predict which would be more volatile, and explain why.

16

SOLIDS, LIQUIDS, AND GASES

COHESIVE VS. DISRUPTIVE FORCES

Thermal energy is **kinetic** energy, or energy of motion, and it has a vital influence on matter. Without it, all matter would lie solid and dead. All the world would be at the "absolute" zero of temperature, 273.16° C below the freezing point of water. Thermal energy causes the component particles of matter to move. The higher the temperature, the greater the vigor of their motion. Indeed, **temperature** is a measure of the vigor of their motion. To reach the same vigor of motion, different substances require different amounts of heat. Temperature does not measure the quantity of heat, but only, in a sense, its quality. As the temperature rises, the components of matter become increasingly independent of one another and tend to break free from the forces that bind them together. All substances break up into independently moving atoms or molecules if the temperature is raised enough. This state of matter is the **gaseous state.**

We are aware that ordinary temperatures, within the range wherein we can survive, are not adequate to change all matter into gases. If all matter at the same temperature possesses the same intensity of motion, why is it not all in the same physical state? The answer lies in the great differences in strength of the forces which hold matter together. The greater the strength of the attractions, the higher the temperature required to overcome them. Therefore, the state of matter under any given conditions depends on the relative strengths of the cohesive forces that hold its atoms or molecules together and the disruptive forces that tend to cause them to fly apart. A solid at ordinary temperature is solid because of the high strength of the forces that hold it together. Liquids are not as tightly held together or they would not change shape so easily. But they too are held together fairly tightly, or their molecules would fly apart altogether as those of gases do. A gas is a substance in which the potential cohesive forces are so weak that they cannot compete effectively with kinetic energy at a given temperature. This energy prevents the individual component particles from clinging together when they collide. It keeps them continually in motion.

Since at a given temperature the disruptive forces are constant, solids must possess the greatest cohesive forces, followed by liquids. Gases have the weakest cohesive forces of all.

No matter how weak the cohesive forces are, they do exist. If the thermal energy is sufficiently reduced, the cohesive forces make themselves evident. Every substance which is gaseous at ordinary temperatures becomes liquid or solid if the particles are slowed enough (cooled enough) to allow the cohesive forces to become effective. Every liquid becomes solid if enough of its kinetic energy is removed by cooling. Therefore many kinds of matter have the ability to exist as either solid, liquid, or gas, depending on the temperature.

It is not necessarily true, however, that all solids can become liquids or all liquids can change to gas. Before a solid or liquid can acquire enough energy to vaporize, its atoms may vibrate back and forth so violently that its chemical bonds break and the substance decomposes. Many solids cannot melt, for similar reasons: energy sufficient to disrupt the lattice energy (the energy holding the particles together in the crystal lattice) may be *more* than enough to break apart the chemical bonds holding together the atoms within the particles.

Have you ever tried to melt a piece of cotton? Or melt and boil a piece of cake?

In summary, all gases can become liquid and then solid, and all liquids can become solid, but all solids cannot necessarily become liquids nor can all liquids become gases, without decomposing. However, if the bonds are strong enough to withstand the thermal agitation required for liquefaction or vaporization, the solid can become liquid, and the liquid can become gas.

Could *all* the chemical elements be melted or vaporized without decomposition? Why or why not?

Let us now consider the nature of the phase transitions that occur when solid phase changes to liquid phase or gaseous phase and liquid changes to gaseous phase.

MELTING

A pure crystalline substance consists of identical component atoms, molecules, or groups of ions. These particles attract each other sufficiently to maintain a fairly rigid structure. That is, each particle tends to keep the same neighbors. Only relatively rarely does a particle move from its symmetrical neighborhood. Unless forcibly shattered or bent, a solid keeps its original shape. The force of gravity is ordinarily not strong enough to distort it. Each component particle remains on the average in a fixed position relative to the surrounding particles.

However, this does not imply a complete lack of motion. On the contrary, the particles of any solid above absolute zero are constantly vibrating, twisting, and bending around their average positions. As the temperature rises, these motions become more vigorous and tend to force the particles somewhat farther apart. This process is called **thermal expansion.**

The crystal expands a little, but remains solid until the temperature reaches a particular point characteristic of that crystalline substance. At this temperature, enough of its particles have sufficient kinetic energy to break down the relatively rigid crystalline structure into a more mobile, fluid form, the **liquid state.** Within a very narrow range of temperature, this collapse of the crystal occurs throughout the solid, because on the average the particles tend to acquire the necessary energy all at once. The temperature at which this process occurs is called the **melting point.** The process is called either **melting** or **fusion.** A pure substance characteristically has a sharp melting point. This means that it all changes from solid to liquid within a very narrow temperature range—less than one degree. Impurities can change the environment of some of the particles more than that of others, reducing the symmetry of the crystal. Therefore, in impure substances, part of the crystal melts before the rest of it has received enough energy to melt. Consequently the melting process occurs over a relatively wide range in temperature—several degrees or more. Sharpness of melting point is taken as a useful criterion of purity. Impurities invariably cause a *lowering* and a *widening* of the melting range. Every pure crystalline solid, unless it decomposes on heating, has its own characteristic and specific melting point.

When a chemist wants to use the melting point not only as a criterion of purity but also to identify a compound, he is wise not to rely exclusively on the sharpness of the melting point and the correctness of the temperature. Among the millions of different known compounds, it is not unlikely that two or more different substances could melt at almost exactly the same temperature. To be sure of the identity of his compound, therefore, he mixes some of it with a pure sample of the known compound he believes it to be. He then determines a *mixed melting point.* If the suspected compound is indeed identical with the known pure compound, mixing them is no different from increasing the supply, and will have no effect whatever upon the melting point. But, if the unknown compound is not the same compound as the known sample, the mixture will have a reduced melting temperature and a wider temperature range of melting, even though independently the components would have the same melting point. Thus, melting point depression in a mixed melting point tells a chemist that his guess as to the identity of an unknown compound was incorrect.

Physical Equilibrium

When a pure compound is melted and then allowed to cool slowly, it usually begins to crystallize when it reaches the melting temperature, since the temperatures of melting and of recrystallization are the same. If a solid compound is warmed within an insulated container until it is about half melted, and then no further heat is added or taken away, the mixture of solid and liquid phases will remain unchanged indefinitely. If we could paint one of the component particles bright blue and watch its motion throughout this mixture, we would discover that sometimes it would be part of the liquid and sometimes part of the solid, tending to transfer readily from one phase to the other. We cannot paint molecules, atoms, or ions a distinctive color, nor could we see them if we did. However, we can tag them by making them radioactive. When this is done, it is discovered by tracing the radioactivity that this mixture of melt and crystal is a dynamic system. That is, its components are constantly interchanging between solid and liquid phases. So long as no heat exchange with the surroundings is permitted, the relative amounts of solid and liquid in this mixture must remain constant, but the individual particles are sometimes part of the solid and sometimes part of the liquid phases.

Such a system is described as being at **equilibrium.** Because individual particles are changing phase, this is a very **dynamic** equilibrium. It involves a physical change, but no chemical change, so it is called a **physical equilibrium.**

Figure 16.1. Solid-Liquid-Gas Equilibrium—Triple Point.

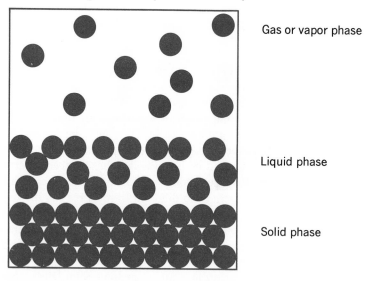

Gas or vapor phase

Liquid phase

Solid phase

At only one temperature, called the **triple point,** can all three phases of a given substance coexist. Here the vapor tensions of solid and liquid phases, a measure of escaping tendencies of atoms, are equal.

If the temperature is now raised only a trifle, the remaining solid melts and the whole system becomes liquid. If the temperature is lowered slightly, the liquid phase crystallizes and all becomes solid. The **melting point** may be defined as the temperature at which the solid and liquid phases of a substance are in equilibrium. Equilibrium is therefore the condition in which two opposite changes are occurring at exactly the same rate of speed. If the two speeds were not identical, one phase or the other would rapidly disappear to form the other phase.

Heat of Fusion

If energy must be put into a solid to cause it to change to liquid, and if energy must be removed from a liquid to cause it to solidify, it appears that the liquid must contain more energy than the solid. In fact, a distinguishing feature of the liquid state of any substance is that it does contain more energy than the solid state at the same temperature. In this light, let us examine the system at equilibrium.

Any system, isolated from its environment, will come to thermal equilibrium with a uniform temperature throughout. In the melting-equilibrium system, the solid and liquid are at the same temperature. If they are at the

Figure 16.2.   Equilibrium Between Solid and Liquid—Melting Point.

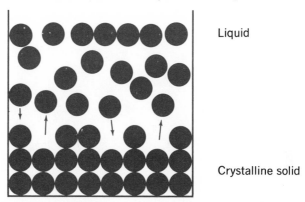

Liquid

Crystalline solid

At the melting point, molecules are continuously and rapidly exchanging between solid and liquid phases. The rate at which crystal molecules (or ions) leave the solid to become liquid is exactly equal to the rate at which liquid molecules (or ions) rejoin the solid.

same temperature, which is a measure of their kinetic energy, how can the liquid contain more energy than the solid? In the liquid, the molecules or other component particles are much more randomly distributed than within the solid. This means that they are not in as favorable a position to attract one another as in the solid. The difference in energy content between liquid and solid, then, does not need to be in *kinetic* energy, which would show a disparity of temperature between the two. It can be in **potential energy** associated with the *position* of the particles. This potential energy can be converted to kinetic energy if the particles resume the positions they held in the solid, but the kinetic energy has to be taken on by something other than the solid, or it would only melt again.

The **heat content** of any substance is the quantity of heat it has taken on in coming from absolute zero ($-273.16°$ C) to its present temperature. We usually do not know the total heat content exactly but it is relatively easy to measure differences in heat content. The difference in heat content between a solid and its liquid at the melting temperature is called the **heat of fusion.** For one gram of a substance, this is the **specific heat of fusion;** for one mole, the **molar heat of fusion.**

VAPORIZATION AND BOILING

Although the molecules of a liquid have the same average kinetic energy if the sample is at a certain fixed temperature, the individual molecular energies are distributed as shown in Figure 16.3. Most of the molecules are nearly

Figure 16.3. Distribution of Molecular Energies.

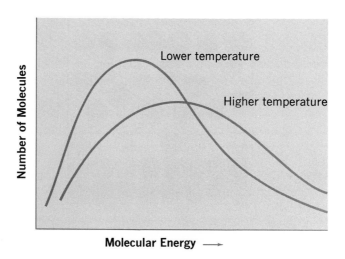

alike in kinetic energy. A few, however, have much higher energy and a few much lower energy. These are accidents of random collisions among molecules. The identity of these few molecules changes constantly, as some slower-moving molecules gain speed at the expense of some of the faster-moving molecules.

Suppose a sample of a pure liquid compound is confined within a closed insulated container larger than the volume of the liquid. If the temperature is kept constant, the space above the liquid fills with vapor up to a certain concentration, which then remains constant. The term **vapor** denotes the gaseous phase of a substance at a temperature at which it is normally liquid or solid. As we shall see in more detail in the following chapter, as the result of their kinetic activity gaseous molecules exert a pressure on any container by colliding continuously with the walls. The pressure exerted at any given temperature is a measure of the concentration of the vapor. We describe this situation by saying that the vapor pressure of the liquid reaches a constant value. Every pure liquid has a characteristic vapor pressure for each temperature. Sometimes this vapor pressure is called the **vapor tension** of the liquid.

As the temperature rises, the proportion of molecules having enough energy to achieve the vapor state increases. Consequently, the vapor tension increases. But as long as the temperature remains constant, the vapor tension does not change. This lack of change does not mean that the liquid suddenly stops evaporating. Rather it means that the vapor molecules are rejoining the liquid at the same rate that new vapor molecules are leaving the liquid. This is another example of a dynamic, physical equilibrium.

In this system, liquid and vapor are at the same temperature but the heat *content* of the vapor is greater. The difference in heat content between a liquid and its vapor at equilibrium is called the **heat of vaporization.** The particles of a liquid are not very far removed from their positions in the solid, so the heat of fusion is relatively small. In a gas the individual molecules are completely free of one another and correspondingly much farther apart than in the liquid, and the heat of vaporization as a rule is much larger than the heat of fusion.

When a liquid is heated in air in an open system, its vapor may escape from the vicinity of the surface and perhaps never return to the liquid. The rate of vaporization of the liquid increases with the temperature until the vapor pressure of the liquid is equal to that of the atmosphere over it. At this point an interesting phenomenon is observed. Up to this point, all vaporization appeared to occur at the surface of the liquid, which remained undisturbed in appearance. Now vaporization can occur *under* the surface as well, forming bubbles around any speck of dust or rough surface of the container. These bubbles are much less dense than the liquid and rise rapidly to the surface and escape. This phenomenon, of course, is **boiling.** It can occur at any temperature at which the liquid has an appreciable vapor tension equal to the pressure of the atmosphere over the liquid. The normal **boiling point** of a liquid is defined as the temperature at which its equilibrium vapor pressure, or vapor tension, equals the pressure of one atmosphere at sea level. A pressure cooker works by confining the vapor of water in a closed system so that it builds up a pressure higher than one atmosphere. This allows the water to remain liquid above its normal boiling point. A ten-degree rise in temperature may approximately double the rate of a chemical reaction, so the pressure cooker speeds up the chemical changes involved in cooking.

SUBLIMATION

In a number of solids the tendency for molecules to escape into the vapor phase is great at temperatures below the melting point. When heated they tend to vaporize directly, rather than first melt and then vaporize. This process is called **sublimation.** When the vapor is cooled, it tends similarly to condense directly to the solid state rather than become a liquid and then solidify. There can be dynamic physical equilibrium between a solid and its vapor. The sublimation pressure depends upon the temperature just as the vapor tension of a liquid depends on the temperature. When the **sublimation pressure** of the vapor over the solid equals the pressure of the atmosphere over the solid, the temperature is called the **sublimation temperature.** However, sublimation begins to occur at an appreciable rate at much lower temperatures. Solid carbon dioxide, called Dry Ice commercially, provides a good example of sublimation. It will not melt unless confined under pressure. Otherwise it simply sublimes into the gas phase with a sublimation temperature of $-78.5°C$.

Since a substance at a given temperature contains more energy as a liquid than in the solid phase and more energy in the gas phase than as the liquid, there is no question that gas molecules have much greater potential energy than molecules in a solid. This energy, called the **heat of sublimation** or the **sublimation energy,** would be evolved in the form of heat if the gas were to resolidify.

ENERGY RELATIONSHIPS AMONG PHASES

In summary, **the gas phase contains the most energy, the liquid phase less, and the solid phase the least energy.** Conversions of a substance from one phase

Figure 16.4. Energy Relationships Among Phases of a Substance.

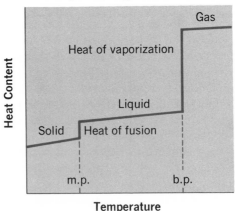

A substance at a specific temperature contains more energy in the gas phase than in the liquid phase. This energy is the **heat of vaporization.**

A substance at a specific temperature contains more energy in the liquid phase than in the solid phase. This energy is the **heat of fusion.**

Notice also that the heat content of any one phase increases as the temperature is raised.

to another are always associated with energy changes. Any process which evolves energy is called **exothermic.** Any process which absorbs energy is called **endothermic.** The changes from gas to liquid, gas to solid, or liquid to solid are all exothermic. Any of these phase changes can be used to absorb or emit heat, depending on their direction. Refrigerators, heat pumps, air conditioners, evaporative coolers, and similar devices are all mechanical arrangements to take advantage of these energy relationships.

Test Your Memory

1. What does temperature measure?
2. What conflicting forces determine the physical state of a substance?
3. What is the cause of thermal expansion?
4. a) What is meant by *melting point?*
   b) What is meant by *mixed melting point?*
5. How are *equilibrium* and *melting point* related?
6. Define *heat of fusion.*
7. a) Define *physical equilibrium.*
   b) How is equilibrium involved in the process of vaporization?
8. Define *boiling point.*
9. What is meant by *sublimation energy?*
10. How do the different states of a given substance vary with respect to heat content?
11. Define *exothermic* and *endothermic.*

Test Your Understanding

1. What is the fundamental difference between a gas and a solid if the particles of both have the same kinetic energy?
2. Why is it impossible for certain solid or liquid substances to exist as gas?
3. How might the vapor tension differ from the vapor pressure of a substance?
4. How can one cause the same liquid to boil at a variety of different temperatures?
5. Give examples of phase changes that are (a) exothermic, (b) endothermic.
6. What can you conclude about the cohesive forces in air?
7. How do you think the cohesive forces in water compare with those in iron?

17

THE RELATIONSHIP OF STRUCTURE TO PHYSICAL PROPERTIES

SOLID, LIQUID, OR GAS?

From the energy relationships among the solid, liquid, and gaseous phases of a substance, it is clear that the forces of association are most effective in solids, less effective in liquids, and least effective in gases. The fundamental causes of these forces are not altered by the temperature, but remain essentially constant. What changes is the relative positions of the component particles. This change is brought about by changes in the kinetic energy, or temperature, of

Figure 17.1. Solid, Liquid, and Gaseous Temperature Ranges of Some Common Substances

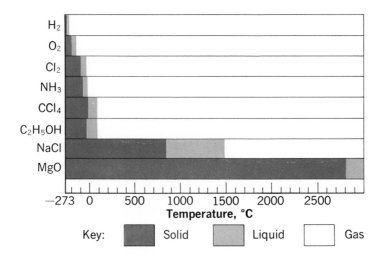

the substance. For any given substance, we can gain some understanding of which phase will be most stable at ordinary temperatures. To predict that phase requires a knowledge of the structure and the types of forces between particles.

For example, we know that any substance that is gaseous at ordinary temperatures is gaseous only because the cohesive forces are relatively weak. This means that the cohesive forces cannot be the strong electrostatic forces associated with highly polar or ionic bonding, nor can they be the covalent bonds that hold some substances in crystal lattices. In fact, they can only be van der Waals forces or attraction between weak dipoles. Where the electronic

What can one conclude about the magnitude of intermolecular forces in air? In gravy? In bone?

arrangement of any molecule has no vacant orbitals left over, but only lone pairs of electrons, the cohesive forces among molecules must be weak. A relatively small molecule with only a few electrons will have weaker cohesive forces, whereas with greater molecular complexity (greater number of electrons and greater number of atomic nuclei per molecule), the van der Waals forces increase. We do not have an exact criterion for predicting whether a given molecular substance will be gaseous or liquid. However, we do recognize that the more electrons there are per molecule, the most likely it is to be liquid. Given the same number of electrons per molecule, we may expect greater cohesive forces between molecules having the greater number of atoms, and in structures allowing closest intermolecular contact.

Instead of being molecular, a compound or element may be assembled through a network of bonds extending indefinitely throughout the substance; this cannot be gaseous or liquid. The atoms are held in positions that are too rigidly fixed to permit motion to different relative positions, as in the liquid state. Any simple combination that would leave low-energy, outer-shell vacant orbitals on one atom and lone pairs of electrons on another undergoes condensation to form larger networks indefinitely if vacant orbitals still remain. An examination of the electronic configuration of the simplest molecule reveals whether this kind of condensation could be expected. If it could then the product must be a solid.

Among the metals we expect moderately strong to very strong bonding. Where only one valence electron per atom is involved, however, and also in the unusual example of mercury, the bonding in metals is somewhat weaker. Since metallic bonding radiates in all directions, metals are expected to be solids. They are certainly not expected to be very volatile because their metallic bonding can persist to a large degree in the liquid state.

If a substance is composed of simple molecules, each having a fairly large number of electrons, we can predict that the van der Waals forces will be large enough to allow the substance to be solid. If the molecules are not too large, however, the substance will be easily melted and vaporized.

Solid, Liquid, or Gas? **189**

Gases

Some examples will be useful to test our understanding of physical states. We predict that H_2, O_2, N_2, Cl_2, CO, CO_2, SO_2, and all the M8 elements should be gaseous, since all lack outer-shell orbital vacancies and have only electrons in pairs, except for H_2 in which *nothing* is left over. The thermal energy at ordinary temperatures will be more than enough to disrupt the very weak van der Waals forces expected for such small numbers of electrons per molecule.

	M. P., °C	B. P., °C
H_2	−259.2	−252.8
N_2	−210	−195.8
O_2	−219	−183.0
Cl_2	−101.0	−34.0
NH_3	−77.7	−33.4
CO_2	−56.6	−78.5 (sublimes)
CH_4	−182.5	−161
HCl	−114.2	−85.0
SO_2	−72.5	−10
H_2S	−85.5	−60.3

Table 17.1. Melting and Boiling Points of Some Representative Gases

In order to make predictions about the physical state of hydrogen compounds, we have to divide them into those capable of forming protonic bridges and those incapable of doing so. Those forming protonic bridges would be expected to be less volatile than those which don't, but how much less volatile is not easily predicted. For example, ammonia (NH_3) boils at −33.4° C, a low temperature, but still much higher than it would be without protonic bridging. Water (H_2O) is a relatively volatile liquid, but it too would be gaseous without protonic bridging. Hydrogen fluoride (HF) is just barely gaseous at ordinary temperatures, with a boiling point of about 19°C. Other hydrogen compounds that form small molecules showing either lone pairs of electrons or nothing are: HCl, HBr, HI, H_2S, H_2Se, H_2Te, PH_3, AsH_3, SbH_3, BiH_3, CH_4, SiH_4, GeH_4, and SnH_4; all of these are gaseous. None can join together by protonic bridging. The van der Waals forces are small here even when the total number of electrons is fairly high, as in BiH_3. The hydrogen atoms protect the molecules against the closer intermolecular interaction that would otherwise be possible. Also, the fact that most of the electrons are around one nucleus instead of spread out over several may be responsible for reduced van der Waals forces.

Liquids

Some volatile liquids are CCl_4, PCl_3, Br_2, and CS_2. In each of these there is no possibility of further condensation to larger molecules. The van der Waals interactions are strong enough to keep the substance liquid at 25°C. Many

	M. P., °C	B. P., °C
CCl_4	−22.9	76.7
$SiCl_4$	−68	57.0
$TiCl_4$	−24.1	236
PBr_3	−41.5	176
SO_2Cl_2	−46	69.3
Br_2	−7.3	58.2
H_2O	0.0	100.0

Table 17.2. Melting and Boiling Points of Some Representative Inorganic Liquids

relatively nonvolatile liquids are known. These usually consist of relatively large complex molecules that cannot easily pack into a nice, neat, orderly crystalline array. Despite strong intermolecular attractions, their molecular size and shape keep them from solidifying easily. Many mixtures are liquid because of the difficulty of forming crystals from particles of different size and shape.

Solids

White phosphorus consists of molecules of P_4. These are regular tetrahedrons that interact with one another sufficiently at 25°C to make a molecular solid. But since these interactions are necessarily very weak, white phosphorus can easily be melted and vaporized. In contrast, red phosphorus, which is composed of molecules containing many more atoms than those of white phosphorus, melts at a much higher temperature and is much less volatile.

Sodium fluoride (NaF) consists of a metal combined with a nonmetal. As in all such combinations, the simplest molecule we can imagine has left-over vacant orbitals on the metal and leftover lone pairs of electrons on the nonmetal. In addition, the metal bears partial positive charge and the non-metal bears partial negative charge. Continued condensation to ionic or co-ordinated polymeric solids is therefore predicted. All such compounds are solids of high melting point and very low volatility.

	M. P., °C	B. P., °C
P_4	44.2	280
S_8	119	444.6
I_2	113.6	184.5
PI_3	61	
NaF	995	1704
NaCl	808	1465
MgO	2802	
CaS	2400	

Table 17.3. Melting and Boiling Points of Some Representative Solids

Carbon in the form of diamond consists of carbon atoms each forming four covalent bonds, directed toward the corners of a regular tetrahedron. A crystal of diamond is therefore held together completely by covalent bonds. It can be called a "giant molecule" or "network solid," and must be solid. When gaseous ethylene (C_2H_4) is made to condense with itself in addition polymerization, it forms very long chains containing hundreds or thousands of carbon atoms, each joined to two hydrogen atoms. Here the van der Waals forces between adjacent chains are very extensive. Thus polyethylene is also a solid.

In summary, although exact predictions of physical state are not yet possible, an understanding of intermolecular forces can provide considerable appreciation of the reasons for some substances being solids, some liquids, and some gases. We need only to apply logically what we know about the way in which their atoms are connected together.

SPECIFIC PHYSICAL PROPERTIES

What do you think would be the melting point of a molecule of sulfur? What would be the density of an atom of lead? Where would one molecule of oxygen boil? How much tensile strength has an atom of iron?

If you think about such physical properties, you will realize that most of them are not the properties of individual atoms or molecules. They are the properties of the *aggregates* of atoms or molecules that result because of their structure and the forces between them. Therefore we cannot expect to find any very consistent or systematic relationship between atomic structure and physical properties of a substance in bulk. We can, however, find a logical relationship between atomic structure and the state of aggregation of the substance—the way in which its atoms are assembled in bulk. We can *then* look for relationships between this state of aggregation and the physical properties in which we are interested. Thus indirectly, if not directly, the properties of matter are the inevitable consequence of the structure of the atoms which compose it.

Melting Point

Obviously, gases tend to have lower melting points than liquids, and liquids lower melting points than solids. Melting points and heats of fusion are closely related because both depend on the same cohesive forces in the substance. If the forces are relatively weak, the melting temperature will be relatively low. The difference in heat content between liquid and solid phases will not be very great. Where stronger cohesive forces exist, greater energy is needed to overcome them. This corresponds to higher temperature and larger heat of fusion. Heats of fusion are relatively low for frozen gaseous substances, somewhat higher for frozen liquid substances, and higher yet for solids.

Among solids, the melting temperatures are lower for those consisting of small molecules held together intermolecularly by weak van der Waals forces, like P_4 or S_8. The heats of fusion are correspondingly small. Molecular crystals made up of larger molecules tend to have somewhat higher melting points. If the molecules are very large, the possibility of thermal decomposition before melting is quite appreciable. Solids consisting of atoms held together throughout the crystal by a network of covalent bonds or by ionic attractions cannot be melted without introduction of enough energy to break at least a large portion of the bonds. Since these are ordinarily quite strong, high temperatures are required and the heats of fusion are relatively high. Ionic compounds in general are relatively high melting, as are "giant molecule" structures of all types.

Boiling Point

Remember that the process of melting disturbs the relative positions of the component particles significantly but does not require that they become separated very far. Evidence of this is the fact that the volume of a substance as liquid usually exceeds the volume as solid but not by a very large amount. On the other hand, vaporization requires the complete separation of the component particles, extending the distances between them to many particle diameters. The attractive forces which diminish with increasing distance are essentially completely overcome. Vaporization is therefore a much more disruptive process than melting of a solid. For this reason, vaporization to the extent of boiling usually requires a much higher temperature than melting. The heat of vaporization is ordinarily much greater than the heat of fusion.

> Can you suggest why the heat of vaporization of water is higher than that of carbon tetrachloride?

In metals, the melting process changes the bonding relatively little. Vaporization therefore requires nearly the whole amount of energy necessary to atomize or otherwise separate the substance into its component particles far removed from one another. Most metals show a relatively wide temperature range in which they are liquid—a wide *liquid range*.

When melting requires the breaking of covalent bonds, vaporization may be possible without much additional bond breaking. The liquid range may be shorter because the boiling point may be closer to the melting point. The melt may contain ions, however, as in the liquid phase of most highly polar compounds. These still exert a strong attraction for one another in the liquid state, and therefore much additional heat is required before they can break loose from one another altogether. In fact, ions do not vaporize as such, but the vapor from such salts consists of molecules. Even though sodium chloride, for example, is nonmolecular in the crystal, it does not vaporize as sodium ions and chloride ions but only as sodium chloride molecules. To some extent these are polymerized as Na_2Cl_2 or Na_3Cl_3, but they are mostly NaCl. Those who insist that this compound is completely ionic claim that these "molecules" in the gas phase are only "ion pairs." There is as yet no way of proving whether these are ion pairs or polar molecules. It is interesting that the bond length in the gaseous molecules is considerably shorter than in the crystal. The correct dissociation energies of the gaseous molecules can be calculated based on the assumption that they are polar covalent molecules rather than ion pairs. Whatever the vapor species may be, stable salts in general tend to have very high boiling points.

When a substance is molecular, relatively weak van der Waals forces are effective in holding it together. Melting disturbs and weakens these forces somewhat, but vaporization must overcome them completely. So long as the same molecules occur in the vapor as in the melt, and no further bond breaking is required for vaporization, molecular substances in general are relatively volatile with relatively low boiling points. The larger the molecules, however, the less volatile the substance. Very large molecules usually decompose thermally before they can absorb enough energy to break free completely to form the gas.

Mechanical Strength

If breaking apart a solid only requires overcoming van der Waals forces between molecules, the solid usually crumbles fairly easily and lacks physical strength. Sulfur, consisting of S_8 molecules weakly attracted to one another by van der Waals forces, is brittle and crumbles rather easily. But if fracture requires breaking of covalent bonds, the solid usually is difficult to break. Diamond, a network lattice of carbon atoms all covalently bound together, is strong and very hard. Sometimes, when very large molecules are closely intertwined, as in a piece of silk or nylon thread, surprisingly great strength is exhibited. The breaking of an ionic salt crystal has a somewhat different nature. Just moving a layer of atoms over by one position in the lattice changes the electrostatic force holding the layers together from attractive, when all the atoms were next to atoms of opposing charge, to repulsive. This slight shift places all the cations next to one another and all the anions next to one another, between the two layers. The forces of attraction are often strong enough to cause the solid to be very hard and strong, but once it starts to break, it often shatters relatively easily. In general, ionic salts tend to be brittle, as do nonmetals. In contrast, the delocalized bonding of metals allows shifts in the relative positions without bond breaking. Some of the strongest of materials are metals, because their close packing permits strong interactions.

When climbing a cliff, would you rather depend on a rope made of small compact molecules or large long molecules? Why?

You may find it interesting to keep in mind that whenever some material substance breaks or changes shape, the atoms are rearranging and bonds are breaking. This is true whether it is your pencil lead, the clothesline, a guitar string, a baseball bat, a steel rail, or a ski tow cable that breaks. Or, as the ski tow brings to mind, even your leg.

Test Your Memory

1. What kind of forces hold together the molecules of a gas when it is condensed?
2. What effect should protonic bridging have on melting and boiling points?
3. What is a *molecular solid?*
4. Why does an "ionic" solid usually melt at a high temperature?
5. Compare melting with vaporization. Which usually requires more energy, and why?
6. How are mechanical properties related to chemical bonds?

Test Your Understanding

1. What state of matter would you predict for zinc chloride ($ZnCl_2$), and why?
2. a) Why is nitrogen a gas?
   b) Why is CO_2 a gas?
3. What does a low melting point indicate about the state of aggregation in a solid substance?
4. What can be said about the cohesive forces in a low-melting, volatile substance?
5. What would be your reaction to a report that a certain gaseous substance has an extremely high heat of vaporization?

18

SOME PROPERTIES OF GASES

THE KINETIC MOLECULAR THEORY OF GASES

Because most gases are invisible, they have always seemed somewhat mysterious. When a gust of wind suddenly whisked the caveman's pink paper napkin off his lap, spilling cake crumbs into his tea, he was far more likely to imagine this to be the deed of some unseen evil spirit than to blame it on

N_2	nitrogen	780,000
O_2	oxygen	210,000
Ar	argon	9,300
CO_2	carbon dioxide	300
Ne	neon	18
He	helium	5.2
CH_4	methane	1.5
Kr	krypton	1
N_2O	nitrous oxide	0.5
H_2	hydrogen	0.5
O_3	ozone	0.4
Xe	xenon	0.08

Table 18.1. Composition of the Atmosphere (molecules per million (10^6) molecules of atmosphere)

the kinetic energy of tiny molecules. The scientific study of gases, however, has contributed much to our general understanding of the nature of matter. As this study developed, it led gradually to the development of the **kinetic molecular theory of gases.** A gas is considered to be a collection of individual molecules in extremely rapid motion at all temperatures above absolute zero (where there is no kinetic energy at all). These molecules have no significant volume compared to the total space filled by their motion. They rebound with perfect elasticity from any other molecules they might happen to strike.

On the basis of this theory it is possible to understand the special qualities and behavior of substances in the gaseous state.

DIFFUSION

One of the properties of gases resulting from their kinetic nature is their tendency to spread out to fill any container uniformly. Each molecule is moving at a high rate of speed in a straight line. It will continue to move in that same direction until something gets in the way, when there will be a collision and presumably a subsequent change in direction. Suppose a sample of gas is introduced into a completely empty container. In other words, the gas is introduced into an evacuated space. The molecules in their random motion will be able to move farther before colliding if they are headed toward the most distant part of the evacuated space. Therefore, the sample spreads out as the result of its own kinetic energy until the molecules have in effect become evenly distributed throughout all the space available to them. Since the initial spreading out was unimpeded by other molecules, this expansion occurs very rapidly. Indeed it must when you consider that the average speed of molecules in air is in the neighborhood of one thousand feet per second. This process of spreading throughout the available space is called **diffusion.** It is a property characteristic of all gases.

Suppose the gas sample had been released into a container that was already filled with air. The space among molecules is so much greater than their volume as individual particles that there is plenty of room for the new sample. However, as it begins to spread out, its molecules begin colliding with air

Figure 18.1. Path of a Gas Molecule.

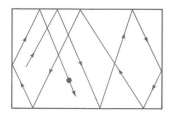

In a vacuum a gas molecule, unrestricted in its motion, bounces in straight-line paths from one wall of a container to another.

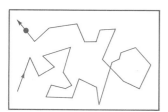

If other gas molecules are present, the straight-line motion of a gas molecule is very rapidly altered by collisions with other molecules. The *mean free path*—its average distance of travel before collision—becomes smaller as the density (pressure) of gas molecules increases.

molecules (primarily oxygen and nitrogen molecules) that are already present. Even though the proportion of free space is very large, the tremendous speed of the molecules causes them to collide very frequently. The average molecule of the sample can travel only a very short distance before colliding. The average distance traveled between collisions is called the **mean free path** of the molecules. Each collision tends to change the direction of molecular motion so the new sample spreads out much more slowly than if no air were present. Diffusion into an enclosed space is greatly slowed, but never prevented, by the presence of a gas already in that space.

The formula for kinetic energy is $1/2\ mv^2$, where m is the particle mass and v is its velocity. At any given instant the distribution of molecular energies follows a pattern like that in Figure 16.3. On the average, the kinetic energy of a molecule is proportional to the temperature. At a given temperature the component particles of all substances have the same vigor of motion, i.e., the same average molecular kinetic energy. If the energies of two molecules are the same but one is heavier than the other, it will move more slowly. You would probably not mind very much being struck in the face with a fast-moving ping-pong ball, but a baseball traveling at the same speed would fracture your skull. The difference in impact relates to a difference in kinetic energy. In order for the much heavier baseball to possess the same kinetic energy as the ping-pong ball, it would have to be traveling much more slowly.

Suppose two molecules, A and B, of different mass, m_A and m_B, have equal kinetic energy. In order for this to be true, the speed of $A(v_A)$ must be different from the speed of $B(v_B)$. Equating their kinetic energies gives

$$\frac{m_A v_A^{\,2}}{2} = \frac{m_B v_B^{\,2}}{2} \quad \text{or,} \quad \frac{m_A}{m_B} = \frac{v_B^{\,2}}{v_A^{\,2}}$$

From this,

$$\sqrt{\frac{m_A}{m_B}} = \frac{v_B}{v_A}$$

The ratio of molecular weights of A and B must exactly equal the ratio of actual masses of molecules A and B, since that is what molecular weight means. Substituting molecular weights (M_A, M_B) for masses in the ratio, we get

$$\frac{v_B}{v_A} = \sqrt{\frac{M_A}{M_B}}$$

This is a mathematical expression of **Graham's Law of Gaseous Diffusion:** the average velocity of the molecules of a gas is inversely proportional to the square root of the molecular weight.

This is an important law. It tells us that at any given temperature, lightweight molecules move faster on the average than heavier molecules. It tells us that if a mixture of gases is allowed to leak through a very small hole, the gases of lowest molecular weight will leak out faster than the rest. The practical importance of this fact is evidenced by the vast diffusion plants for the separation of uranium isotopes. The average uranium atom has a nucleus of 92 protons and 146 neutrons, giving a total mass of 238. A very small fraction of the atoms of natural uranium consist of the isotope having only 143 neutrons per nucleus. This isotope, uranium-235, is **fissionable,** meaning that its nucleus can be caused to break up with the evolution of enormous quantities of nuclear energy. It is therefore desirable to separate it from the bulk of the natural uranium. Uranium forms a fluoride, UF_6, which is a gas. The uranium isotopes can be separated by converting them to the fluoride and taking advantage of the slightly more rapid diffusion of the hexafluoride molecules containing uranium-235. The gas that leaks through a porous wall is richer in uranium-235. Chemical separation is not possible, for the chemistry of the two isotopes is identical.

> What effect, if any, would slow leakage from an inflated tire have on the composition of the air within the tire?
>
> Can you suggest a means of separating helium from methane?

PRESSURE

The incessant motion of the very large number of gas molecules causes them to collide with the container walls so frequently that a steady pressure on the walls results. Individually, a gas molecule has so little mass that even when it collides at a speed of a thousand miles per hour, the force of the impact is negligible. Collectively, however, moving gas molecules can perform feats of amazing strength, such as bursting balloons, blowing out tires, uprooting trees, and demolishing cities. The force exerted by the molecules of a gas on each unit area of the container walls is called the **pressure** of the gas.

Pressure in scientific measurement is usually measured in terms of the height of a column of mercury the pressure will support, in **millimeters** or **torr** (1 mm mercury = 1 torr). Higher pressures are measured in **atmospheres,** one atmosphere being equal to 760 mm mercury.

Devices used for measuring pressures are called **manometers.** The mercury manometer was invented by the Italian scientist named E. Torricelli (1608–1647). If a long enough tube closed at one end is filled with mercury and then inverted so the lower open end is in a pool of mercury, the tube will drain under the influence of gravity until the remaining column is about 760 mm in height where the mercury level remains steady. When the mercury falls from the closed end of the tube, it leaves above it a vacuum, containing only mercury vapor. Since the vapor tension of mercury at 25° is only about 2×10^{-3} mm, its influence on the height of the column is negligible. One may interpret the entire difference between height in the tube and level of mercury in the pool as the result of the pressure of the outside atmosphere. This pressure bears down on the pool, supporting the column inside the tube. When

Figure 18.2.   Some Simple Laboratory Devices for the Measurement of Gas Pressure.

Barometer. This is the simplest type, devised by Torricelli. A long tube closed at one end is filled with mercury and inverted with its open end in a dish of mercury. The mercury drains down to the level at which it is supported by the atmosphere. The height of the column of mercury is therefore a measure of the pressure exerted by the atmosphere. Unit: 1 mm Hg = 1 torr.

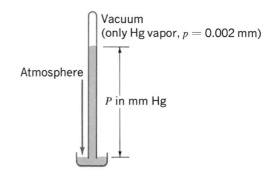

Vacuum
(only Hg vapor, $p = 0.002$ mm)

Atmosphere

P in mm Hg

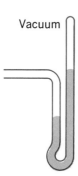

Vacuum

Manometer. In scientific experiments this type of manometer can be used to measure vapor tensions of liquids or pressures of gases inside an enclosed system. The difference in mercury levels gives the pressure in mm Hg. It can be read simply by use of a meter stick.

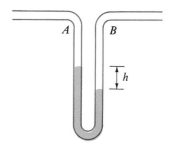

A B

h

Differential manometer. A simple U-shaped transparent tube containing mercury can be used to measure a difference h in gas pressure between the two sides of the U-tube. In the figure, the pressure of gas in side B is greater than the pressure of gas in side A by the amount h.

used to measure the atmospheric pressure, such a device is called a barometer. The principle is the same in ordinary mercury manometers used in scientific apparatus for the study of gases and vapors.

In the seventeenth century, Robert Boyle (1627–1691), the scientist who contributed so much to the concept of a chemical element, experimented with gases and found them to be highly compressible. He found that if the pressure is doubled, the volume is halved. In general, for a given sample of gas, the product of the pressure times the volume is a constant:

$$PV = k$$

The magnitude of k is of course dependent on the size of the particular sample of gas chosen, and on the temperature, which must be held constant. But since

P and V can be anything, as long as they depend on each other in this manner, we can write

$$PV = k = P'V'$$

One pressure and corresponding volume are P and V and another pressure and corresponding volume, for the same sample of gas, are P' and V'. Either of these expressions can be taken as a mathematical statement of **Boyle's Law.** It is one of the **gas laws** that describe the approximate behavior of gases under common conditions.

Problems using Boyle's law are among the simplest in elementary chemistry. Yet they are extremely important, too. Chemists working with gases could hardly do without Boyle's law. So let us look at a couple of examples.

Figure 18.3.   Boyle's Law.

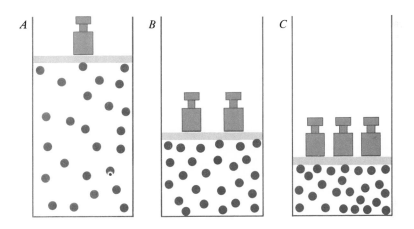

Each gas sample contains the same number of molecules at the same constant temperature, confined by a weightless piston on which weights are placed.

In A, the molecules occupy unit volume, and exert only enough pressure to support one weight.

In B, they occupy only one-half unit volume, and so exert enough pressure, by colliding with the piston twice as frequently, to support two units of weight.

In C, by occupying only one-third unit volume, they exert enough pressure to support three units of weight because they strike the piston three times as frequently as in A. 1 unit volume $\times$ 1 unit weight = $\frac{1}{2}$ unit volume $\times$ 2 unit weights = $\frac{1}{3}$ unit volume $\times$ 3 unit weights.
Or, $PV = k$, which is Boyle's Law. $P_A V_A = P_B V_B = P_C V_C = k$. For this particular sample, $k = 1$. The numerical value of k depends on the number of molecules in the sample and the units of volume and pressure used.

Example 18.1. *A sample of ammonia* (NH_3) *occupies a volume of* 1.00 *liter at a pressure of* 380 *mm* (*or* 380 *torr*). *If it is allowed to expand into a total volume three times as large, what pressure will it then exert?*

The initial pressure is 380. mm and the volume 1.00 liter. The new volume is 3.00 liter and the pressure is P. By Boyle's law, $3P = 380$ mm $\times$ 1 liter, from which $P = 127$. mm.

Example 18.2. *The volume of* 500. ml *of oxygen is decreased until the pressure has increased from an initial* 25. mm *to* 600. mm. *What is the final volume?*

The initial volume is 500. ml and the pressure 25. mm. The final volume is V and the pressure 600. mm. By Boyle's law, $600V = 25 \times 500$, from which $V = 12500/600$ or 20.8 ml.

CHARLES' LAW

Boyle's law is only applicable if the temperature is kept constant. A change in temperature means a change in the average speed of the molecules. This means a change in the force of their collisions with the walls of the container and a change in the pressure. When a scientist named Jacques Charles (1746–1823) investigated the effect of temperature on a gas kept at constant pressure, he found that the volume increases directly with the temperature, provided the correct temperature scale is used. It was observed that a given sample of gas decreases by 1/273 of its volume at 0°C for every degree of cooling below 0°C. If continued, this cooling would result, at −273°C, in a volume of zero for the gas. In fact, however, nobody has ever observed a gas to disappear when cooled sufficiently, for actually it *appears*. Its appearance marks the change from the invisible gas to the visible liquid form, and then to the visible crystalline solid. In other words, all real gases condense from the gaseous state when enough of the kinetic energy of their molecules has been removed. But as long as they remain gaseous, then they approximately follow the volume contraction rate described above. Above 0°C there is a corresponding expansion: The volume increases by 1/273 of its 0°C volume for each degree above 0°C.

The temperature at which the hypothetical gas would disappear is also the temperature at which all kinetic energy would be gone, the **absolute zero of temperature.** The absolute temperature scale is often called the **Kelvin scale** after Lord Kelvin (1824–1907), an Englishman who performed many important experiments. Degrees are the same size for the Celsius or centigrade scale but are numbered from absolute zero instead of from the freezing point of water. The relationship between the two temperature scales is given by °K (Kelvin) or °A (Absolute) = °C + 273°.

Figure 18.4. Charles' Law.

Each sample of gas contains the same number of molecules and each exerts the same pressure. Only the temperatures are different.

A higher temperature in B allows the molecules to occupy a larger volume than in A without reducing their pressure. They are moving faster; therefore they strike the walls more frequently and harder.

In C, the temperature is still higher. To keep from increasing the pressure, the volume is expanded even more than in B.

When T is the absolute temperature (°C + 273°),

$$V_A/T_A = V_B/T_B = V_C/T_C = k, \quad \text{or,} \quad V = kT.$$

This is called **Charles' Law.**

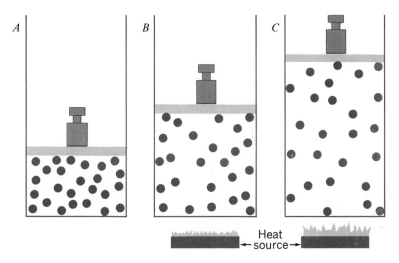

According to **Charles' Law,**

$$\frac{V}{T} = k$$

where T is the *absolute* temperature and k is a constant determined by the quantity of gas and the pressure. At constant pressure, $V/T = k = V'/T'$. From this equation we can determine any one volume or temperature if we know the other three quantities.

Example 18.3. *To keep the pressure constant, to what volume must a sample of gas be allowed to expand if one liter at 25° is heated to 125°?*

The very first thing to do in preparation for solving a problem involving gases at different temperatures is to change the temperature, if necessary, to the absolute scale. If you neglect to do that, you will almost invariably obtain an entirely wrong answer. For example, casual inspection of the above temperatures (given in Celsius) gives the impression that the temperature is being increased by a factor of 5, since 125 is 5×25. But this is not true at all. $25°C + 273°C = 298°K$, and $125°C + 273°C = 398°K$. The actual temperature change is from $298°$ to $398°K$.

The initial volume is one liter. The new volume will then be $398/298$ liters. $1/298 = V/398$, from which $V = 398/298 = 1.33$ liters.

PRESSURE AND TEMPERATURE

If the volume instead of the pressure or temperature is kept constant, then the gas pressure is directly proportional to the temperature. We could write a third gas law: $P/T = P'/T' = k$. This equation describes the pressure build-up in an automobile tire which becomes heated without much change in volume.

Suppose the reaction inside a 10-ml firecracker produced 100 liters of gas at 1000°C. If the container did not burst, what would be the internal pressure?

THE COMBINED GAS LAWS AND THE IDEAL GAS

If $PV = k$ is combined with $V/T = k$ and $P/T = k$, all the k's having different values, and all three are applied to the same sample of gas, we have $PV/T = K$ as a combined gas law. This can be rewritten, $PV = KT$. Since K depends on the size of the gas sample, we could choose exactly one mole of gas for the sample and then K would have a value that is specific for one mole. This is called the **gas constant,** and is given the symbol R. For one mole of gas, we write

$$PV = RT$$

and for n moles of gas,

$$PV = nRT$$

This is the usual form of the combined gas law.

These relationships hold strictly only for the hypothetical ideal gas. All actual gases differ from the ideal in two important respects: (1) the molecules of an ideal gas individually occupy no space, whereas real molecules do; and (2) the molecules of an ideal gas exert no influence on one another, whereas real molecules exert van der Waals attractions. At low and ordinary pressures and at temperatures well above their boiling points, ordinary gases obey the ideal gas laws quite well. But at high pressures or at temperatures near condensation, deviations occur. Under these conditions, the volume of the individual molecules themselves cannot be ignored. Furthermore, when they are forced close together they exert attractions upon one another that have the same effect as would an increase in external pressure. These two effects tend to cancel one another: The volume is larger than expected because of the volume contribution of the molecules, but it is smaller than expected because of the cohesive forces pulling the molecules closer together. Therefore, the ideal gas laws are applicable over a somewhat wider range of conditions than would otherwise be expected. But we will count on their being most reliable only at relatively low pressures of one atmosphere or less, and at temperatures well above the boiling points of the substances.

Standard Conditions of Gas Volume Measurement

If the volume of a given sample of gas can change with both pressure and temperature, it is clear that we cannot know the quantity of the sample from its volume unless we also know the pressure and temperature at which that volume was measured. It is convenient to convert gas volumes to a set of **standard conditions (SC)** of temperature and pressure, sometimes abbreviated STP for Standard Temperature and Pressure in order to compare them with other volumes. These standard conditions are a pressure of **760 mm (torr)** and a temperature of **0°C or 273°K.** When measured at these conditions, one mole of gas is found to occupy **22.4 liters.** This is the standard volume of a mole or **molar volume** of a gas. This is a very important number to memorize along with the standard conditions of pressure and temperature. Its importance, as we shall see, is that it gives us a direct relationship between the weight of a gas and its volume—a measurement of gas density—thus allowing us to determine volumes by weighing and to weigh by measuring volume. It allows us to calculate the molecular weight of any volatile substance.

These values can be used to evaluate the gas constant R. If the pressure is measured in atmospheres, the volume in liters, and the temperature in degrees Kelvin, then for $PV = RT$ we can write $1.00 \text{ atm.} \times 22.41 = 273° \times R$, from which $R = 0.082$ liter-atmospheres per degree. If the pressure is measured in millimeters and the volume in liters, then $760 \text{ mm} \times 22.41 = 273°R$, from which $R = 62.3$ liter-millimeters per degree.

Volume-Volume or Similar Relationships

It is not necessary to know the identity of a sample of gas or what fraction of a mole it may be if all we wish to do is to determine what volume or pressure or temperature would result from a change in the conditions. We simply make use of the combined gas law form, $PV/T = P'V'/T'$. Rearranged, this formula can be written:

$$V = V'\left(\frac{P'}{P}\right)\left(\frac{T}{T'}\right)$$

To find a new volume under new conditions when the volume under certain other conditions is known, we simply multiply the old volume by a pressure factor and a temperature factor.

Instead of trying to memorize which is P and which P', and which is T and which is T', we can more usefully reason out what effects the changes in pressure and temperature should be expected to have separately. First, we look at the pressure to see whether it goes up or down. If the new pressure is higher, then the volume must be smaller. We place the larger of the two pressures in the denominator, to make the pressure factor smaller than 1.0. If the new pressure is lower, then the volume must be larger. The smaller of the two pressures is made the denominator, to make the pressure factor greater than 1.0.

Next we look at the temperature to see whether it goes up or down. If the final temperature is higher than the initial temperature, then this effect should expand the gas and the temperature factor must be greater than 1.0. The smaller temperature is made the denominator. But if the final temperature is lower than the initial temperature, we know at once that this cooling must have the effect of causing the gas to contract. The temperature factor is therefore made less than 1.0 by placing the higher temperature as the denominator. Remember that the temperatures must always be expressed in degrees Kelvin.

By following this reasoning carefully we should encounter no difficulty in obtaining the correct answer. Just remember that the new volume equals the old volume multiplied by a pressure factor and a temperature factor, plus the fact that gases expand under reduced pressure or higher temperature, and contract under higher pressure or lower temperature.

Example 18.4. *A chemist carries out a reaction in which a gaseous compound is liberated, and he finds that confined within a volume of 350 ml, at 27°C, this gas sample exerts a pressure of 206 mm. Before he can have a clear idea of how much gas this is, he wants to convert this volume to standard conditions. In other words, what volume would this gas occupy at 0°C and a pressure of 760 torr?*

First, he converts the 27°C to absolute temperature: $27 + 273 = 300°K$. Then he applies the equation:

$$V = 350 \times \text{pressure factor} \times \text{temperature factor}$$

He notes that the pressure rises from 206 to 760 which must tend to diminish the volume, so he chooses as the pressure factor the ratio 206/760, which is smaller than 1.0. He also notes that the temperature is reduced from 300° to 273°K, which also makes the factor less than 1.0, or 273/300.

$$V = 350 \times \frac{206}{760} \times \frac{273}{300} = 86.3 \text{ ml}$$

If the identity of a gas is known, the weight of a sample can easily be determined from its measured volume, corrected to standard conditions. For example, if the gas is known to be carbon dioxide (CO_2), the molecular weight of which is 44 (12 + 16 + 16), you can calculate that 25 ml of it at standard conditions should weigh 0.049 g (25/22400 × 44 g). This is very useful information since experimentally it is usually much easier to measure accurately the volume, pressure, and temperature of a gas sample than it is to weigh it. This is especially true if the sample of gas is very small. In chemical research using gases, quantities of the gases are usually measured out by volume rather than by weight. The weight can then be easily calculated. The determination is often more accurate than a direct weighing would be.

If the identity of a gas is unknown, one of the most helpful clues one can obtain as to its possible identity is its molecular weight. This can be determined by measuring the volume of a weighed sample and converting the volume to standard conditions. No matter what gas it is, one mole will occupy very nearly 22.4 liters. This is the volume of Avogadro's number of gas molecules at standard conditions. It arises from **Avogadro's Law,** which states that: Equal volumes of all gases, measured under the same conditions of pressure and temperature, contain identical numbers of molecules. The molecular weight (M) of the gas is given by the equation:

$$M = \frac{22,400 \text{ ml}}{(\text{volume in ml at STP})} \times (\text{weight of sample in g})$$

The gas law equation $PV = nRT$ can be very useful here, for we can solve for n, the number of moles, if we know the volume, pressure, and temperature of the sample at any set of conditions.

Example 18.5. *Suppose we find that* 0.164 g *of an unknown gaseous compound occupies* 250 ml *at* 24°C *and exerts a pressure of* 150 mm. *What is its molecular weight?*

First, how many moles of it are in the sample? We know that $P = 150$ mm, $V = 0.25$ liter, R is 62.3 1-mm per degree, and $T = 273 + 24$ or 297. Therefore,

$$150 \times 0.25 = n \times 62.3 \times 297$$

or,
$$n = \frac{150 \times 0.25}{62.3 \times 297} = 0.0020 \text{ mole}$$

Now, if 0.0020 mole weighs 0.164 g, one mole must weigh 0.164/0.0020, or 82 g. The molecular weight is 82.

Test Your Memory

1. What is the *kinetic molecular theory* of gases?
2. What is the cause of diffusion?
3. What is the effect on diffusion of a gas through a container that results from gas already present in the container?
4. State Graham's law of diffusion in words and write an equation expressing it.
5. What is the cause of gas pressure and how is it measured?
6. How are a barometer and a manometer related?
7. State Boyle's law both in words and mathematically.
8. What is meant by *absolute zero?*
9. State Charles' law and give its mathematical expression.
10. If volume is held constant, how are pressure and temperature related?
11. What are *standard conditions?*
12. How are the gas laws combined?
13. What is the standard molar volume of a gas?
14. What information is needed to obtain the molecular weight of a sample of gas?

Test Your Understanding

1. List the following gases in order of decreasing diffusion rate: hydrogen, chlorine, hydrogen chloride, carbon dioxide, oxygen, and ammonia.
2. A slight leak in a tire should result in a slight enrichment of which of the two chief gases in the air in the tire?
3. If the temperature is kept constant, what happens to the pressure when a one liter container of methane is opened to a previously evacuated volume of nine liters?
4. A McLeod gage is a device for measuring very low pressures by compressing a relatively large volume of gas into such a small space that its pressure becomes easily measurable on an ordinary manometer. If the pressure is 10^{-6} mm, into how small a volume must 200 ml of gas be compressed to bring its pressure up to 10 mm?
5. What would be the pressure inside a 500 ml flask if all the air at one atmosphere in a room $6 \times 6 \times 6$ meters could be forced into it?
6. If the pressure remains constant, how hot must the air in a balloon be to keep it the same size it was at 25°C when it had twice as much air in it?
7. Determine the weights of the following gas samples at STP: (a) 500 ml ammonia; (b) 500 ml carbon dioxide; (c) 200 ml of methane; (d) 25 liters of hydrogen; and (e) 1000 liters of oxygen.
8. A sample of chlorine gas occupies 250 ml at 300 mm and 23°C. What is its volume at standard conditions, and how much does it weigh?

9. A sample of unknown gas occupies 65.0 ml at 450 mm and 27°C, and weighs 0.246 g. What is its molecular weight?
10. Which is heavier, 1000 ml of oxygen at 700 mm and 37°C or 1000 ml of nitrogen at 690 mm and 15°C?
11. Carbon dioxide is soluble in liquid water but not in ice. Why would it be hazardous to freeze the contents of a coke bottle solid?

19

THE NATURE AND PHYSICAL PROPERTIES
OF SOLUTIONS

KINDS OF SOLUTIONS

A solution is a mixture, but unlike ordinary mixtures, the mixing is on a molecular level. The individual atoms, molecules, or ions of one substance are completely separated from one another by the molecules of another substance. These in turn are separated from their normal condition by the intervention of the first. Therefore a solution is homogeneous down to the molecules that make it up. It has the appearance of a pure substance.

Several kinds of solutions are possible. The components may be the following: gas in gas, gas in liquid, gas in solid, liquid in liquid, liquid in solid, solid in liquid, and solid in solid. For the present, we are primarily concerned with solutions in which a gas, liquid, or solid is dissolved in a liquid. The substance that is dissolved is called the **solute.** The liquid that dissolves it is called the **solvent.** When liquids form a solution, it is not clear which should be called the solvent, for each dissolves the other. The usual practice is to consider the component that is present in larger quantity to be the solvent, although this practice is not always followed. For example, a solution containing 95 per cent alcohol and 5 per cent water is called a 95 per cent alcohol solution. Although it might more logically be regarded as a 5 per cent solution of water in alcohol, in this case the emphasis is on the alcohol.

When two liquids dissolve in one another in all proportions, they are called **miscible.** The mixture of water and ethyl alcohol is an example. If their mutual solubility is only partial, each is called **partially miscible,** and if the solubility of each in the other is very small, each is called **immiscible.** Because of the relatively loose open structure of liquids they can usually accommodate at least a few foreign molecules within them. Therefore, pairs of liquids that cannot dissolve even a tiny trace of one another are relatively rare.

Figure 19.1. Miscibility of Liquids.

(A) The two liquids form separate layers with a clearly discernible interface and the denser liquid at the bottom. Even with the most immiscible liquids, each layer will contain a few stray molecules of the other component.

(B) The interface persists, but each layer is a solution of both components. The lower layer contains mostly the denser component.

(C) The interface completely disappears. The two components become thoroughly mixed at the molecular level.

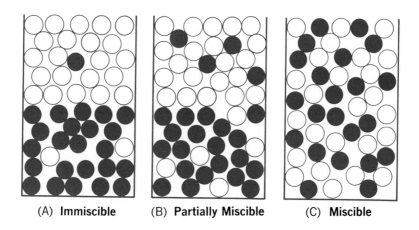

(A) **Immiscible**   (B) **Partially Miscible**   (C) **Miscible**

HOW DISSOLUTION TAKES PLACE

We know very well from everyday observations that not all liquids will dissolve all substances, and that different solvents will not dissolve a given substance to the same extent. The ability of solvents to dissolve solutes has a high degree of specificity. In order to understand it, we must examine the nature of the process by which a solution forms. This process of dissolving is called **dissolution.**

General Principles

The dissolution of a gas is the easiest to understand because the individual molecules of a gas are already completely separate from one another. For the same reason that the substance is a gas, its molecules are not likely to be attracted very strongly to the molecules of a solvent any more than to one another. The attraction can only be by van der Waals forces unless some chemical reaction occurs. For this reason gases are ordinarily not very soluble in liquids. Their solubility is found to be directly proportional to the pressure of the gas over the solvent. This suggests that the gas molecules bombarding the surface of the liquid occasionally find holes in the surface and become trapped within the interior. If the gas is very soluble in a liquid, the explanation usually is more chemical than physical. Such reactions will be considered later.

Any solute that is a liquid or a solid exists in that phase because of strong **cohesive forces** among its component particles. If these were absent, it would be a gas. The process of dissolution requires that these cohesive forces be overcome, because within the solution the component particles are highly dispersed. No substance held together by cohesive forces can be expected suddenly to fly apart. Energy must be expended to separate its components. If the cohesive forces are merely van der Waals forces, dissolution will not be greatly hampered. However, if they are electrostatic forces among oppositely charged ions, which are usually strong, a lot of energy will be required to separate the ions. Polar or nonpolar covalent bonds may have to be broken before dissolution can occur.

Similarly, any liquid solvent is a liquid because of the existence of cohesive forces. The dissolution process requires that the solvent molecules become somewhat separated in order to allow the solute particles to be distributed among them. Again, considerable energy is needed.

Both these processes essential to dissolution require the absorption of appreciable energy. Yet experimental observations show that dissolution frequently occurs spontaneously when the solute and solvent come into contact, often with the evolution of heat. Where does the energy come from?

Since water is the most common and most important solvent, let us consider its action on solutes as examples of specific aspects of the dissolution problem.

Water as a Solvent

Liquid water has a relatively high boiling point, relatively low volatility, relatively high heat of vaporization, and relatively high melting point and heat of fusion. All these facts indicate that the cohesive forces in water are strong. Their origin, as has been mentioned, is the protonic bridging which occurs so readily among water molecules. Each oxygen of a water molecule bears partial negative charge and two lone pairs of electrons. These can attract the protonic hydrogen of other water molecules. It also bears two partially positive hydrogen atoms, each capable of attracting an electron pair on the oxygen of another water molecule. Each water molecule is thus capable of forming up to four protonic bridges simultaneously. As we have seen in Figure 15.1, it does this when cooled to its freezing point. Above that temperature, the protonic bridging is not as complete and is constantly breaking and reforming. Nevertheless, on the average the protonic bridging is extensive enough at ordinary temperatures to give water unusually strong cohesive forces for a liquid.

Despite this relatively stable, structured quality, water is one of the most general, effective, and useful of solvents. Almost everything will dissolve in water, at least in traces. Only certain general types of substances will dissolve in appreciable concentrations.

One type is that usually called *ionic*. Ionic substances are believed to be held together principally by relatively strong electrostatic forces between oppositely charged ions. In general, this results in relatively high melting points and very low volatility. Yet many, although by no means all, ionic substances dissolve in water rather easily. One of these is table salt (sodium chloride, NaCl). This is a salt so stable that its crystal lattice is not even disrupted by heat until a temperature above 808°C is reached. Yet there is considerable evidence that in a solution of sodium chloride in water, the salt is dispersed throughout the solvent as separate sodium and chloride ions. How does the action of water overcome the strong electrostatic attractions in the crystal? How can these ions overcome the protonic bridging of the water in order to move in between the water molecules?

The only reasonable answer seems to be that the interaction between solute and solvent evolves sufficient energy to disrupt the crystal lattice and the protonic bridges. To visualize this we must recognize the polar nature of the water molecule. Its oxygen is joined to two hydrogens with a bond angle of 104.5°. Since the bonds are polar, the geometrically unsymmetrical molecule must also be polar. The hydrogens are positive and the oxygen is negative. Water, coming into contact with ions or partially charged atoms on the surface

Figure 19.2. Dissolution by Hydration of Ions.

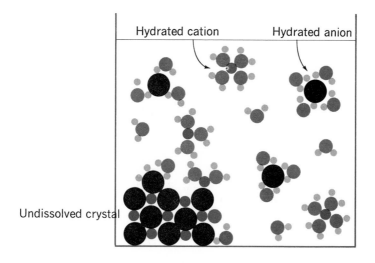

The energy of hydration of the ions helps to provide the energy needed to separate the ions from the crystal. Water attaches to anions through its protonic hydrogen and to cations through its negative oxygen. Once the ions are in dilute solution, then their electrostatic interactions are reduced, by orientation of the water dipoles that separated the ions, to about 1/80 the value expected if they were in a vacuum. This property of water is called its **dielectric constant** (about 80 at 25°). A high dielectric constant is an asset to a solvent in the dissolution of substances as ions.

of the sodium chloride crystal, attaches itself to the charged atoms with release of considerable energy. Positively charged sodium attracts the negative oxygen while the negatively charged chlorine attracts the positive hydrogens. As each ion interacts with water molecules at the crystal surface, it leaves the crystal environment to enter a nearly equivalent polar environment within a sphere of hydrating water molecules as shown in Figure 19.2. In fact, the hydration energy of Na^+ and Cl^- ions nearly equals the energy of association of the ions in the crystal.

The process of dissolution always implies an attraction operating between solute particles and solvent molecules that compensates for the attraction among solute particles and among solvent molecules that had to be overcome. Furthermore, it should be noted that there is a natural tendency for systems to become as random as possible. The disruption of a neat, orderly crystal to form a random mixture such as a solution is aided by this tendency. **Entropy** is a measure of the extent of disorder or randomness. Thus, the process of dissolution increases the entropy of the system. (Entropy is an important topic in chemistry but detailed discussion is usually presented at an advanced level.)

Many ionic substances scarcely dissolve in water at all. Apparently in these cases the interaction between water molecules and ions is not sufficiently strong to overcome the strong interactions within the crystal. Unfortunately we still lack a comprehensive theory of solubility.

Magnesium hydroxide is very insoluble in water but magnesium chloride dissolves readily. What conclusion can be drawn about the crystal energies of these two compounds?

Another and quite different type of solute that will dissolve in water consists of molecules which contain atoms or groups capable of protonic bridging. For example, sugars and alcohols contain OH groups often not very different in condition from those of water molecules. Such compounds are usually held together by cohesive forces that consist largely of protonic bridges. If the protonic bridges among solute molecules and among water molecules can be replaced by protonic bridges between solute molecules and water molecules, high solubility or even complete miscibility can be expected. If however, hydroxyl groups of the solute comprise but a small part of the solute molecules, it is possible that not enough protonic bridges between water and solute can form to compensate for the numerous protonic bridges among water molecules that would be broken to accommodate the large solute molecule. Such a solute would have only limited solubility in water. For example, although ethyl alcohol (C_2H_5OH) is completely miscible with water, butyl alcohol (C_4H_9OH) is only slightly soluble in water. The 4-carbon group is too large.

A solute may have cohesive forces, but have nothing to offer to water molecules in exchange for breaking their own protonic bridges. Such a substance is not expected to be very soluble. This is true for such substances as

Figure 19.3. Dissolution Through Protonic Bridging.

Ethyl alcohol (C_2H_5OH) has a hydroxyl group (OH) resembling that of water, HOH. Ethyl alcohol is like water in that it is a liquid because of molecular association through protonic bridging. When the two liquids are mixed, protonic bridging seems readily interchangeable, causing water and ethyl alcohol to be completely miscible.

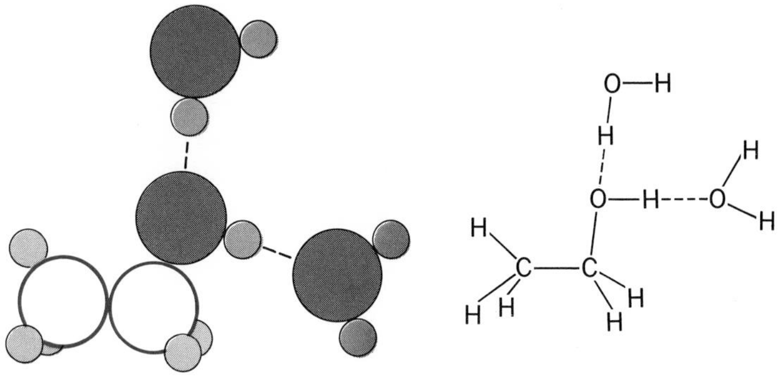

Most hydrocarbons are quite insoluble in water because they offer no association with water to compensate for breaking the protonic bridges among water molecules. If an organic molecule contains a hydroxyl group for every one or two carbon atoms, however, this permits enough protonic bridging with water to compensate for the hydrocarbon portion. Such compounds are ordinarily very soluble in water.

carbon tetrachloride (CCl_4) or any of the gasoline hydrocarbons, such as hexane (C_6H_{14}). The molecules of these are held together only by relatively weak van der Waals forces which are easily overcome. (In fact, the two examples given are miscible with one another.) To mix them with water molecules, however, would require breaking many protonic bridges in the latter without replacing these bridges with anything. Neither carbon tetrachloride nor hexane molecules have any means of attracting water molecules strongly enough to accomplish this. Therefore water will not dissolve appreciable concentrations of either of these compounds.

EXPRESSING CONCENTRATIONS OF SOLUTIONS

Weight Per Cent

A common way of expressing concentrations of solutions is by weight per cent, which means simply the number of parts by weight of *solute* per 100 parts by weight of the *solution*. A 10% solution of NaCl, for example, would contain 10 g NaCl for every 90 g H_2O.

How many grams of sugar would be needed to make
a kilogram of 15 per cent solution?

Mole Fraction

If both solute and solvent are measured in moles, then the concentration of a solution can be expressed in terms of how many molecules or ions of solute there are per molecule of solvent or per total number of molecules of solute plus solvent. The ratio of the number of moles of solute to the total number of moles of solute plus solvent is called the mole fraction. It must always be less than one since the denominator must always be larger than the numerator. For example, in a solution with mole fraction of sugar 0.1, one out of every ten molecules is sugar and the other nine are water.

What is the mole fraction of $CaCl_2$ in a 20 per cent
solution?

Molality

Frequently instead of measuring the solvent in moles, the concentration of a solution is expressed in the number of moles of solute per 1000 grams of solvent. This is called the **molality.** Is is used to express concentrations chiefly for assessing the effects of solutes on the physical properties of solvents as will be described later in this chapter.

If it takes 125 g of water to dissolve one mole of A,
what is the molality of the solution?

What weight of NaCl is present in 529 g of one
molal solution?

Molarity

Weighing, even on the newest and most automatic balances, is usually less convenient than measuring liquid volumes. The latter method employs a variety of specially designed types of laboratory apparatus including graduates (graduated cylinders), volumetric flasks, pipettes, and burets. A solution can be poured into a container with marked calibrated walls and measured up to a fixed mark much more readily than it could be weighed out exactly. For this reason, in scientific work the concentrations of solutions are most frequently expressed in **moles of solute per liter of solution,** or **molarity.** Do not confuse this word and its meaning with the word similar to it, **molality.**

When any solute is dissolved in water, volume changes occur, such that the volume of the final solution is seldom the exact sum of the initial volumes

Figure 19.4. Some Types of Volumetric Apparatus.

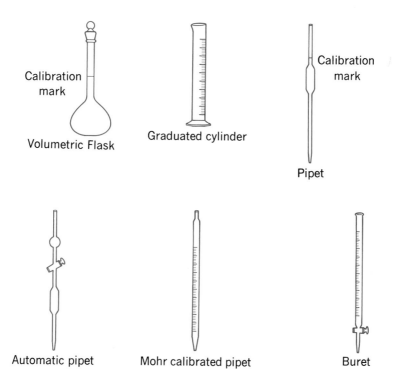

Calibration mark

Volumetric Flask

Graduated cylinder

Calibration mark

Pipet

Automatic pipet   Mohr calibrated pipet   Buret

of the solute and solvent separately. A solution is most commonly used as a source of the solute. The quantity of water to accompany the solute is relatively unimportant. Thus, molarity does not indicate the exact amount of water present in any solution, since this varies from solute to solute and from concentration to concentration. But we do not care. What we wish to know when we measure out 10 ml of a solution, for example, is how much solute it contains. If this is a 0.5 M (molar) solution, then we know that 10 ml (0.01 l) must contain 0.005 mole of solute. It is much easier to measure out 10 ml of the prepared solution than to weigh out exactly 0.005 mole of the solute and dissolve it in enough water to total 10 ml of solution. The solute had to be weighed just once—when the solution was originally prepared. Once the molarity of the solution is determined, the exact quantity of solute in any measured volume of the solution is easy to calculate from the molarity.

How many moles of ethyl alcohol are in 0.5 ml of a 2M solution?

What is the molarity of chloride ion in 3M $MgCl_2$ if the salt is completely ionized?

To measure out samples each containing 1 g of NaOH, what volume of 0.2M NaOH would you use?

Expressing Concentrations of Solutions **217**

Normality

A normal solution is defined as one containing a **gram equivalent weight** of solute per liter of solution. To understand the importance of this we must understand the concept of **equivalent weights.** Let us limit ourselves for the time being to considering only solutions of solutes that dissolve as ions. An equivalent weight of any ion is the weight of one mole divided by the charge on the ion. An equivalent weight of any compound that dissolves as ions is the weight of one mole, divided by the total positive *or* negative charges on ions formed from one formula unit of the compound. An equivalent weight of a metal that forms ions is the weight of one mole divided by the charge on the ions it forms.

For example, HCl dissolves as H^+ and Cl^- ions. The charge on each ion is one. The equivalent weight of hydrogen ion is the same as the weight of one mole of hydrogen ions. This is 1 g, the same as the weight of one mole of hydrogen atoms, because the tiny mass contributed by the electron can be neglected. Similarly, the equivalent weight of chloride ion is the same as the weight of one mole of chloride ions: 35.5 g. The equivalent weight of hydrogen chloride is 36.5 g. Magnesium chloride ($MgCl_2$) dissolves as Mg^{++} ions and Cl^- ions. One mole of $MgCl_2$ obviously would give one mole of magnesium ions and two moles of chloride ions. But one equivalent weight of magnesium is the weight of one mole divided by the charge on the ion (2), or 12 g (24 g/2). One mole of magnesium chloride therefore contains two equivalent weights. One equivalent weight must be half the weight of one mole, or 47.5 g. Similarly, aluminum forms the tripositive ion, Al^{+++}. One mole of aluminum weighs 27 g. One equivalent weight of aluminum is one-third of this or 9 g.

The purpose of equivalent weights is to identify *chemical* equivalence. In reactions where electrons are supplied by metals, the equivalent weight of a metal is that weight which will supply one mole of electrons. One mole of sodium will supply one mole of electrons, so one mole and one equivalent weight of sodium are the same quantity. One mole of magnesium will supply two moles of electrons. The amount to supply one mole of electrons is therefore half a mole or one equivalent weight, 12 g. One mole of aluminum will supply three moles of electrons, so one-third of a mole of aluminum is all that is required to provide one mole of electrons. As suppliers of electrons, therefore, 23 g of sodium, 12 g of magnesium, and 9 g of aluminum are all exactly equivalent to one another. The amount of chlorine, oxygen, or other nonmetal that is required to react with each of these amounts of metal is one equivalent weight. For instance, oxygen tends to acquire two electrons, so its equivalent weight is half a mole of atoms, or 8 g. An equivalent weight of oxygen is exactly enough to react with an equivalent weight of a metal. The 8 g of oxygen will react with 23 g of sodium to form Na_2O, or with 12 g of magnesium to form MgO, or with 9 g of aluminum to form Al_2O_3.

The most familiar application of equivalent weights to solution chemistry is in expressing the concentrations of acids, of which the characteristic species is the hydrogen ion, H^+. An amount of acid that can produce one mole of hydrogen ions is called an equivalent weight of that acid. Some acids produce one mole of hydrogen ions per mole of acid, some two moles of hydrogen ions, some three. For example, hydrochloric acid (HCl) furnishes one mole of hydrogen ions per mole of acid; sulfuric acid (H_2SO_4) produces two; and phosphoric acid (H_3PO_4) produces three. A one-molar solution of hydrochloric acid would not, therefore, have the same acidity as a one molar-solution of sulfuric acid or a one-molar solution of phosphoric acid. But if the solution concentrations are expressed in *normality,* then one molar HCl is also one normal (1 *N*), but one molar H_2SO_4 is 2 *N*, and one molar H_3PO_4 is 3 *N*. Correspondingly, a 1 *N* solution of sulfuric acid contains one-half mole of H_2SO_4 per liter of solution. A 1 *N* solution of phosphoric acid contains one-third mole of H_3PO_4 per liter of solution. The equivalence lies in the fact that one liter of any 1 *N* acid provides the same quantity of H^+ ions, 1 g.

Although this may seem unduly confusing at this point, when you become more familiar with solution chemistry, you will appreciate that although you could get along without expressing solution concentrations in normality by just using molarity, the idea of normality can be quite useful.

> How many grams of solute are there in 10-ml samples of each of the following solutions: 0.02*N* HCl, 0.4*N* $ZnCl_2$; 6*N* H_2SO_4; 3*N* H_3PO_4.

DISSOLUTION EQUILIBRIUM

The process of dissolution is a reversible one. Let us again use a sodium chloride solution as an example. As the concentration of hydrated sodium and chloride ions increases, the probability increases that their movement through the solvent will bring them close to any undissolved remainder of their original crystal. When they return to the crystal, they may rejoin it, shedding their covering of water molecules. The rate of dissolution will not be greatly affected. It probably slows somewhat as the immediate environment at the surface of the crystal begins to show a decreased concentration of water molecules, but the rate of recrystallization will certainly increase as the concentration of dissolved solute increases. When the rate of recrystallization becomes equal to the rate of dissolution, no further net change in solution concentration can occur. The processes continue indefinitely, another example of physical equilibrium.

It has long been debated whether dissolution is a physical or a chemical process and whether this equilibrium should be called physical or chemical. No doubt the process of dissolution is partly chemical, but removal of the solvent ordinarily leaves the solute as it was before it dissolved. The action is therefore usually thought of as essentially physical, although many examples do exist of a solute dissolving through chemical change, such that evaporation of the solvent cannot serve to recover the original solute. This is definitely

chemical dissolution. If the solute can be recovered by evaporating the solvent, we will call the dissolution physical.

The concentration of solute in a solution that equals the concentration at equilibrium is called the **solubility** of the solute. A solution that contains this equilibrium concentration is called a **saturated solution.** If the solution contains less than that concentration, no undissolved solute can be present without further dissolution occurring. The solution is called **unsaturated.** Perhaps surprisingly, a solution can also be **supersaturated,** having a higher concentration of solute than would be possible at equilibrium. Such supersaturated solutions can be prepared by taking advantage of the fact that temperature usually changes the solubility. Often, but not always, an increase in temperature corresponds to a large increase in solubility.

A saturated solution is prepared at a temperature where the solubility is high. If the clear solution, freed of undissolved crystals, is allowed to cool carefully, it may reach a temperature where the solubility would be much less, without depositing its excess solute.

The reason this is possible is that crystallization cannot easily start just by two ions coming together. There must be some nucleus upon which the new crystal can begin to build. It may be a speck of dust, or a tiny scratch on the surface of the container. Best of all, a tiny crystal of the same material may deliberately be added to help the crystallization along. The cooled solution is now supersaturated, but this is a highly unstable situation. **Precipitation** can be initiated by dropping in a small crystal of solute substance, stirring vigorously, or even by rubbing the stirring rod against the edge of the container. Precipitation is the formation of solid by crystallization out of solution. Once it begins, the supersaturated solution quickly becomes a saturated solution as the excess solute rapidly crystallizes. In the process the mixture becomes warmer because heat is given out by the formation of the crystal and the more stable saturated solution.

Imagine that someone handed you a clear liquid in a beaker, told you it was a solution of salt A, and asked you to determine whether any more of A could be dissolved. When you dropped in a crystal of A to find out, instead of it dissolving, a large mass of crystals appeared. Explain.

PHYSICAL PROPERTIES OF SOLUTIONS

Melting Point

One effect of dissolving a solute in a solvent is to dilute the solvent. Any properties of the solvent that depend on the concentration of its molecules will therefore be affected by the presence of a solute. The properties of a liquid that are usually of most interest are melting point, volatility, and boiling point. The melting point is the temperature at which solid and liquid phases are at equilibrium. In other words, the liquid phase must be returning to the solid phase exactly as fast as the solid is transforming to liquid. Let us consider the cooling of a dilute solution until crystals appear. If the cooling has not lowered the solubility of the solute so much that it begins to precipitate, the crystals will be of pure solvent.

If we isolate this system of pure solid solvent with solution and examine it, we find that the solvent molecules are not as highly concentrated in the solution as they are in pure solvent. Therefore, the rate at which they can crystallize is reduced from what it would be in pure solvent. If melting occurs at the same speed as when no solute was present, and recrystallization is slowed, melting must be occurring more rapidly than recrystallization. This state of affairs cannot exist very long before all the crystals have melted. But what we did was cool the solution until crystals appeared—in other words, until the rate of melting was slowed to that of recrystallization. Therefore the temperature, if equilibrium exists, must be lower than that of the equilibrium involving only pure solvent. In other words, **the freezing point, or melting point, of the solvent is lowered by the presence of the solute.**

Perhaps this may be clarified by a little different explanation of the situation. Suppose we prepare an ice and water mixture in a flask insulated so that it is isolated from its surroundings. Equilibrium is soon attained. Water molecules from the pure liquid are joining the ice crystals at exactly the same rate as molecules from the ice are becoming liquid. Now, without allowing any heat exchange with the environment, we drop in a little solute. It dissolves. It dilutes the solvent, slowing the rate of recrystallization. But nothing has happened to the rate of melting, so it remains the same; it must now be greater than the rate of recrystallization. Therefore, the ice begins to disappear, for it is melting faster than it is forming. Remember, however, that melting is an endothermic process. In order to go on melting, the ice must receive energy from somewhere. The result is that the mixture grows colder as it gives up heat to the melting ice. As the ice-and-solution mixture cools, the rate of melting is slowed, until it reaches a new equilibrium with the rate of recrystallization now being equal. But this must be at a lower temperature than before. **The melting point of the solution is lower than that of the pure solvent.**

As will be discussed below, this has important scientific applications. It also has very practical application in removing layers of ice from streets and sidewalks. A thin layer of liquid water on the surface of the ice is enough to dissolve the salt that is strewn upon it. This lowers the temperature at which crystallization can occur, and the ice melts.

Vapor Tension and Boiling Point

In a system of liquid in equilibrium with its vapor, the vapor tension is the equilibrium vapor pressure corresponding to equal rates of vaporization and liquefaction. The rate of liquefaction is proportional to the concentration of the molecules in the vapor. The rate of vaporization is proportional to the concentration of the molecules in the liquid. Introduction of a solute decreases the concentration of the liquid, thus slowing its rate of vaporization. For the moment, equilibrium is upset while vapor becomes liquid faster than liquid becomes vapor. But this reduces the concentration of vapor until a new equilibrium is reached. **A solute lowers the vapor tension of the solvent.**

If a solute lowers the vapor tension of the solvent at any given temperature, and the boiling point is defined as the temperature at which the vapor tension equals one atmosphere, then the solute must raise the boiling point by making a higher temperature necessary in order to reach the same vapor tension. **A solute reduces the vapor tension of a solvent and elevates its boiling point.**

What could you predict about the boiling point of an aqueous solution that freezes below 0°C?

Molal Quantities

In reasonably dilute solutions, the effects of solutes on the melting point, vapor tension, and boiling point of a solvent are found to be dependent only on the *concentration of particles* of solute. They are independent of the nature of the particles. A solution containing one mole of *particles* in 1000 g of solvent is called a **one molal** solution. In a given solvent, all one molal solutions have identical physical properties. That is, they melt at the same temperature and boil at the same temperature. For each solvent these temperatures are unique. For water, the melting point of a one molal solution is $-1.86°C$. Its boiling point is $100.52°C$. The difference between the melting point of the pure solvent and that of the one molal solution is called the **molal freezing point depression.** The difference between the boiling point of the solution and the boiling point of the pure solvent is called the **molal boiling point elevation.** These quantities are characteristic properties of each liquid compound that can act as a solvent.

Electrolytes and Nonelectrolytes

Notice above that the molal effects on physical properties were said to depend on the number of moles of "particles." This was deliberate, for the number of particles is not always the same as the number of formula units. Normally we would describe the molality of a solution in terms of the number of moles, according to the formula of the solute, per 1000 grams of solvent. But a substance like NaCl gives two particles, a sodium ion and a chloride ion, for each formula unit dissolved. $MgCl_2$ gives three particles, one magnesium ion and two chloride ions per formula unit. Since the effect on solvent properties is the effect of particle concentration, a one molal solution of sodium chloride would be equivalent to a two molal solution of particles. A one molal solution of magnesium chloride would be equivalent to a three molal solution of particles.

Two broad classes of compounds are recognized with respect to their effects on the solvent. One consists of those for which one mole of solute gives one mole of particles in solution, the other consists of those for which one mole of solute gives more than one mole of particles in solution, and, therefore, abnormally affects the properties of the solvent.

Study of the electrical properties of these different classes of solutions shows that they could similarly be classified in terms of their ability to conduct an electric current. The type that gives abnormally large effects is found to conduct an electric current well. The type that gives normal effects does not conduct an electric current appreciably. The former are called **electrolytes** and the latter **nonelectrolytes.** Many substances are **weak electrolytes** conducting an electric current only feebly. Putting these classifications together, we recognize that ions give to a solution the ability to conduct the electric current, and also have an abnormally great effect on solvent properties.

HOW MOLECULAR WEIGHTS OF NONVOLATILE COMPOUNDS CAN BE DETERMINED

The method of determining molecular weights from vapor or gas density has already been described. It is applicable only to those substances volatile enough to produce an easily measurable vapor under convenient experimental conditions. Preferably the substance has a vapor tension of at least a few torr at 25°C. But many compounds exist that are only volatile at high temperatures. Some even decompose at low temperatures before developing appreciable vapor tension. For these, this method of molecular weight determination is inadequate. However, almost all molecular compounds, unless their molecules are extremely large, will dissolve in some liquid. Chemists can make use of one or more of their effects on the physical properties of that liquid to determine the molecular weight.

The molality of any solution made by dissolving a weighed amount of an unknown compound into a weighed amount of solvent is equal to the ratio of the observed freezing point depression or boiling point elevation to the depression or elevation for a *one* molal quantity. For example, the molal freezing point depression for benzene (C_6H_6) as solvent is 5.12°C. Benzene freezes at 5.50°C. If a benzene solution freezes at 2.94°C, the depression is 5.50 − 2.94 or 2.56°. The ratio of this to 5.12° is 2.56/5.12 or 0.500. From this the molality of the solution is known to be 0.500. Then, from the weights of solute and solvent in the solution used for melting point determination, it is easy to compute the weight of solute that would correspond to 1000 grams of solvent. If this is also 0.50 mole, then the molecular weight is found simply by multiplying by 2.

This method is subject to the same limitations that affect the change in physical properties of the solvent by the solute. Namely, the observed effects depend on the concentration of *particles*. One should keep in mind that this method determines only the *apparent* molecular weight of the species present in solution. The solute may be dissolved as ions. If so, the apparent molecular weight would only be the average of the formula weights of the separate ions. The solute may be present as molecules that are dimeric or otherwise polymerized in the solvent. Or, the solvent may have depolymerized the solute on dissolution. For example, in some solvents, aluminum chloride has an apparent molecular weight corresponding to Al_2Cl_6, and in others, $AlCl_3$. But in most applications, a molecular compound will dissolve as the same kind of molecules that make up its crystalline form. Careful chemists are usually aware of the possibilities for error or of being misled. They usually have some idea of what the unknown compound is likely to be and how it is likely to behave in the particular solvent. Table 19.1 lists some typical molal freezing and boiling point constants.

Table 19.1.   Some Molal Freezing and Boiling Point Constants (°C)

Solvent	Freezing point	Lowering	Boiling point	Elevation
benzene	5.50	5.12	80.1	2.53
acetic acid	16.7	3.9	118.5	3.07
camphor	180	40	208.3	6.0
carbon tetrachloride	−22.9	30	76.5	5.02
cyclohexane	6.5	20	80.9	2.79
water	0.0	1.86	100.0	0.52

Example 19.1.   *An unknown crystalline solid has been purified so that it melts sharply and appears to be a pure compound. To determine its molecular weight, a sample weighing 0.345 g is dissolved in 10 g of camphor.* (Notice that this particular solvent, an organic compound containing carbon, hydrogen, and oxygen, is a solid that must be heated above its melting point before it will dissolve the solute readily.) *The melting point of the solution is found to be 170°. What is the molecular weight?*

The melting point is 10° below that of pure camphor, so the depression, or *lowering,* is 10°. From Table 19.1, the molal lowering is 40°, so the molality of the solution must be 10/40 or 0.25. Now, if 10 g of camphor contains 0.345 g of unknown compound, how much would 1000 g of camphor contain? Evidently 100 times as much, or 34.5 g. We now have the information that 34.5 g = 0.25 mole, from which, 1.0 mole = 4 × 34.5 g or 138 g. Therefore the molecular weight of the unknown compound is 138.

Example 19.2.   *A sample of compound X weighing 0.16 g is dissolved in 5.42 g of cyclohexane, and the solution is found to boil at 81.5°C. What is the molecular weight of X?*

First, we note that pure cyclohexane boils at 80.9°, so the elevation observed is 81.5 − 80.9 = 0.6°. The molal elevation is 2.79°. Therefore the molality of the prepared solution must be 0.6/2.79 or 0.22.

Now, if 5.42 g of solvent contains 0.16 g of solute, what would 1000 g of solvent contain?

$$\frac{1000}{5.42} \times 0.16 = 29.5 \text{ g of solute}$$

Finally, if 29.5 g of the compound X is 0.22 mole, how much is one mole? $29.5/0.22 = 134$ g; so the molecular weight is 134.

Test Your Memory

1. Distinguish between *solute* and *solvent*.
2. What is meant by *partially miscible?*
3. What is *dissolution?*
4. What cohesive forces are involved in the dissolution process, and how?
5. Name two main types of compounds that may be soluble in water.
6. What is *entropy?*
7. Define *mole fraction.*
8. How are *molarity* and *molality* different?
9. Define *normality.*
10. What is the equivalent weight of magnesium and how does this differ from one mole?
11. Define *solubility.*
12. What is meant by a *saturated solution?*
13. How can a *supersaturated* solution be possible?
14. How might one initiate precipitation from a supersaturated solution?
15. How does the presence of a solute affect the melting point of a liquid? Why?
16. Why should a solute change the vapor tension of a liquid?
17. Define *molal freezing point depression.*
18. What determines whether an electrolyte is called weak or strong?
19. What kinds of substances are nonelectrolytes?
20. How would you proceed to determine the molecular weight of a compound that is nonvolatile?

Test Your Understanding

1. Name three pairs of liquids that you believe to be immiscible. Would you know offhand if they were partially miscible?
2. Explain why water can sometimes dissolve a salt.
3. What quality of compounds containing OH groups appears to aid their solubility in water?
4. Why are gasoline and water immiscible?
5. Calculate the mole fractions of a solution of sulfuric acid that contains 50 weight per cent water.
6. A solution that is $2M$ in HNO_3 has how many grams of HNO_3 per liter?
7. To what volume would you have to dilute a liter of $10M$ solution of ethyl alcohol to reduce its concentration to $2M?$

8. What is the molarity of chloride ion in a solution that is 0.004 M in $AlCl_3$?

9. What is the normality of each of the following: 0.05 M H_2SO_4; 0.135 M HCl; 1.64 M H_3PO_4?

10. What are the final molarities of each ion when 400 ml of $3M$ H_2SO_4 is diluted to one liter?

11. What would be the molarity of a solution made by dissolving 20 g sugar ($C_{12}H_{22}O_{11}$) in a volume of 2 liters?

12. a) What is the molality of a solution of 20 g sugar in 2 liters of water?
    b) What is the melting point of this solution?

13. What is the molecular weight of a compound if a solution of 0.0500 g in 6.50 g benzene boils at 82.2°C?

20

THE NATURE OF CHEMICAL CHANGE

ELECTRICAL BASIS OF CHEMICAL CHANGE

What is chemical change? It is any process in which the kind and/or number of chemical bonds changes. Perhaps the first thing we wish to know about it is *why* it occurs. We also want to know how a chemical change occurs, and under what conditions. These are apparently simple questions, but the answers are complex, subtle, and indeed not wholly attainable within our present state of knowledge.

Our understanding would presumably be helped tremendously if we knew why opposite charges attract and like charges repel, for these properties of electrical charge are at the heart of chemical change. Being only human, however, we shall never be able to achieve the ultimate in understanding anything. The facts of electrical charge interactions are experimentally established. We may have confidence in their reliability even though we may never fully understand why they occur. So let us accept these properties of electrical charges as the fundamental basis upon which to build some understanding of the nature of chemical change.

THE INFLUENCE OF BOND ENERGY

Throughout Nature there is a tendency for forces to balance one another. Systems tend to become stable by losing as much energy as possible. A stable system is one of relatively low energy. An apple, when its stem breaks loose in the wind, speedily adjusts its position to greater stability by moving as close to the center of gravity of the earth as is possible. So two atoms, each possessing effective positive charge at their surface, are drawn together by the mutual attraction of these charges for the negative charges of the electrons of the other atom. It takes energy to lift up the apple to its original position on the tree above the ground. It takes energy to separate the two atoms from their closely bonded position.

Since electronegativity is a measure of the attraction which an atom can exert on outside electrons, atoms of high electronegativity should strongly influence chemical change. Since chemical bonds are more stable with increasing polarity, highly electronegative atoms tend to form the most polar bonds possible. This means that they will favor bonding with atoms that offer the lowest resistance to electron removal. The chemical changes most likely to occur are those that will produce the greatest evolution of energy, thereby forming the most stable compounds.

Another property that can influence chemical change is the tendency toward the result with highest probability. Chemical change tends to occur not only in the direction of forming the strongest chemical bonds, but also in the direction of highest probability. In the absence of other factors, the most probable state is the one of greatest disorder or randomness. The degree of randomness is measured as the **entropy** of the system. We will not consider entropy effects in detail in this book, but it is important to realize that bond energies are not solely responsible for the direction of chemical change. At ordinary temperatures, however, entropy effects are usually quite small. Therefore, as a rough approximation, **chemical change can be expected to occur in the direction of forming the strongest bonds possible.** Another way of saying this is to say that of all possible reactions, the most exothermic one will tend to be favored.

MECHANISMS OF REACTION AND REACTION RATES

No matter how favored a certain chemical change may seem to be by the energy of the reactants compared to that of the products, no change will occur unless some reasonable mechanical means for the reaction is available. Fluorine can form much stronger bonds to sodium than to sulfur. Yet when it is already combined with sulfur in SF_6, the fluorine fails to react with molten sodium. Hydrogen and oxygen can react very vigorously to form water with the release of a large amount of heat. Yet hydrogen gas and oxygen gas may be mixed together and allowed to stand for years without reaction. As the gasoline in your automobile tank is consumed, air takes its place. The gasoline and oxygen of the air become thoroughly mixed by the agitation of driving on rough roads. Nevertheless, no appreciable reaction occurs within the gas tank. The act of joining to other atoms to form a molecule of a compound or an element seems to protect any atom from further chemical attack. It does this by covering up its most reactive position, an originally vacant or half-filled orbital.

Reagents consisting entirely of single, gaseous atoms, could react rapidly upon collision, if the reaction energy could be dissipated. But ordinarily all reagents are already chemical combinations of atoms, either of the same element, as in H_2, or in compounds. **Before new bonds can form,** as required for chemical change, **old bonds must break.** Since these bonds were all created with the evolution of energy, they require energy absorption before they can be broken.

Remember that at any given temperature, all molecules do not have exactly the same amount of energy. At any given instant, the energy is distributed unevenly. Most of the molecules have an average energy corresponding to the observed temperature, but a few have much less, at that instant, and a few have much more. Sometimes enough of the molecules have a sufficiently higher-than-average energy to permit a reaction to start spontaneously the instant the reactants come into contact. In such cases, all that is necessary to promote a chemical change is to let the reactants come together, and the reaction will begin at once. It may even occur explosively fast. For most reactions, however, some means of providing the reagents with extra energy is necessary if a chemical change is to occur.

Activation Energy

This extra energy for initiating a chemical reaction is called the **activation energy.** It can be supplied by heat, electrical spark or discharge, or various

Figure 20.1. Reaction Energy Diagram.

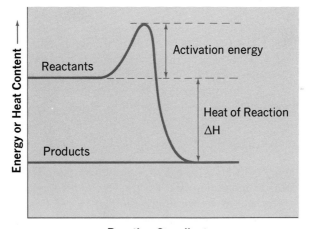

Reaction Coordinate

Represented here is an exothermic reaction requiring a considerable activation energy. Since the heat content of the products is lower than that of the reactants, heat must be *evolved* when reactants form products. This is the heat of reaction; it is assigned a negative sign.

The fundamental significance of a negative heat of reaction is that on the average the bonds are stronger in the products than in the reactants. Reactions tend to occur in the direction of forming stronger bonds. First, however, the old bonds must be broken, which helps explain the need of activation energy.

related sources of energy, such as sunlight. If the reaction being sought is exothermic after it begins, the initiation of the reaction at a single point is all that is necessary. As soon as the reaction begins, it evolves enough energy to activate the remaining reagent. The reaction proceeds without further outside help. Sometimes, however, the energy released by a reaction is insufficient for the reaction to become self-sustaining. A continuous supply of energy from an outside source must be supplied. For instance, it might prove necessary to maintain the reaction mixture at a certain high temperature to keep the reaction going—like baking bread in an oven. Or perhaps it must be continuously irradiated with an ultraviolet lamp, depending on the nature of the activation process required.

Reaction Mechanisms and Rates

One of the simplest of reaction mechanisms, other than the simple joining of two individual atoms or molecules, is represented by the hypothetical interaction of A_2 and B_2 to form $2AB$. We assume that if A_2 is heated with B_2 in the vapor state, they may react with one another to form AB according to the equation:

$$A_2 + B_2 \rightarrow 2\ AB$$

The rate of the reaction depends on the rate of collision between A_2 molecules and B_2 molecules. Only a small percentage of the total collisions are effective in bringing about a reaction. The rate of collision between reagent molecules must be directly proportional to their concentrations. Both concentrations are equally important. A **rate equation** can be written in which S_1 is the speed or rate of the forward reaction in the equation as written above:

$$S_1 = k_1\ [A_2]\ [B_2]$$

The proportionality constant k_1 is called the **rate constant.** The concentrations of atomic, ionic, or molecular species are represented by the appropriate symbols within brackets as shown. Since the rate of reaction here is proportional to both the concentration of A_2 molecules and the concentration of B_2 molecules, it is proportional to their product.

If the compound AB is heated to the same temperature, some of it forms A_2 and B_2:

$$2\ AB \rightarrow A_2 + B_2$$

The rate of this reaction, S_2, can be expressed as above, only changing the reactants and products appropriately:

$$S_2 = k_2[AB][AB] = k_2[AB]^2$$

Notice that the concentration of AB occurs twice. The reason for this is that an AB molecule does not fly apart to atoms all by itself. Two AB molecules must collide before the A_2 molecule and B_2 molecule can be formed. Squaring the concentration of AB is therefore merely multiplying the concentration of one kind of molecule times the concentration of the other kind of molecule, as before, except that this time one kind happens to be the same as the other kind.

The mechanism of this reaction is assumed to involve the formation of an **activated complex** when two molecules collide under the right conditions:

$$A_2 + B_2 \rightleftharpoons \begin{Bmatrix} AB \\ AB \end{Bmatrix} \rightleftharpoons 2\,AB$$

The activated complex is a very unstable association of two A atoms with two B atoms. It decomposes rapidly either to give A_2 and B_2 or to give two AB. The reaction between A_2 and B_2 is thus reversible, and the reaction equation could have been written:

$$A_2 + B_2 \rightleftharpoons 2\,AB$$

Consider initiating the reaction with only A_2 gas and B_2 gas present. The rate of formation of AB must at the beginning be at a maximum since only at the beginning are maximum concentrations of the reactants present. As soon as any AB forms, some of the A_2 and the B_2 are used up, reducing their concentrations and, therefore, slowing their rate of combination. The more AB, the lower the concentration of the remaining A_2 and B_2 and the slower the forward reaction.

Now, what of the reverse reaction? Initially it could not occur, because the concentration of AB was zero. But, as soon as some AB formed, it became possible to reform A_2 and B_2. The rate of forming A_2 and B_2 increased as the concentration of AB increased. We therefore must consider, in the same system, two opposing reactions occurring simultaneously. One begins at maximum speed and slows down. The other begins at zero speed and speeds up. The two speeds cannot possibly pass one another. As soon as they become equal, no further net changes in the concentrations of any of the components of the system can occur. The system has achieved **chemical equilibrium.**

When the two speeds have become equal, then:

$$S_1 = k_1[A_2][B_2] = S_2 = k_2[AB]^2$$

or, in terms of the equilibrium constant, $K = k_1/k_2$,

$$\frac{k_1}{k_2} = K = \frac{[AB]^2}{[A_2][B_2]}$$

EQUILIBRIUM CONSTANTS

Equilibrium Expressions

The system described above is said to be at chemical equilibrium because the two *opposite* chemical changes are occurring simultaneously at exactly the *same speed*. The ratio of the rate constants for the forward and reverse reactions, K, is called the equilibrium constant for the reaction written as shown above. For the reverse reaction, the constant would be $1/K$. The activation energy in this reaction is the energy necessary for the creation of the activated complex.

Equilibrium constants for all chemical reactions that are reversible can be expressed in the same way, but this does not mean that the reaction mechanisms are the same. In fact, very few reaction mechanisms are as simple as that described above. For the general equation,

$$aA + bB \rightleftharpoons cC + dD + eE$$

where a is the number of moles of reagent A, and so on, the equilibrium constant at a given temperature can be written:

$$K = \frac{[C]^c[D]^d[E]^e}{[A]^a[B]^b}$$

The **equilibrium constant** for a chemical reaction at any given temperature is equal to the product of the concentrations of the products, each raised to a power corresponding to the number of moles of it appearing in the equation, divided by the product of the concentrations of the reagents, each raised to a power corresponding to the number of moles of it appearing in the equation. This is a perfectly general expression, independent of the mechanisms of the various steps by which the overall reaction may occur.

Of what use is an equilibrium constant? Its numerical value tells us whether, when equilibrium is reached, a good yield of products is obtained. If the value is greater than one, the yield is good. If it is much larger, the reaction as written must go almost to completion, with excellent yields. (**Yield** is a term used to describe the extent to which reactants are converted to products.) If the value of the equilibrium constant is much smaller than one, the extent of the reaction as written is quite slight. Special means must be applied to obtaining good yields of products. The form of the equilibrium expression suggests what can be done to improve the yield at equilibrium. By increasing the concentration of either of the reactants we can speed the forward reaction, requiring the concentrations of products to increase also in order to maintain the equilibrium constant. The attainment of equilibrium can be prevented by removing one or more products as fast as they form, thereby forcing the reaction to go to completion from left to right even though the equilibrium constant has a very small value.

The concentration of a gas is measured by its pressure. In fact, when all the reactants and products are gaseous, we can write equilibrium constant expressions using only pressures for concentrations. Gas pressure can easily be varied. Therefore, gas concentrations are variable and belong in the equilibrium expression. But what about pure liquids and solids? How can their concentrations be changed? Remember, concentration means number of component units per unit *volume*. The only way the concentration of a solid or liquid reagent can be changed is to change its density. Neither solids nor liquids are readily compressible; even under tremendous pressures their volumes diminish only a little. Thus, except possibly under very extraordinary conditions, and certainly for all reactions carried out at ordinary atmospheric pressure, the concentrations of solids and liquids do not change. There is no point in including them in the equilibrium constant expression. If, however, the reaction is being carried out with one or more of the reactants dissolved in a solvent, the concentration of the solution is variable from zero to the limit of the solubility in that solvent. Under these conditions, the concentration of a liquid or solid can be changed if it is a dissolved solute that is participating in the reaction. In aqueous solutions, ions are usually the reactive species. The concentrations of the ions can frequently be varied within rather wide limits. The concentrations of liquid or solid reactant should certainly be included in the equilibrium expression if they are in solution and therefore variable.

Let us consider a few examples of reversible reactions for which we might write an expression for the equilibrium constant.

Example 20.1. $2 SO_2 + O_2 \rightleftharpoons 2 SO_3$

All the components of this system are gases, so we would write,

$$K = \frac{[SO_3]^2}{[SO_2]^2[O_2]} \quad \text{or} \quad K = \frac{p^2_{SO_3}}{p^2_{SO_2} p_{O_2}}$$

Example 20.2. $CaCO_3 \rightleftharpoons CaO + CO_2$

Here calcium carbonate ($CaCO_3$) is a solid. So is calcium oxide (CaO). The only component of this system whose concentration can be varied is carbon dioxide gas (CO_2). Therefore, the equilibrium constant is simply the concentration of carbon dioxide:

$$K = [CO_2], \quad \text{or} \quad K = p_{CO_2} \quad \text{where } p \text{ is the pressure of } CO_2.$$

Example 20.3. $NH_3 + HCl \rightleftharpoons NH_4Cl$

Here ammonia and hydrogen chloride are gases but ammonium chloride is a solid. (The smoke formed by a reaction between ammonia and hydrogen chloride gases is a suspension of very finely divided solid in the air.) For this reaction,

$$K = \frac{1}{[NH_3][HCl]}$$

Example 20.4. $CO_3^= + H_2O \rightleftharpoons HCO_3^- + OH^-$

This reaction takes place among species all in aqueous solution. Ordinarily in such reactions the water is present in an overwhelming surplus, since it is the solvent and the other reactants are relatively dilute. For this reason, the concentration of water is not considered changed or changeable, and it is left out of the equilibrium expression:

$$K = \frac{[HCO_3^-][OH^-]}{[CO_3^=]}$$

Chapter 24 discusses in detail some of the chemistry of solutions. The subject of equilibrium constants will be reconsidered there.

Write equilibrium constant expressions for each of the following: $H_2 + Cl_2 \rightleftharpoons 2 HCl$; $CaO + H_2O(g) \rightleftharpoons Ca(OH)_2$; $N_2 + 3 H_2 \rightleftharpoons 2 NH_3$

LE CHATELIER'S PRINCIPLE

When systems at dynamic equilibrium are placed under some stress that tends to upset the equilibrium, the system becomes altered in the direction of absorbing or counteracting the stress. This is a statement of the famous principle of Henry Louis Le Chatelier (1850–1936), who devised this practical rule long before our present knowledge of chemical equilibria was available. It is extremely useful because it tells us what to expect of a system at chemical or physical equilibrium when some stress is placed upon it. This in turn gives us some idea of what kind of stress to use on a system to make it behave in a certain way.

For instance, what will be the effect of increasing the pressure on a reaction system? If the system does not include gaseous components, no effect will be observed, except under special circumstances where enormous pressures are brought to bear to influence a reaction of liquids or solids. If one or more of the reactants or products is gaseous, an increase in pressure will have the effect of increasing the rate of reaction of the gases. If the total number of moles of gas is the same on both sides of the chemical equation, both the forward and reverse speeds will be increased by the same amount by the increase in pressure. No net effect on the equilibrium will be observed. But if the number of moles of gas on one side of the equation is less than that on the other side, Le Chatelier's principle tells us that the reaction that relieves the excess pressure will be favored. Since this can be done by reducing the number of gaseous molecules, the reaction in the direction producing the fewer gas molecules is favored. A familiar example is the synthesis of ammonia from nitrogen and hydrogen:

$$N_2 + 3 H_2 \rightleftharpoons 2 NH_3$$

As the equation is written, four moles of gas form two. An increase in pressure therefore gives better yields of ammonia at equilibrium.

What about the thermal decomposition of limestone? Here the equilibrium constant is the same as the pressure of carbon dioxide, so its value is variable with the pressure. Elevating the pressure results in more rapid reverse reaction until the pressure is reduced to its equilibrium value again. Once more Le Chatelier's principle helps us predict that the reaction causing the disappearance of gaseous molecules would be favored by the increase, or attempted increase, in pressure.

What is the effect of increasing the temperature? An equilibrium constant is constant only at a constant temperature. Its value will be changed by a change in temperature. But in what direction? Remember that every reaction involves a change in energy content. Therefore, a reversible reaction will be exothermic in one direction but endothermic in the opposite direction. Le Chatelier's principle tells us that if we try to raise the temperature of a system at chemical equilibrium, the system would react in the direction of resisting that temperature increase. This it can do by absorbing the heat as potential rather than kinetic energy. In other words, **the endothermic reaction is favored by any elevation of the reaction temperature.** If the reaction equation is written in the exothermic direction, the new equilibrium constant will be smaller. The decomposition of limestone is clearly endothermic. Therefore, better yields of decomposition products are expected at higher temperatures. But the synthesis of ammonia is exothermic. Higher temperatures here would only favor its decomposition, giving poorer yields.

The effects of changing concentration also can be predicted by applying Le Chatelier's principle. Any attempt to change the concentration of any component will be opposed by the system. If we try to decrease the concentration of a component, the reaction that increases it will be favored. If the concentration is increased, the reaction that uses it up to form products is favored.

By gaining a thorough understanding of chemical systems at equilibrium, and by applying Le Chatelier's principle, industrial chemical manufacturers have been able to develop important processes which would have been unsuccessful because of poor yields of products had the processes not been modified by this understanding.

OTHER REACTION MECHANISMS

As previously noted, the synthesis of AB, as described above, is an exceptionally simple reaction mechanism. Most reactions occur through much more complicated mechanisms, many of which are imperfectly understood or completely undetermined. The probability of three molecules colliding in exactly the right way at exactly the same moment, while not impossible, is *much* less than that of two molecules colliding. But what about those chemical reactions for which several molecules of one reactant must encounter several molecules of another reactant? What is the probability that these could all meet at the same time? Practically zero. Yet we know that such reactions proceed, and often at a rapid rate. Studies of reaction rates which make up the important branch of physical chemistry known as **kinetics,** show that reactions described by relatively complicated chemical equations actually occur by a succession of separate steps.

If one of these steps is much slower than the rest, this step is then essentially the **rate determining step.** It is the bottleneck in the stepwise reaction, for which all the subsequent steps must wait, even though once beyond this step they may be able to react extremely rapidly. The study of kinetics yields much interesting information about chemical reactions. If interpreted accurately, which is not always easy, such information can suggest how the reactions may proceed. The form of the mathematical expression telling how the rate changes as one of the components is used up depends somewhat on the reaction mechanism. It can suggest reasonable pathways for the reaction to follow.

A fairly common general type of reaction mechanism is the **free radical** mechanism, usually involving a **chain reaction.** A free radical is an atom or a group of atoms with one half-filled orbital not involved in bonding. Such a species is usually very short-lived because it is so reactive, but it is crucial to many chemical reactions. A single atom of an active element can be regarded as a free radical, because it too tends to react rapidly. One might think that the reaction of hydrogen with chlorine could proceed in the fashion described for the hypothetical reaction of A_2 with B_2. However, although two equations may look similar and the products may be similar, the mechanisms may be altogether different. This is true here. Chlorine (Cl_2) is capable of absorbing visible radiation such as sunlight, and thus of acquiring enough energy to atomize its diatomic molecules:

$$Cl_2 + h\nu \rightarrow 2\ Cl$$

The quantum of light absorbed is $h\nu$, h being Planck's constant and ν the frequency of the light absorbed.

In a mixture of H_2 and Cl_2, no reaction occurs until sunlight enters. Then an explosion is likely, with the evolution of considerable heat and the formation of HCl. The reaction is believed to follow a course such as this:

$$Cl_2 \rightarrow 2\ Cl$$

$$Cl + H_2 \rightarrow HCl + H$$

$$H + Cl_2 \rightarrow HCl + Cl,\ \text{etc.}$$

Thus the absorption of a single quantum of energy can initiate a whole chain of reactions leading to the formation of many molecules of hydrogen chloride. The chain would be broken, of course, and thus terminated, if any of the intermediate free radicals (single atoms) should encounter another of its own kind to form the diatomic molecule again. This is more likely to occur at the wall of the container where atoms of the container can absorb the energy released by the formation of the diatomic molecule. Two single atoms would have a difficult time uniting without the presence of a third party to absorb at least part of the energy of their union. In the absence of such a third party, the diatomic molecule would hold enough energy to decompose itself again.

CATALYSIS

Two types of substances, classified according to their probable modes of action, can sometimes serve to increase a reaction rate. One type usually acts in the same phase with the reactants and is therefore called a **homogeneous catalyst.** The other type, called a **heterogeneous catalyst,** usually acts through certain sites on its surface, which is in a different phase from the reactants. The exact means by which a catalyst affects the rate of a reaction is usually unknown. Presumably a homogeneous catalyst forms some kind of intermediate chemical complex, with one or more of the reactants, that lowers the activation energy requirement for the reaction, thus speeding it along. For example, the catalyst might permit the reaction to proceed by a mechanism requiring less activation energy but giving the same final products.

A heterogeneous catalyst, often called a **contact catalyst,** uses its residual valence forces at certain sites on the surface to **adsorb** the reactants. By holding them to its surface in such a way as to render them more vulnerable to chemical attack, it thus reduces the activation energy requirement. In any case, a catalyst helps in the uncoupling of old bonds and the formation of new ones, but it is equally helpful in both reaction directions. Therefore, **a catalyst does not improve the yield of a reaction. It merely speeds the rate of attainment of equilibrium.** This in itself is a great help. For example, although the magnitude of the equilibrium constant for the synthesis of ammonia indicates that excellent yields of ammonia are to be expected at $25°C$, we would probably wait forever for equilibrium to be reached at that temperature. A catalyst is indispensable for persuading the very stable nitrogen molecules to atomize and combine with hydrogen. Even with a catalyst, elevated temperatures are needed in this instance to raise the rate of reaching equilibrium. Although this is essential, it is not ideal. The equilibrium yield is smaller at the higher temperatures, since the synthesis of ammonia is exothermic.

Substances that slow reactions are called **negative catalysts** or **inhibitors.** Often they are most effective in slowing chain reactions, for they usually operate in a self-sacrificing manner. For example, oxygen tends to react with automobile engine oil in an undesirable manner, forming oxidation products that are corrosive or form harmful deposits on metal surfaces. This oxidation is slow and seems to occur by chain mechanisms. If the chain can be stopped before it goes very far, all the oil molecules that might have become oxidized as the chain proceeded are spared from reaction. A very small quantity of an easily oxidizable substance that is soluble in the oil can serve as an **oxidation inhibitor.** Each molecule of this inhibitor can effectively stop one chain by combining with the active species that propagates the chain. This renders both the propagator and the inhibitor inactive. However, because a single chain reaction can account for a large number of oxidized oil molecules, relatively few inhibitor molecules can serve to prevent a large amount of oxidation.

Test Your Memory

1. a) What two factors have major influence on the direction of chemical change?
    b) Which is more important under ordinary conditions?
2. Define *activation energy*.
3. To what is the speed of a chemical change proportional?
4. What is an *activated complex?*
5. Write the expression for the equilibrium constant for the synthesis of hydrogen iodide.
6. What kinds of substances can be changed in concentration?
7. State *Le Chatelier's principle*.
8. What is meant by *kinetics?*
9. What is the *rate determining step?*
10. a) What is a *free radical?*
    b) How may it become involved in a chain reaction?
    c) Write equations for a chain reaction.
11. How does a container wall sometimes function in a chemical reaction?
12. a) Distinguish between homogeneous and heterogeneous catalysis.
    b) What is a *contact catalyst?*
13. How might an oxidation inhibitor work?

Test Your Understanding

1. At ordinary temperatures, carbon tetrachloride (CCl_4) is quite an un-reactive compound, yet in principle it should hydrolyze readily to form CO_2 and HCl. Account for this difference between practice and principle.
2. How would you explain the fact that gasoline burns in an automobile engine but not in the gasoline tank? How could you cause it to burn in the latter? What would prevent its burning in the engine?
3. Why does the reaction between A_2 and B_2 not go to completion?
4. Write equilibrium constant expressions for each of the following reactions:
    a) Nitrogen plus hydrogen form ammonia.
    b) Calcium hydroxide loses water when heated, to become calcium oxide.

c) NO_2 forms N_2O_4, both gaseous.

d) The burning of hydrogen forms steam.

e) The reaction between hot coke and steam forms hydrogen and carbon monoxide.

5. How would the reaction in question 4(c) be affected by an increase in the external pressure?

6. How would temperature changes affect the yield of hydrogen from decomposing steam by heat?

Part 3

Chemical Properties

21

OXYGEN, WATER, AND OTHER OXIDES

COMBUSTION AND THE ROLE OF OXYGEN

By far the most abundant element at the surface of the earth is oxygen. Out of every hundred atoms, 53 are of oxygen, and they make up nearly half the total mass. One fifth of the atmosphere is oxygen gas (O_2) with traces of ozone (O_3), in the upper atmosphere where it helps to shield us from the ultraviolet radiation of the sun. Combustion in its most familiar form is the combination of other elements with oxygen. In its most spectacular form of fire and flame, combustion has been frightening, comforting, exciting, destructive, cleansing, and indispensable to mankind since the beginning of history. Yet its true chemical nature has only been recognized since about the time of the American Revolution, probably because of the invisible and therefore mysterious nature of gases.

An ingenious explanation of burning was devised by a German chemist and physician named Georg Ernest Stahl (1660–1734). He invented a strange, invisible something he called **phlogiston,** from a Greek word meaning *to set on fire*. According to his scheme, materials able to be burned were rich in phlogiston, whereas incombustible materials had none. Burning, he proposed, was simply the release of phlogiston into the air. Removal of all the phlogiston from a piece of wood would leave only its ashes. Stahl did have the insight to recognize a similarity between active burning and the rusting of metal. He ascribed the latter process to the loss of phlogiston by the metal to the air. The formation of free metal by heating its ore with carbon was then explained as the result of phlogiston passing from the carbon, which contains lots of it, to the ore, which contains none of it. This transfer changes the ore into metal which is now phlogiston-rich and the carbon into phlogiston-poor ash.

To us today it seems extraordinary that although a grievous discrepancy in this theory was discovered, it was not considered important enough to discredit the theory. The discrepancy was that although the ashes left behind when wood burns weigh much less than the original wood, a fact attributed to the loss of phlogiston, the metals *gain* weight by rusting, a process which also was claimed to involve a loss of phlogiston. This could only be true if phlogiston had a *negative* weight. Aside from being somewhat fantastic, this would be inconsistent with the results observed on burning wood. With the passion of the modern scientist for accurate measurement and consistent results, it is almost impossible to understand how the phlogiston theory could have been accepted as universally as it was by chemists and other intelligent scholars and scientists of that day.

The first thing that had to be accomplished to dispel the ignorance of the phlogiston theory was the discovery of oxygen. Oxygen was discovered in 1771 by Karl Wilhelm Scheele (1742–1786), a Swedish chemist, and in 1774 by an English clergyman named Joseph Priestley (1733–1804), whose great hobby was chemistry. But in those days as now, credit for a discovery is usually accorded to him who first publishes his results. Scheele's publisher was exceedingly slow, failing to print Scheele's report on oxygen until 1777. Consequently, Priestley is usually credited with this important discovery.

Priestley prepared oxygen by heating the red powder we know as mercuric oxide (HgO) with the aid of a large magnifying glass (burning glass). He discovered that mice could live in a limited supply of it much longer than in the same amount of air. He also found, to his great excitement, that burning is much more vigorous in the new gas than in air. These experiments failed to enlighten Priestley concerning the true nature of combustion, but fortunately he was destined soon to describe his experiments to someone much better able to interpret them.

This person was Antoine Lavoisier, (1743–1794), a brilliant French scientist who has become known as the father of modern chemistry. Recognizing the nature of combustion as the combination of matter with oxygen in the air, Lavoisier carried out many quantitative experiments demonstrating the truth of his conclusions. His work resulted in the eventual overthrow of the phlogiston theory, although its many partisans were most reluctant to change their views. Joseph Priestley himself clung to the phlogiston theory. Thirty years after his discovery of oxygen and its ability to support combustion, he died still a staunch supporter of the old and discredited theory.

A Russian chemist named Mikhail V. Lomonosov (1711–1765) appears to have rejected the phlogiston theory nearly twenty years before the work of Lavoisier, correctly suggesting that combustion involves combination with a part of the air. Even today scientific communication is imperfect, but in those days it was much worse. Lomonosov's work was published in Russian and unavailable to the scientists of western Europe who therefore could only proceed on their own, in complete ignorance of what had been done elsewhere.

Lavoisier's great contribution, other than setting straight the ideas of combustion, was to emphasize the vital importance of quantitative measurements in chemical research. He would no doubt have continued to make outstanding contributions had he not been selected, in the prime of his life, for decapitation by the zealous patriots of the French Revolution.

PREPARATION OF OXYGEN

The methods of preparing oxygen today include the one used by Priestley, although a Bunsen burner usually replaces the burning lens. In the laboratory it is very convenient to prepare small quantities of pure oxygen gas by heating mercuric oxide:

$$2 \, HgO \rightarrow 2 \, Hg + O_2$$

The reason this works is that mercury atoms characteristically form relatively weak bonds easily broken by heat. Consequently the stability imparted by a strong double bond between the two oxygen atoms in O_2 (119 kcal per mole) favors the oxygen's leaving its weak union with mercury when heat is provided.

Among all the chemical elements, **oxygen is second only to fluorine in its high electronegativity.** Consequently it tends to attract electrons from all the other active elements except fluorine, forming polar bonds in which the oxygen is partially negative. The strength of these bonds tends to increase with increasing polarity. Therefore, the weakest bonds to oxygen, those most easily broken by heat, occur in compounds having only slightly polar bonds, in which oxygen has not acquired a very high negative charge because of the competition offered by other oxygen atoms or because of the high electronegativity of the other elements. Consistent with this reasoning, oxygen gas can also be liberated by heating such compounds as potassium chlorate ($KClO_3$), sodium nitrate ($NaNO_3$), or potassium permanganate ($KMnO_4$):

$$2 \, KClO_3 \rightarrow 2 \, KCl + 3 \, O_2$$

$$2 \, NaNO_3 \rightarrow 2 \, NaNO_2 + O_2$$

$$2 \, KMnO_4 \rightarrow K_2MnO_4 + MnO_2 + O_2$$

Oxygen can also be prepared by decomposing water by electricity, as will be described in Chapter 25. For industrial use, it is separated from the air by liquefaction followed by fractional distillation. Nitrogen boils at $-196°C$, thirteen degrees lower than oxygen at $-183°C$, and can be distilled away, leaving the oxygen. Enormous quantities are prepared in this way for use in the iron and steel industry and as an oxidant in rocket propulsion.

WATER

If we were forced to the impossible task of choosing the single most important compound on earth, we would probably choose water. Water is indispensable for all life as we know it. It is the medium in which most biological processes occur. It is an excellent solvent for many inorganic as well as organic compounds. Water is tremendously important in weather and in geological processes. It is also a great help in swimming and boating, and on a hot summer day there is nothing quite like a good cold drink of it.

The properties of water, like the properties of all other compounds, are the inevitable consequence of the special qualities of the atoms that compose it. It was Henry Cavendish (1731–1810), a shy and eccentric English millionaire, who discovered that water is formed by the combustion of hydrogen. Let us review what we know of hydrogen and oxygen, to see what should be expected of their combination. Then we can compare our predictions with the observed facts.

First, consider the hydrogen atom. With its single electron in the $1s$ orbital, it clearly has the capacity to form only one single covalent bond. With its half-filled outer shell, it, like other elements with half-filled outermost shells, has an electronegativity that is intermediate among all the elements but a little above the median. We expect hydrogen to be univalent, reasonably resistant to the removal of its electron, and moderately able to attract electronic charge from other atoms.

Oxygen atoms have the electronic configuration represented by 2-6. This we interpret as meaning that the first principal quantum shell is filled with two electrons. In the second principal quantum shell there must be two electrons in the $2s$ orbital and four electrons in the $2p$ orbitals. The three p orbitals, like any other set of orbitals of equal energy, tend to be filled with one electron per orbital until pairing becomes absolutely necessary. Therefore two of the oxygen's $2p$ orbitals will be singly occupied; the third necessarily accommodates a pair of electrons. We recognize here the capacity to form two single covalent bonds, using these two half-filled orbitals. Because of the presence of electron pairs in the other two outer-shell orbitals of oxygen, these two half-filled orbitals must form an angle of approximately 109°. Next to fluorine, oxygen has the highest electronegativity of all the elements, tending in almost all its compounds to acquire partial negative charge.

From this much knowledge of the nature of hydrogen and oxygen atoms, there is little difficulty in predicting what should happen when they come together. Each oxygen atom can form a covalent bond to each of two hydrogen atoms. The bond angle should be approximately 109°, giving a molecule of bent structure and of formula H_2O. The greater electronegativity of oxygen must result in polarity in these covalent bonds to hydrogen. The oxygen becomes partially negative at the expense of the hydrogen which is left partially positive. The intermediate electronegativity of the hydrogen, however, limits the polarity of these bonds. Each hydrogen atom can be calculated to bear a partial positive charge of 0.12. The oxygen atom correspondingly bears a partial negative charge of -0.25. On the basis of this charge distribution and the observed bond lengths, the atomization energy of water has been calculated to consist of a covalent contribution of 100 and an ionic contribution of 124 kcal per mole, for a total of 224. A relatively high dipole moment (product of charge and distance of separation) is expected.

Figure 21.1. Predictions of Water and Its Properties.

What is an atom of hydrogen like?
With one half-filled orbital, it can form one covalent bond. Its electronegativity is 2.31.

What is an atom of oxygen like?
With two outer-shell lone pairs and two half-filled orbitals, it can form two covalent bonds. Its electronegativity is 3.46.

What should their compounds be like?
The formula must be H_2O. The two lone pairs of electrons on the oxygen should repel the bonding pairs, leading to a bond angle between the two O-H bonds near to the tetrahedral angle of $109°28'$. The more electronegative oxygen should become partially negative at the expense of the two hydrogen atoms which would be left partially positive.

What is water like?
It has a formula of H_2O, as predicted. The bond angle is $104.5°$, a little smaller than predicted because the two lone pairs repel more effectively than the two bonding pairs of electrons, which are therefore forced a little closer together.

The bonds are indeed polar: oxygen bears a partial negative charge of -0.25, and the hydrogens each bear a partial positive charge of $+0.12$.

What else might easily be predicted about water?
It has a negative side and a positive side, and therefore should have a dipole moment. It does—about 1.84 Debye units. With small, negative oxygen and positive hydrogen, it should associate through protonic bridging. It does, causing melting and boiling points higher than otherwise expected. With lone pairs on negative oxygen, water should be able to coordinate as an electron donor. It does, forming thousands of complexes.

The properties of water are the inevitable and logical consequence of the qualities of the hydrogen and oxygen atoms which compose it. In general, all properties of all substances are similarly derived. This is the fundamental basis of the **science** of chemistry.

246 Oxygen, Water, and Other Oxides

If we now consider the facts about water derived experimentally, we find that it consists of molecules of formula H_2O. The bond angle between the two OH bonds is $104.5°$. These molecules are polar with a dipole moment of about 1.84 **Debye units** (number of charges × charge on an electron × distance of separation in Å). The experimental atomization energy of water is 222 kcal per mole, indicating an average bond energy of 111 compared to the calculated value of 112 kcal per mole. Thus, on the basis of a relatively simple picture of the behavior of hydrogen and oxygen atoms, we have achieved a rather remarkable understanding of the compound water.

What else might be predicted about water? From the presence of two lone pairs of electrons on each oxygen, plus the partial negative charge, we can recognize the ability of a water molecule to act as an electron donor in coordinate covalent bonds to acceptor ions or molecules. The formation of hydrates is thus explained. The positively charged hydrogen atoms are seen to have the necessary characteristic to attract an electron pair from another molecule to form a protonic bridge. The water molecule would therefore seem capable of becoming bridged to four other water molecules, at the corners of a tetrahedron. Two protonic bridges would be formed by its two protonic hydrogen atoms, and the other two by its two lone pairs of electrons. If enough of the kinetic energy were removed from water, then, it should become joined together in a tetrahedral structure.

This is, in fact, the structure of ice. But in the packing together of molecules or atoms or any type of particle, a coordination number of four does not represent the closest possible packing. Such a structure must therefore be relatively open. If it were to begin to collapse, closer packing could be achieved. Water has long been observed to have the unusual property of expanding when it freezes, and it contracts when it melts, until the temperature becomes high enough to cause thermal expansion. The expansion of water as it freezes is an important property. The expansion within cracks and fissures of rocks contributes to their weathering and structural breakdown. Ice has a lower density than water, causing it to form on top of a body of water instead of at its bottom. This is very convenient for ice skaters. The fish appreciate this property of water, too. Although unusual, like the other properties of water its density is explained by a sufficient knowledge of the properties of the component atoms.

As our study of chemistry proceeds we will find that, in general, the behavior and properties of water are quite consistent with what we can predict from what we know about its atoms. This is also true of all other compounds. All properties, physical and chemical, of all compounds are a reflection of the condition of the combined atoms. In turn this is the inevitable consequence of the inherent nature of the atoms before combination. Chemists do not yet understand in detail all the interrelationships between the structure of atoms and the properties of their compounds. The closer they approach such an understanding, the more completely the science of chemistry unfolds.

The Ionization of Water

By ordinary standards water is a nonelectrolyte. It cannot conduct an electrical current easily, if it is pure. However, impurities are often present in water as ions, and ions in effect conduct electrons through a liquid. Impure water is a much better conductor. Even in the very purest water, however, a few ions occur; they originate when protons transfer from one oxygen to another within the water. This kind of transfer is quite an improbable one and happens relatively infrequently. Yet, as we shall see, it is very significant in the chemistry of aqueous solutions. When a proton leaves one water molecule to join another, it leaves its original electron behind, giving the rest of the water molecule a negative charge and imparting its own positive charge to the neutral water molecule it joins. This process thus results in two ions:

$$H_2O + H_2O \rightleftharpoons H_3O^+ + OH^-$$

This process is called **self-ionization** or **auto-ionization.**

Figure 21.2. Ionization of Water.

There is **no** reason for a proton (a hydrogen ion, H^+) to separate spontaneously from a hydroxide ion (OH^-) for the two species are very strongly attracted to one another: $H^+ + OH^- \rightarrow H_2O$.

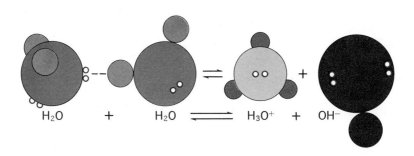

$$H_2O \quad + \quad H_2O \rightleftharpoons H_3O^+ \quad + \quad OH^-$$

Occasionally, however, a proton from one water molecule can become attached to a lone pair of electrons on the oxygen atom of another water molecule, as shown above.

Note the large changes in partial charge which this involves. In the hydronium ion, H_3O^+, H is more positive than in water, but the oxygen, being less negative, can no longer donate its remaining electron lone pair. In the hydroxide ion, OH^-, H is not protonic, but the oxygen is much more negative than in water and its lone pairs are very readily donated to electron acceptors such as H^+. Consequently, H_3O^+ and OH^- can coexist in the same solution only when separated by water molecules.

As soon as they meet, the hydroxide oxygen takes a proton from the hydronium ion, forming two water molecules. This reverse of the ionization of water is called *neutralization.*

248 Oxygen, Water, and Other Oxides

Many authors describe the ionization of water by the equation:
$$H_2O \rightleftharpoons H^+ + OH^-$$
Does this make sense to you? Why or why not?

If we calculate the partial charges on the hydrogen in the **hydronium ion** (H_3O^+), we find the charge on hydrogen to be 0.35 and that on oxygen to be -0.06. For the **hydroxide ion** (OH^-) the charge on oxygen is -0.64 and the charge on hydrogen, -0.36. Compare these with those on water itself: -0.25 on oxygen and 0.12 on hydrogen. How different is the condition of these atoms in the different ions and molecule! The hydronium ion and the hydroxide ion are quite the opposite of one another, and the water molecule is intermediate. The differences in charge make the oxygen of the hydroxide ion an excellent donor, the oxygen of water a good donor, and the oxygen of the hydronium ion no donor at all. The very positive hydrogen of the hydronium ion gives it the power of attracting electrons, which is much greater than the power of hydrogen on water to attract electrons. The negative hydroxide ion cannot attract electrons at all.

Two such opposite species as the hydronium ion and the hydroxide ion might be expected to react at once if they met. Indeed they do. The reaction is exactly the reverse of the ionization equation:

$$H_3O^+ + OH^- \rightarrow 2H_2O$$

If this reaction occurs readily, then how can the ions form in the first place? Although we do not know exactly, we do know that they appear to become separated from one another quickly enough to build up small but significant concentrations. These reach their maximum when the rate of recombination equals the rate of formation. At this equilibrium the concentration of each kind of ion equals 10^{-7} mole per liter. More than 550 million water molecules exist in this solution for every pair of ions. This is why water is not a good electrical conductor. Since the concentration of water is not changed by any significant amount in this auto-ionization process, we leave it out of the equilibrium expression, and simply write an ion product:

$$K = [H_3O^+] [OH^-] = 10^{-7} \times 10^{-7} = 10^{-14}$$

The really significant part of the hydronium ion is the extra proton. Often this is written simply as the hydrogen ion, H^+, with the understanding that such an ion could not exist free in water. It must be hydrated since the bare proton would certainly attach itself to any available pair of electrons. In fact, some chemists object to calling the ion "hydronium" with formula H_3O^+, because this ion would be further hydrated. The lone pair of electrons on the oxygen would hardly be available to form a protonic bridge because of the low negative charge on this oxygen. However, the three protonic hydrogen atoms could easily form bridges to three other water molecules, leading to a tetrahydrated hydrogen ion. Experimental evidence for this has been found. Certainly the hydrogen ion cannot exist in water unhydrated. The hydronium

Figure 21.3. Hydronium Trihydrate.

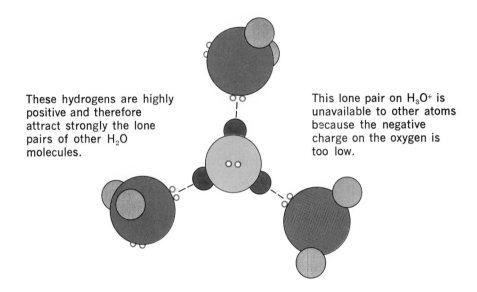

These hydrogens are highly positive and therefore attract strongly the lone pairs of other H_2O molecules.

This lone pair on H_3O^+ is unavailable to other atoms because the negative charge on the oxygen is too low.

A hydronium ion readily forms three protonic bridges to water, producing a **trihydrate.** In other words, the proton, H^+, is tetrahydrated. However, the first water molecule, forming H_3O^+, is by far the most firmly bound.

ion represents the initial stage of hydration. It has exactly the same concentration whether it is called "hydrogen ion" or "hydronium ion" or "tetrahydrated hydrogen ion." From here on, unless there is some special reason for doing otherwise, if we speak of the **hydrogen ion,** or represent it as H^+, the hydration is simply being assumed without being specified.

Aqueous Acids and Bases

There are many compounds which when placed in water provide a source of either hydrogen ions or hydroxide ions. It is therefore possible to prepare solutions in water which have concentrations of hydrogen ion much larger than 10^{-7} mole per liter. These range up to several moles per liter. The characteristic properties of such solutions are found to be those of the **hydrogen ion.** They have a **sharp or sour taste,** tend to **corrode the more reactive metals, dissolve metal oxides,** and they **cause characteristic color changes to occur in certain dyes called indicators.** Such solutions are formed, for example, when hydrogen chloride gas (HCl) dissolves in water:

$$HCl + H_2O \rightarrow H_3O^+ + Cl^-$$

Here is an example of the dissolution of a gas by chemical reaction with water. Thus, it becomes much more soluble than gases normally are. Aqueous solutions in which the hydrogen ion concentration is greater than 10^{-7} mole per liter are called **acidic.** The substance that provides the hydrogen for the hydrogen ion formation is called an **acid.** Here the solution is called hydrochloric acid.

It is also possible to prepare solutions in water which have concentrations of hydroxide ions that are greater than 10^{-7} mole per liter. Certain metal hydroxides will dissolve in water, forming solutions containing their ions:

$$NaOH \rightarrow Na^+ + OH^-$$

Sodium hydroxide is very soluble in water. It can therefore furnish a high concentration of hydroxide ions. An aqueous solution containing more than 10^{-7} mole of hydroxide ion per liter is called a **base** or an **alkali.** Their characteristic properties are those of the **hydroxide ions.** These cause the solution to **taste flat and bitter,** to have a **soapy feel, to absorb carbon dioxide gas,** and **to cause indicator dyes to change color from that imparted by acids.** In general, basic solutions are *very* different from acidic solutions.

It is impossible to increase simultaneously the concentrations of both hydrogen ions and hydroxide ions in water. **The ion product equilibrium constant of pure water is the same for all aqueous solutions.** If we were to increase the hydrogen ion concentration of water by adding hydrogen chloride, the probability of hydrogen ion finding hydroxide ion would also increase. Equilibrium would be momentarily upset as the rate of hydrogen and hydroxide ions forming water exceeded the rate at which the water ionized. But as this combining proceeded, it would reduce the hydroxide ion concentration to well below the original 10^{-7} mole per liter present in pure water. Finally, even with the large excess of hydrogen ion present, the chance of encounter between hydrogen ion and hydroxide ion once more would equal the chance of water ionizing. In the acidic solution at the new equilibrium, the hydrogen ion concentration would be far higher than in pure water and the hydroxide ion concentration far lower, yet their product would remain exactly the same at 10^{-14}.

Similarly, if a source of hydroxide ions were added to pure water, the equilibrium in the water would be momentarily upset. The probability of encounter between hydrogen ions and the now much more numerous hydroxide ions would be momentarily increased. As the hydroxide ions reacted with hydrogen ions to form water, the concentration of hydrogen ions would be reduced far below their concentration in pure water. The hydrogen ions would become so scarce that despite the abundance of hydroxide ions, the rate of combination would again equal the rate of ionization of the water. In the basic

Figure 21.4. The Ion Product of Water.

There is just as good a chance of an encounter between hydronium and hydroxide ions whether there are

6 H⁺ and 1 OH⁻
$6 \times 1 = 6$

or

3 H⁺ and 2 OH⁻
$3 \times 2 = 6$

or

2 H⁺ and 3 OH⁻
$2 \times 3 = 6$

or

1 H⁺ and 6 OH⁻
$1 \times 6 = 6$

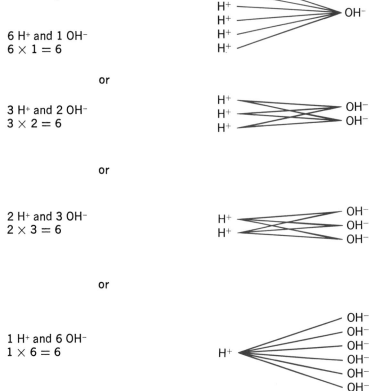

Therefore at equilibrium the H⁺ and OH⁻ ion concentrations may vary over a wide range, subject only to the requirement that the PRODUCT of their concentrations at 25°C must remain constant.

$$[H^+][OH^-] = 10^{-14} \qquad [H^+][OH^-] = 10^{-14} \qquad [H^+][OH^-] = 10^{-14}$$

solution at the new equilibrium, the hydroxide ion concentration far exceeds that in pure water, but the hydrogen ion concentration is much lower.

Therefore, no solution can simultaneously be both strongly acidic and strongly basic. The acid ions and the basic ions react with one another, forming neutral water. This reaction is called **neutralization.** One of the most important characteristics of acids and bases is that they neutralize each other:

$$H_3O^+ + OH^- \rightarrow 2H_2O$$

When an aqueous acid and an aqueous base are mixed together, they neutralize one another, forming water, but the metal ion of the base and the nonmetal ion of the acid remain uninvolved in the neutralization. Ions that appear merely to be bystanders while their partners undergo a reaction are called **spectator ions.** In the neutralization reaction, the reaction of hydrogen and hydroxide ions leaves the spectator ions in the solution. If the solvent were then removed, they would crystallize out as a **salt.** For example, if a sample of hydrochloric acid is neutralized by a sample of sodium hydroxide in exactly the correct amount to neutralize the acid, with no acid or base left over, the solution would then contain nothing but water, sodium ions, and chloride ions (plus the ions of water in their normal low concentrations). The number of chloride ions would exactly equal the number of sodium ions. An identical solution could have been formed by simply dissolving the appropriate amount of sodium chloride in water. This would also give us sodium and chloride ions in equal numbers, and water.

The neutralization of an aqueous acid by an aqueous base can be described as a process forming water and a salt.

> What salt would result from the neutralization of sulfuric acid by calcium hydroxide? From phosphoric acid by sodium hydroxide?

METAL OXIDES

As a class of elements, metals are characterized by having not only fewer low-energy, outer-shell electrons than vacancies, but also a relatively weak hold on those electrons. That is, they tend to be relatively low in electronegativity. In the competition that occurs when they come in contact with oxygen, the oxygen is usually able to become quite highly negative at the expense of the metal. Oxygen therefore readily combines with most metals. The simplest molecules, through coordination of vacant orbitals of the metal with lone pairs on oxygen, polymerize to stable solids held together by highly polar bonds. The partial charge on oxygen depends on the electronegativity of the metal and also on the relative numbers of atoms of metal and oxygen. Whenever several different oxides of the same metallic element are known, the oxygen is more negative the fewer there are other oxygen atoms with which it must compete. Consequently, it is most negative in the oxide having the highest metal-to-oxygen ratio and least negative in the oxides with the lowest metal-to-oxygen ratio. As we shall see, the properties vary accordingly.

The most characteristic property of negatively charged oxygen is that of being basic. In one sense that means tending to form hydroxide ions in water:

$$O^= + H_2O \rightarrow 2OH^-$$

A more general meaning of **basic** is, having ability to act as an **electron pair donor.** This is the principal characteristic of negative oxygen or of a hydroxide ion. When a hydroxide ion acts as a base to neutralize a hydrogen ion, it acts as a donor to take on the proton as acceptor. The properties of basicity and acidity are closely related to the properties of electron donating and electron accepting. Indeed it is often convenient to classify such properties together. Any oxide of a metal in which the oxygen atom has acquired a fairly high negative charge will usually be basic. When such an oxide comes in contact with water, the water can donate a proton to it, whereupon the hydroxide ion that is left can join also to the metal. For instance, calcium is a metal of low electronegativity, which allows the oxygen in CaO to acquire a high negative charge. When calcium oxide (commonly known as **quicklime**) encounters water, it acquires one proton from the water and also acquires the hydroxide ion which results, forming the hydroxide $Ca(OH)_2$ (commonly known as **slaked lime**).

$$CaO + H_2O \rightarrow Ca(OH)_2$$

Calcium hydroxide readily releases hydroxide ions in water solution. It is therefore known as a strong base.

Notice that here water appears to resemble an acid, in that it provides a proton to a base. In fact, since water ionizes to give ions characteristic of both acid and base, it can be regarded as both acidic and basic. Substances capable of reacting both as acid and as base are called **amphoteric.** They are only weakly acidic and weakly basic, but can react either way. Toward a strong acid they are basic, and toward a strong base, acidic.

If metal oxides are basic, they can be expected to neutralize acids and form salts. Indeed they do. The following equations give some representative examples:

$$CaO + H_2SO_4 \rightarrow CaSO_4 + H_2O$$

$$CaO + 2\ HCl \rightarrow CaCl_2 + H_2O$$

$$3\ CaO + 2\ H_3PO_4 \rightarrow Ca_3(PO_4)_2 + 3\ H_2O$$

$$CaO + 2\ HNO_3 \rightarrow Ca(NO_3)_2 + H_2O$$

Table 21.1 lists some of the more important metal oxides and their acid-base properties. Notice that being a metal oxide is not enough to ensure basicity.

Table 21.1. Some Metal Oxides and Their Acid-Base Properties

Na_2O	strongly basic
CaO	strongly basic
ZnO	amphoteric
Al_2O_3	amphoteric
MnO_2	amphoteric
CrO_3	strongly acidic
Mn_2O_7	strongly acidic

If the competition among oxygen atoms is too strong, no one oxygen atom may become very negative. In this case the oxide may be weakly basic or not basic at all. Also, if the metal is not very low in electronegativity, the oxygen may not be able to acquire a very high basicity. We shall consider some more information about metal oxides after we have learned something about non-metal oxides.

NONMETAL OXIDES

Nonmetals are characterized by their smaller, more compact atoms of higher electronegativity. The number of outer-shell electrons is at least equal to, and usually exceeds the number of low-lying orbital vacancies. Oxygen forms many compounds by combining with nonmetals. Nonmetal oxides, as a class, are quite different, indeed almost opposite, from metal oxides. In these compounds the high electronegativity of the other nonmetal prevents oxygen atoms from acquiring a very large partial negative charge. The bonds are much less polar, and therefore not as strong. Furthermore, the presence of electrons in all the orbitals not involved in the bonding prevents the kind of coordination or condensation that is typical of the metal oxides. Most nonmetal oxides tend to be molecular and relatively volatile. Some polymeric nonmetal oxides occur but most of these tend to break up into smaller molecules rather easily.

Nonmetal oxides take on water to become hydroxy compounds, much as metal oxides do. There is an important difference, however, in that nonmetal hydroxy compounds are formed by water acting as base instead of acid. That is, the negative oxygen on the water molecule donates an electron pair to the nonmetal oxide. Next, one of its protons finds a more stable position on the oxygen atom of the oxide. For example:

$$SO_3 + H_2O \rightarrow H_2SO_4 \ [O_2S(OH)_2]$$
$$N_2O_5 + H_2O \rightarrow 2 \ HNO_3 \ (O_2NOH)$$
$$P_4O_{10} + 6 \ H_2O \rightarrow 4 \ H_3PO_4 \ [OP(OH)_3]$$

The hydroxides that are formed by action of water on nonmetal oxides are acidic, as are the nonmetal oxides themselves. One would expect such oxides to neutralize bases, which they do. Some representative examples are given by the following equations:

$$SO_3 + 2 \ NaOH \rightarrow Na_2SO_4 + H_2O$$
$$CO_2 + 2 \ NaOH \rightarrow Na_2CO_3 + H_2O$$
$$N_2O_5 + 2 \ NaOH \rightarrow 2 \ NaNO_3 + H_2O$$
$$P_4O_{10} + 12 \ NaOH \rightarrow 4 \ Na_3PO_4 + 6 \ H_2O$$

Table 21.2 lists some typical nonmetal oxides and their acid-base properties.

N_2O_5	strongly acidic
SO_3	strongly acidic
CO_2	weakly acidic
P_4O_{10}	moderately acidic
Cl_2O	very weakly acidic
Cl_2O_7	strongly acidic
SO_2	weakly acidic

Table 21.2. Some Nonmetal Oxides and Their Acid-Base Properties

ACID AND BASE ANHYDRIDES AND NEUTRALIZATION

An oxide that adds water to form a basic hydroxide is called a **base anhydride.** This means simply, the remainder of the base after the components of water have been removed. The oxide of sodium, Na_2O, is the anhydride of NaOH, because removal of H_2O from 2 NaOH leaves Na_2O, and because addition of water to Na_2O forms 2NaOH. The oxide of calcium, CaO, is the anhydride of calcium hydroxide, $Ca(OH)_2$.

An oxide that adds water to form an acidic hydroxide is called an **acid anhydride.** SO_3 is the acid anhydride of sulfuric acid (H_2SO_4). HNO_3 is

Figure 21.5. Comparison Between the Condition of Oxygen and Its Effects on Properties of Metal Oxides and Nonmetal Oxides.

Oxygen in a metal oxide tends to be larger and quite negative. The oxide tends to be a nonmolecular solid, stable to heat. The relatively high negative charge on oxygen makes it basic and ordinarily nonoxidizing. A metal oxide tends to react with nonmetal oxides to form oxyacid salts.

Oxygen in a nonmetal oxide tends to be smaller and only slightly negative. The oxide tends to be unstable to heat, molecular, and a volatile liquid or gas. The relatively low negative charge on oxygen leaves it strongly oxidizing and acidic, and the molecule may act as an electron pair acceptor. A nonmetal oxide tends to react with metal oxides to form oxyacid salts.

formed when water is added to N_2O_5, the acid anhydride of nitric acid. P_4O_{10} is the acid anhydride of phosphoric acid (H_3PO_4).

Notice that gradually the concept of acids and bases has been broadening. If acid and base anhydrides are included, then neutralization can include reactions in which no water is formed, but an acidic oxide joins with a basic oxide to form a neutral salt. The following reactions are all of essentially the same nature:

$$CaO + SO_3 \rightarrow CaSO_4$$
$$CaO + H_2SO_4 \rightarrow CaSO_4 + H_2O$$
$$Ca(OH)_2 + SO_3 \rightarrow CaSO_4 + H_2O$$
$$Ca(OH)_2 + H_2SO_4 \rightarrow CaSO_4 + 2\,H_2O$$

List some compounds, solutions of which might be used to absorb (a) CO_2, (b) NH_3 from the air.

AMPHOTERIC ANHYDRIDES

Certain oxides, such as ZnO, Al_2O_3, and water, which was discussed earlier, form hydroxides that can act either as acid or base. Such oxides, as well as their corresponding hydroxides, are called **amphoteric** oxides and hydroxides. The following reactions may be written:

$$ZnO + SO_3 \rightarrow ZnSO_4$$
$$Zn(OH)_2 + SO_3 \rightarrow ZnSO_4 + H_2O$$
$$ZnO + H_2SO_4 \rightarrow ZnSO_4 + H_2O$$
$$Zn(OH)_2 + H_2SO_4 \rightarrow ZnSO_4 + 2\,H_2O$$

These are examples of zinc oxide and hydroxide functioning as bases. With strong bases, however, they can function as acids:

$$ZnO + Na_2O \rightarrow Na_2ZnO_2$$
$$ZnO + 2\,NaOH \rightarrow Na_2ZnO_2 + H_2O$$
$$Zn(OH)_2 + Na_2O \rightarrow Na_2ZnO_2 + H_2O$$
$$Zn(OH)_2 + 2\,NaOH \rightarrow Na_2ZnO_2 + 2\,H_2O$$

CAUSES OF ACID-BASE PROPERTIES OF OXIDES AND HYDROXIDES

An old and respectable rule about oxides is that metal oxides tend to be basic and nonmetal oxides tend to be acidic. This is a fairly reliable generalization, but there are numerous exceptions. Some metal oxides are acidic, while some nonmetal oxides show weakly basic properties. But the rule would be much more meaningful if based on fundamental principles.

Causes of Acid-Base Properties of Oxides and Hydroxides **257**

The fundamental basis for this rule has already been suggested. In oxides where oxygen has been able to acquire a fairly high partial negative charge, the oxygen is able to share its electron pairs as a donor to a proton or any other appropriate acceptor. It neutralizes an acid by acquiring its protons, forming water. But when the partial negative charge on oxygen is not very large, its ability to act as an electron pair donor becomes much smaller while at the same time the atom to which the oxygen is attached becomes more effective as an electron pair acceptor. Thus the trend, with decreasing partial negative charge on oxygen in oxides, is from strongly basic properties toward amphoteric—weakly basic and weakly acidic—properties and then toward stronger acidic properties. Since this trend corresponds to that from active metal to active nonmetal, we find that metal oxides tend to be basic because their oxygen is highly negative. Nonmetal oxides tend to be acidic because their oxygen is not very negative.

We can compare the polarity of the bond between oxygen and hydrogen with that between oxygen and the other element, E, in the hydroxide E-O-H. Since the oxygen and hydrogen atoms remain the same, any differences among the hydroxides must arise from the nature of E. If E is of low electronegativity, the oxygen will acquire fairly high negative charge from it, and the hydrogen will be more nearly neutral. But if E is of high electronegativity, the oxygen will not acquire much negative charge from it, so it will withdraw more charge from the hydrogen, which becomes more positive.

In order for E-O-H to ionize in solution, polar bonds must become ionic. In order for hydroxide ions to be formed, the O-H must remove an electron completely from E. In order for hydrogen ions to be formed, the E-O must remove an electron completely from H. If the O-H already holds a substantial negative charge taken from E, separation as hydroxide ion will be relatively easy. The hydroxide will be strongly basic. If the O-H has not acquired a very high negative charge from E, the formation of hydroxide ions may occur but not very easily. At most, the hydroxide will be weakly basic. At the same time the hydrogen will be more positive. The chance of forming hydrogen ions being greater, the hydroxide may also be weakly acidic, making it amphoteric in character. But if the oxygen has been able to acquire only a small negative charge from E, it will then draw a larger amount of charge from the hydrogen. The O-H bond will be highly polar, and the ease of separation of hydrogen ions will be at a maximum. Such a hydroxide will be a strong acid.

Consider sodium hydroxide (NaOH). Sodium is one of the elements of lowest electronegativity. It loses its electron relatively easily to the oxygen. The oxygen in fact becomes so negative that it even shares its electronic wealth with the hydrogen, which also becomes negative. When sodium hydroxide is placed in water, there is no problem whatever about separation of hydroxide ions. The solution becomes strongly basic. With negative instead of positive charge on the hydrogen, there is no likelihood of separation of a proton. Sodium hydroxide is not acidic at all.

Compare this with the hydroxide O_2NOH. This, of course, is only nitric acid, usually written HNO_3, but it is nevertheless a hydroxide. Here the oxygen of the hydroxyl group is trying to withdraw an electron from a nitrogen atom. The nitrogen itself is of high electronegativity and reluctant to release charge to oxygen. In addition, the nitrogen is already attached to two other electron-seeking oxygen atoms. It is not difficult to predict for the hydroxyl oxygen a minimum of success in attracting negative charge under these highly competitive circumstances. The chance of separating into NO_2^+ and OH^- in water is so slight that nitric acid is not basic in aqueous solution at all. The hydrogen, however, being the least electronegative atom in the molecule, must become quite positive. Its separation as a proton is therefore not difficult. In dilute solution, nitric acid is a strong acid. This means dissociation to hydrogen and nitrate ions is essentially complete:

$$H_2O + HNO_3 \rightarrow H_3O + NO_3^-$$

Zinc hydroxide, $Zn(OH)_2$, is an intermediate example. Here the zinc is sufficiently electronegative itself to resist the removal of electrons by the oxygen atoms, yet they can become partially negative at its expense. They must also draw electronic charge from the hydrogen, making it partially positive. Placed in water, zinc hydroxide (which is actually quite insoluble) may be expected to furnish both hydroxide ions or hydrogen ions, but each only very weakly. Zinc hydroxide is amphoteric.

COMPLEX OXIDES

Let us now consider the nature of the complex oxides that form when a metal oxide combines with a nonmetal oxide. This is the special variation of neutralization discussed earlier. In general, we may expect any basic oxide to be able to form a complex addition product with any acidic oxide, to form a "neutral" salt that is neither acidic nor basic. Some examples are shown in the following equations:

$$CaO + SO_3 \rightarrow CaSO_4$$
$$Na_2O + CO_2 \rightarrow Na_2CO_3$$
$$ZnO + N_2O_5 \rightarrow Zn(NO_3)_2$$

Some of these **complex oxides** (perhaps better thought of as salts of **oxyacids**) are very stable, but some are not stable enough to be easily formed. For stability, either the acidic oxide or the basic oxide, or both, must be strongly acidic or strongly basic. A compound between a weakly basic oxide and a weakly acidic oxide, or an amphoteric oxide and a weakly basic or acidic oxide, is not likely to be very stable. For example, most salts of sodium hydroxide and most salts of sulfuric acid are stable. But salts of weak oxyacids and weak bases tend to decompose rather easily into their component oxides.

Test Your Memory

1. On what basis would you predict the formula H_2O for water?
2. What causes a water molecule to be bent rather than linear?
3. Why does water expand when it freezes?
4. Write the chemical equation for the auto-ionization of water.
5. a) How does the partial charge on oxygen compare in water, hydronium ion, and hydroxide ion?
   b) How does this charge affect their electron pair donating properties?
6. What is the *ion product* for water?
7. a) What are the distinctive properties of acids?
   b) What are the distinctive properties of bases?
8. What is meant by *neutralization?*
9. What is a *spectator ion?*
10. Write an equation for the reaction of sodium hydroxide with hydrochloric acid.
11. Define *amphoteric.*
12. How do nonmetal oxides tend to differ from metal oxides?
13. How do different oxides of the same element compare?
14. What is meant by *anhydride?*
15. a) Write an equation showing ZnO acting as an acid.
    b) Write an equation showing ZnO acting as a base.
16. How are salts of oxyacids formed?

Test Your Understanding

1. What combination of circumstances makes the water molecule, as a unit, polar?
2. If hydronium ion is acidic and hydroxide ion is basic, why is water amphoteric?
3. Identify each of the following hydrogen ion concentrations as representing solutions that are either acidic or basic: 10^{-3}, 10^{-10}, 10^{-7}, 5×10^{-7}, 10^{-2}, 10^{-8}, 10^{-13}, 10^{-5}, 2×10^{-6} mole per liter.
4. Write equations for the neutralization of H_2SO_4 by (a) Na_2O, (b) ZnO, (c) $Ca(OH)_2$, (d) NH_4OH, (e) Al_2O_3.
5. Write equations for the neutralization of CaO by (a) Cl_2O_7, (b) SO_3, (c) HCl, (d) H_2SO_3, (e) HNO_3.
6. Write an equation for reaction of an amphoteric anhydride (a) with an acid anhydride; (b) with a basic anhydride.
7. Write an equation for the combination of a nonmetal oxide with a metal oxide.
8. Rate the following groups as acids and tell why the differences occur: (a) HNO_2, HNO_3; (b) $Mn(OH)_2$, Mn_2O_7; (c) H_2SO_3, H_2SO_4; (d) HOCl, $HOClO$, $HOClO_2$, $HOClO_3$.

22

OXIDATION-REDUCTION AND OXIDATION NUMBERS

ELECTRON TRANSFER REACTIONS

Oxygen forms compounds with nearly all the other chemical elements. In all of these, except those with fluorine, it acquires a partial negative charge by removing electrons from other atoms. Consequently the word **oxidation** has come to mean any chemical reaction in which electrons are transferred. The substance from which electrons are removed is said to be **oxidized.** The substance that removes the electrons is called the **oxidizing agent.** The oxidizing agent is not necessarily oxygen but can be chlorine, fluorine, or any of a number of different elements or compounds.

Metals invariably react chemically by at least partial loss of electrons. Therefore, they bear positive charge in all their compounds. The compounds of metals that serve as natural sources of free metals are called **ores.** The process of obtaining a metal from its ore has long been termed **reduction.** This involves returning to the metal atoms any electrons that were removed from it in forming the compound in the ore. Therefore, the word *reduction* has come to mean *supplying* electrons. A **reducing agent** is any substance that supplies electrons. Any substance that acquires electrons is said to be **reduced.**

Oxidation and reduction must take place simultaneously. No substance can be oxidized without a substance also being reduced. No substance can give up electrons without another substance taking on those electrons. Chemical reactions that involve a transfer of electrons are classified as **oxidation-reduction reactions,** or **redox** reactions.

Why is the burning of a candle classified as oxidation? What is the reducing agent?

OXIDATION NUMBER

The custom has developed of assigning, quite arbitrarily in many applications, a number to each element. This number is called its **oxidation number.** It indicates what **oxidation state** the element is in. Oxidation number and oxidation state are essentially the same. The following rules are helpful in assigning oxidation numbers:

1. **All elements in the free state are said to have an oxidation number of zero.** This means that their atoms are electrically neutral. No electrons have been added or withdrawn, even partially.

2. **Ions represent the elements with oxidation numbers equal to the charge on the ions.** Magnesium ion (Mg^{++}) is an example of magnesium in the $+2$ oxidation state. Or we might say that magnesium here has an oxidation number of $+2$. Sodium ion (Na^+) is sodium in the $+1$ oxidation state. Sodium has an oxidation number of $+1$ in the ion. Chlorine in chloride ion (Cl^-) has an oxidation number of -1.

3. **Oxygen is always assigned the oxidation number of -2 in its compounds,** except when one of the atoms to which an oxygen atom is attached happens to be another oxygen atom. Then the oxidation number is -1.

4. **When like atoms form a covalent bond together, this bond is subtracted from their usual oxidation number in compounds** (as indicated for oxygen under rule 3).

5. **The halogens, M7 elements fluorine, chlorine, bromine, and iodine, all have the oxidation number of -1 in their halide salts, M_mX_n, where M is** the metal and X the halogen.

6. **Hydrogen most commonly has the oxidation number of $+1$ in its compounds.** Actually the oxidation number is -1 if the hydrogen is joined to a less electronegative element, and $+1$ if it is joined to a more electronegative element.

7. Finally, **the sum of the oxidation numbers in a compound formula must be zero. The sum of the oxidation numbers in the formula of a complex ion must be equal to the charge on the ion.**

From these rules it is possible to assign oxidation numbers to most of the elements in their common compounds. Consider, for example, the element sulfur, which in the free state has the oxidation number zero. Combined with hydrogen, sulfur forms hydrogen sulfide (H_2S). Taking the hydrogen atoms as $+1$ each, since sulfur is more electronegative than hydrogen, this leaves -2 for the oxidation number of the sulfur. When sulfur burns in air it forms sulfur dioxide (SO_2). The oxygen atoms each have oxidation number -2. This makes it necessary for the sulfur to have the oxidation number of $+4$ in order for the sum to equal zero. When sulfur dioxide is burned with oxygen in the presence of a catalyst, it forms SO_3. Here the oxidation number of sulfur must be $+6$ to balance the three oxygens of -2 each.

In ammonia (NH_3), nitrogen must be assigned the oxidation number of -3 to balance the three hydrogens of $+1$ each. When nitrogen unites with oxygen to form NO, the oxidation number of nitrogen must be $+2$. When

$NaCl$	Na	$+1$	Cl	-1		
H_2O	H	$+1$	O	-2		
H_2SO_4	H	$+1$	O	-2	S	$+6$
H_2SO_3	H	$+1$	O	-2	S	$+4$
H_2S	H	$+1$	S	-2		
NH_3	H	$+1$	N	-3		
HNO_2	H	$+1$	O	-2	N	$+3$
HNO_3	H	$+1$	O	-2	N	$+5$
$CHCl_3$	H	$+1$	Cl	-1	C	$+2$
Na_2SO_4	Na	$+1$	O	-2	S	$+6$
$Al_2(SO_4)_3$	Al	$+3$	O	-2	S	$+6$
H_2O_2	H	$+1$	O	-1		
Ca_3P_2	Ca	$+2$	P	-3		
$Ca_3(PO_4)_2$	Ca	$+2$	O	-2	P	$+5$
$CO_3^=$	C	$+4$	O	-2		
$[Cr(NH_3)_6]^{+++}$	Cr	$+3$	N	-3	H	$+1$

Table 22.1. Oxidation Numbers in Various Compounds and Ions

the oxide is N_2O_3, the oxidation number of nitrogen must be $+3$ to balance the three oxygens of -2. When the oxide is NO_2, the nitrogen is in the $+4$ oxidation state. It has an oxidation number of $+4$. When the oxide is N_2O_5, the nitrogen must be $+5$ to balance the total -10 of the oxygen atoms.

The term **oxidation-reduction** is defined on this quite arbitrary basis: An oxidation-reduction reaction is any reaction in which there is a change in oxidation number by any of the elements. Oxidation is defined as involving a decrease in negative oxidation number or increase in positive number. That is, an element is oxidized when its oxidation number becomes less negative or more positive. An element is reduced when its oxidation number becomes less positive or more negative.

For example, MnO has manganese in the $+2$ oxidation state. If the manganese is converted to the $+3$ oxidation state, as in Mn_2O_3, or the $+4$ oxidation state, as in MnO_2, or the $+7$ oxidation state, as in Mn_2O_7, any of these conversions is called *oxidation*. To produce MnO_2 from Mn_2O_7 would require *reduction* of the manganese. Nitrogen is reduced when ammonia is formed, for the nitrogen goes from the zero oxidation state to -3. It is oxidized when nitric acid is formed, for then it is in the $+5$ state.

The oxidation number tells us absolutely nothing about how thoroughly electrons have been gained or removed. Such information is obtained from partial charge calculations. Oxidation number is merely an arbitrary description of the state of an element, indicating whether it has tended to lose or gain electrons, and how many, but not to what extent. Oxidation number is used widely to differentiate among compounds of the same element.

An alternative representation of oxidation state that is helpful in naming chemical compounds is to write the oxidation state in Roman numerals in parentheses following the name or symbol of the element. For example, the oxides of manganese mentioned above were previously distinguished from one another by calling MnO *manganous oxide*, Mn_2O_3 *manganic oxide, manganese sesquioxide* (*sesqui-* means one-and-one-half), or *dimanganese trioxide,* MnO_2 *manganese dioxide,* and Mn_2O_7 *manganese heptoxide* or *dimanganese heptoxide.* This practice has led to much inconsistency and ambiguity. For example, B_2O_3 was *boric oxide,* Al_2O_3 was *aluminum oxide,* Fe_2O_3 was *ferric oxide,* La_2O_3 was *lanthanum sesquioxide.* The more systematic method, now widely used, names the manganese oxides *manganese(II) oxide* (MnO), *manganese(III) oxide* (Mn_2O_3), *manganese(IV) oxide* (MnO_2), and *manganese(VII) oxide* (Mn_2O_7). B_2O_3 becomes *boron(III)* oxide, Al_2O_3 is called *aluminum(III) oxide,* Fe_2O_3 is *iron(III) oxide,* and La_2O_3 is *lanthanum(III) oxide.* This system is usually used only when there is need to make a distinction and not when only one oxide of an element is known. Chemists rarely call aluminum oxide anything but that or **alumina,** because only the one oxide is important. This system of naming, following the element name with its oxidation state in Roman numerals, is called the **Stock system.** It is generally applicable not just to oxides, but also to other compounds such as sulfates, chlorides, fluorides, bromides, sulfides, iodides, and so on.

In studying chemistry, one must become familiar with the various names chemists use. Although great efforts have been made, and are still being made, to systematize logically the nomenclature of chemistry, it is very difficult or impossible to displace the more familiar *trivial* names, as they are called, that have been used for many years. Even chemists will go on quenching their thirst with *water,* not *hydrogen(I) oxide,* or just *hydrogen oxide,* or *dihydrogen oxide.*

Test Your Memory

1. a) Define *oxidation.*
   b) Define *reduction.*
2. What is meant by *oxidation number?*
3. What is the usual oxidation number of oxygen in oxides?
4. What is the oxidation number of molecular oxygen?
5. What is the use of the concept of oxidation number?
6. What is the most common oxidation state of hydrogen?
7. What is the oxidation number of fluorine in CoF_2? In CoF_3?
8. What is the oxidation number of the element in Na^+, Al^{+++}, Fe^{++}, H^-, $S^=$, $P^\equiv$?

Test Your Understanding

1. Give the oxidation number of each element in each of the following: (a) $S_2O_7^=$, (b) $Mg_2P_2O_7$, (c) CO_2, (d) Al_4C_3, (e) NO_3^-, (f) NH_3, (g) $(NH_4)_3PO_4$, (h) NaH, (i) H_2S.
2. Name each of the following by the Stock system: $FeCl_2$, $FeCl_3$, $MnCl_2$, $MnCl_4$, OsO_2, OsO_4, TiO_2, Ti_2O_3, TiO.

23

THE PERIODICITY OF OXIDE CHEMISTRY

OXIDES ACROSS THE TABLE

The use of the periodic table in organizing the chemical elements according to their atomic structure, and in discussing physical properties that result from atomic structure, sometimes tend to create the impression that the table applies only to the elements. A systematic study of the chemistry of the elements soon reveals that the periodicity of their *compounds* is also especially noteworthy. Let us examine the periodic variations of properties of the compounds of elements with oxygen.

Period 2

Lithium. A lithium atom has the capacity to form one covalent bond, as shown by its electronic structure of 2-1. We can predict that two lithium atoms can become attached to one oxygen atom in a bent molecule with bond angle about 109°. But there are two reasons why we would expect such molecules to condense further. One is the existence of lone pairs of electrons on the oxygen and vacant orbitals on the lithium atoms. The other is that lithium is very low in electronegativity and must therefore form highly polar bonds to oxygen. The highly negative oxygen can then attract the positive lithium of another molecule, and through coordinated polymerization form a stable crystalline solid of empirical formula Li_2O.

We predict that the highly negative charge on oxygen will make it strongly basic and thus an excellent electron donor. In water the oxygen from the lithium oxide will quickly acquire a proton from the H_2O, simultaneously forming one hydroxide ion and leaving another. Meanwhile the two positive lithium atoms will become hydrated lithium ions in solution. The solution will then be strongly basic.

The experimental facts are in accord with these predictions. This shows once more that if we know enough about the nature of the component atoms, we can approach a reasonable understanding of the compound they form. Lithium metal easily combines with oxygen to form Li_2O, a stable white solid that reacts with water to form a solution of lithium hydroxide (LiOH), a strong base:

$$Li_2O + H_2O \rightarrow 2\ LiOH$$

Beryllium. The next element in this period is beryllium. It differs from lithium in having one more proton in the nucleus and one more electron in its outer shell. The effective nuclear charge of beryllium is stronger than that of lithium because the final electron added does not effectively shield the extra positive charge at the nucleus. Consequently, beryllium atoms are considerably smaller and more compact than lithium atoms. They also have a higher electronegativity.

A beryllium atom is restricted to two covalent bonds by the fact that it has but two outer-shell electrons. An oxygen atom is restricted to two covalent

If both outer-shell electrons of beryllium are paired in the 2s orbital, how can beryllium be expected to form two bonds?

bonds by the fact that it has but two outer-shell vacancies. Oxygen atoms should combine with beryllium atoms one to one. In order to make fullest possible use of the extra electron pairs on oxygen and the vacant orbitals of the beryllium, this should be a polymeric oxide having no individual molecules. BeO should be a stable solid, which indeed it is. Each beryllium atom is surrounded at the corners of a tetrahedron by four oxygen atoms. Each oxygen atom is surrounded at the corners of a tetrahedron by four beryllium atoms.

For two reasons, the oxygen should be much less negative in BeO than in Li_2O. One reason is the higher initial electronegativity of the beryllium compared to lithium: 1.61 compared to 0.9. The other is the higher valence of beryllium. Instead of an oxygen having two lithium atoms from which to withdraw electrons, it has only one beryllium atom. Although the oxygen in BeO cannot be as highly negative as in Li_2O, it should still be able to attract a proton from water to form beryllium hydroxide, $Be(OH)_2$. This compound cannot be nearly as basic as lithium hydroxide. In fact, $Be(OH)_2$ does form from BeO and H_2O. It is only very weakly basic, and even a little acidic, and it is classified as amphoteric.

Boron. The next element in this period is boron, atomic number 5, with electronic configuration 2-3. Although the ground state of boron would have two of the outermost electrons in the $2s$ orbital, one is easily promoted and boron provides three sp^2 hybrid orbitals for covalent bonding. Therefore, the formula of the oxide should be B_2O_3. Here three oxygen atoms are competing for the electrons of only two boron atoms. Furthermore, boron atoms are considerably more electronegative than are beryllium atoms. For these two reasons, we cannot expect the oxygen to become even as negative as in beryllium oxide. If beryllium oxide was so weakly basic as to be amphoteric, then boron oxide should not be expected to have any basicity. It should be exclusively acidic.

In fact, B_2O_3 is the formula. The compound is a white solid, and although polymerized from simple molecules like the preceding oxides we have considered, it melts and volatilizes more readily. It reacts with water to form boric acid, $B(OH)_3$. This is only extremely weakly acidic, as one might judge from its use as an eye washing lotion in dilute aqueous solution. It has no basic properties.

Carbon. The next element in this period is carbon, with atomic number 6 and electronic configuration 2-4. Electron promotion followed by hybridization should permit a carbon atom to form four equal single covalent bonds. The formula CO_2 is predicted for its oxide. As to its physical state, however, we could not say unless we knew from experimental observation. We do know that carbon and oxygen both are among the relatively few elements that easily form multiple bonds. We would not be sure whether these would be favored over single bonds. Single bonds would mean a polymeric solid in which each carbon atom is surrounded by four oxygens at the corners of a tetrahedron and each oxygen atom is joined to two carbon atoms. Double bonds would mean a substance composed of CO_2 molecules, with no vacancies left over for further condensation. It would therefore be volatile and probably a gas.

By rather simple methods somewhat beyond the scope of this book, it has recently become possible to calculate the bond energies for the single and double bonds between carbon and oxygen. By this means it has been shown that although more commonly a double bond is not twice as strong as a single bond, here a double bond is more than twice as strong. Therefore, the molecular compound is favored over the polymeric single-bonded form by about

Figure 23.1.   A Molecule of Carbon Dioxide.

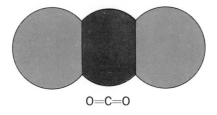

O=C=O

Carbon dioxide remains molecular even when cooled to solidification. No polymerization occurs even in the crystal, which is the molecular substance called *dry ice.*

50 kcal per mole. On this basis we could indeed predict that carbon dioxide should be molecular and, therefore, probably a gas rather than a solid. We know, of course, that carbon dioxide has the formula CO_2 and is a gaseous compound. A single-bonded polymeric form has never been observed.

The double-bonded structure, $O=C=O$, seems so stable that it is difficult for it to unite with water. The hypothetical product, carbonic acid, H_2CO_3, is so unstable that it never has been isolated. It is known only in solution. We would predict that carbonic acid would be a weak acid but stronger than boric acid, since the oxygen in carbon dioxide, for the reasons cited above, is less negative than in B_2O_3. With an electronegativity of 2.5 compared with 1.9 for boron, carbon offers greater resistance to the removal of electrons by oxygen. Also, instead of three oxygen atoms competing for electrons of two boron atoms, here we have two oxygen atoms competing for the electrons of the same carbon atom. Carbonic acid is indeed a weak acid, but much stronger than boric acid. As one should expect, it is not basic at all.

Nitrogen. Nitrogen forms such a variety of oxides that it would be confusing to consider each one here. Let us consider then the anhydride of nitric acid, N_2O_5. In this oxide, nitrogen has the maximum positive oxidation state that could be predicted from the presence of five outer-shell electrons. Nitric acid is well known to be a strong acid, in keeping with the fact that the only atoms except hydrogen are all high in electronegativity: N 2.9 and O 3.5. It also is a good oxidizing agent. Here is an important general observation: whenever a highly electronegative atom like that of oxygen is incorporated in a compound with other atoms high in electronegativity so that it cannot have acquired much negative charge, the compound may safely be predicted to be potentially a strong oxidizing agent. There is a strong tendency for any highly electronegative atom to leave a combination in which it has failed to become very negative, in favor of joining a new combination which could supply it with electrons more readily. Oxides in which the oxygen has a reasonably high negative charge do not function as oxidizing agents. Oxides in which the negative charge on oxygen is quite low are invariably oxidizing agents.

Fluorine. If fluorine and oxygen are considered, there is no difficulty in predicting the formula of their combination, since the fluorine can form but one single covalent bond and the oxygen two: OF_2. This is written OF_2, rather than F_2O, following the custom of writing the symbol of the more negative component last. Since fluorine is the one element more electronegative than oxygen, the oxygen must here have a $+2$ oxidation number instead of the usual -2. The bonds, although slightly polar, are polar in the opposite direction from usual. This compound should be called **oxygen difluoride** rather than "fluorine oxide." As expected from the complete lack of vacant orbitals in the molecule, preventing further condensation, oxygen difluoride is a gas. It is somewhat unstable and a powerful oxidizing agent.

From the viewpoint of making reasonable comparisons, it would have been well to stop at oxygen in crossing this period, for in no other period is

Figure 23.2.   A Molecule of Oxygen Difluoride.

Only in combination with fluorine does oxygen acquire a partial positive charge. Naturally a compound combining two such highly electronegative elements must have strong oxidizing powers, as the component elements seek better sources of electrons than each other.

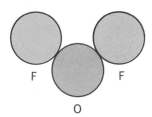

there an element more electronegative than oxygen. The trend in properties of the oxides from lithium to nitrogen was quite striking. The valence of oxygen remained constant, but the valence of the other element increased steadily from one in lithium to five in nitrogen. At the same time, the electronegativity increased steadily from very low to high. As a consequence of both these trends, the partial charge on oxygen went from high to low. As the condition of the combined oxygen changed, so did the physical state and properties, and the chemical properties. The physical state changed from nonvolatile, stable, crystalline solid to volatile, unstable, molecular compound. The basicity changed from very high to low to amphoteric to weakly acid to strongly acid. The oxidizing ability changed from none at all to very strong. The change in oxide properties from left to right across the periodic table is fully as spectacular as the change in the properties of the elements themselves, from highly reactive metal to highly reactive nonmetal.

Period 3

Let us go back now and begin again, but this time one row lower in the periodic table. Sodium, of atomic number 11 and electronic configuration 2-8-1, is like lithium since it has but one outer-shell electron, and thus has the capacity to form but one covalent bond. Two sodium atoms can be predicted to join to one oxygen atom, giving the molecule Na_2O, with a bond angle of about 109°. Its bonds should be highly polar since the sodium was originally very low in electronegativity and the oxygen high. Since the simplest molecule possible would still have vacant outer-shell orbitals on the sodium atoms and unused electron pairs on the oxygen, further condensation would be predicted to form a nonmolecular crystalline solid. Since the oxygen bears high negative charge in this compound, we would expect it to have lost its oxidizing power but to be highly basic. Na_2O should take on a proton from water to form 2 NaOH, which should be a strongly basic hydroxide.

All that we have predicted is experimentally verified, except for one point that really could not have been known in advance. It is important to realize the possibility of some such point existing. We do the best we can to understand the chemistry of the elements from what is known of their atomic structures. For the most part, this can be a satisfyingly successful effort. But there is no advantage to pretending that everything about chemistry is known and understood—this will never be true.

The unexpected feature of the sodium-oxygen combination is that when sodium burns in oxygen, the principal product is not Na_2O as predicted, but the unpredicted sodium **peroxide,** Na_2O_2. This is also a white solid which reacts with water to form not only sodium hydroxide but also to liberate oxygen:

$$2\,Na_2O_2 + 2\,H_2O \rightarrow 4\,NaOH + O_2$$

It has been determined that the peroxide group $O_2^=$ is joined to two Na^+ ions in the sodium peroxide crystal. Since the charge on the two oxygen atoms together is only -2, each must have the oxidation number of -1. The single bond between the two oxygen atoms neither enhances nor detracts from the charge on each oxygen. Potassium, rubidium, and cesium in this M1 group all react differently with oxygen, forming **superoxides** of formula MO_2. Here the metal does not have the oxidation number of $+4$ as we might judge from the formula. Instead, the oxygen occurs as O_2^- ion.

Now that the existence, properties, and general nature of peroxides and superoxides have been determined, it is not surprising to find them formed most readily only by the most reactive metals, those that give up their electrons most readily, for oxygen molecules (O_2) would be forced to break into atoms before they could form an oxide like Na_2O. This would take considerable energy. If O_2 can find a source of electrons so available that this initial breaking up into atoms can be avoided, it will be able to acquire electrons as a molecule. Thus it becomes a molecule ion, $O_2^=$ or O_2^-. Now that this is known, it can be rationalized to some extent. We might shrug and say that we should have known it all the time. But we did not, and truthfully, we could not have predicted these unusual combinations from our limited knowledge of the elements.

Although it is very important to appreciate the limitations of chemical theory, it is equally important not to become so panicked by its occasional failure that all faith in it is lost. Once in a while, an anomaly or apparent contradiction is recognized that proves an entire theory incorrect. Much more commonly, however, such a discovery merely points out the limits of applicability of the theory, or the need for minor revision, or for a logical extension. This is the way knowledge grows, with a continuous reshuffling of facts and theories along the borderline between the newly discovered and the great unknown. Only rarely does some discovery shake the structure of knowledge down to its very roots.

The M1 oxides are not entirely anomalous. In fact, an oxide of predictable formula M_2O *can* be prepared for each of these metals. These oxides have just the properties expected of them. Na_2O, for example, is a stable white solid that is strongly basic. With water it forms the very soluble strong base, sodium hydroxide (NaOH).

Magnesium. The next element in this period is magnesium, of atomic number 12 and electronic configuration 2-8-2. Magnesium atoms are expected to be considerably smaller than sodium atoms for the same reason that beryllium atoms are smaller than lithium atoms. The same factor of increased effective nuclear charge also causes magnesium to have an electronegativity considerably higher (1.4) than that of sodium (0.9). For the combination of magnesium, which can form two bonds per atom, and oxygen, which also can form two bonds per atom, the formula MgO is predicted. The compound should consist not of simple molecules but of a solid, nonmolecular, crystalline form of high stability. The solid will use more effectively the otherwise vacant orbitals on the magnesium and the otherwise unused electron pairs on the oxygen. In MgO, each oxygen atom will have on the average only one magnesium atom to serve as supplier of electrons, in contrast to Na_2O where two sodium atoms served that function. Furthermore, the magnesium is not as easily relieved of its valence electrons as is the sodium. For these two reasons, the bonds in magnesium oxide cannot be nearly as polar as in sodium oxide. The basicity must therefore be considerably less than that of sodium oxide. Water should form $Mg(OH)_2$, but this should not be a strong base.

Magnesium does indeed form magnesium oxide (MgO). In fact, the brilliant light emitted when magnesium burns in oxygen has often been used in photography. The compound is very stable, with a crystalline structure similar to that of NaCl: each magnesium atom is surrounded equally by six oxygen atoms and each oxygen atom by six magnesium atoms. Although this compound is commonly termed an "ionic oxide," the oxygen appears to have only a moderately high negative charge which makes it only moderately basic. Since magnesium hydroxide is very insoluble in water, its basicity must be judged indirectly from the general chemical properties of magnesium compounds. It is insoluble in bases but readily soluble in acids. This property shows us that although not the strongest of bases, it has no acidic qualities.

Aluminum. The next element in this period is aluminum, of atomic number 13 and electronic configuration 2-8-3. We expect of aluminum the availability of three hybrid sp^2 orbitals, each containing one electron and capable of forming a single covalent bond. The combination with oxygen should therefore have the formula Al_2O_3. The electronegativity of aluminum (1.5) is higher than that of magnesium. Each aluminum has to supply with electrons on the average one-and-one-half oxygen atoms instead of only one as in magnesium oxide. For these reasons, the oxygen in aluminum oxide is not expected to be highly negative and should certainly be less basic than it is in

MgO. In fact, aluminum does form a very stable oxide, Al_2O_3, which is amphoteric.

Silicon. With its electronic configuration of 2-8-4, the ability of silicon to form four covalent bonds using hybrid sp^3 orbitals can easily be predicted. From this, the formula SiO_2 comes naturally. But here our powers of prediction are put to a real test: Should SiO_2 be molecular like CO_2, or composed of single bonds and thus polymeric and solid? Our general knowledge of the elements tells us that only elements of the second period readily form ordinary double bonds, so SiO_2 can be predicted as a polymeric solid. This would prevent its dissolving in water. What about its acid-base properties as deduced from other evidence? Silicon is more electronegative (1.7) than aluminum, and on the average, two oxygen atoms are competing for the valence electrons of each silicon atom. Surely SiO_2 must be less basic than Al_2O_3, which is amphoteric and therefore only weakly basic. A reasonable guess is that silicon dioxide probably has no basic properties and is more acidic than aluminum oxide. These predictions indeed fit well with the observed experimental facts.

Silicon dioxide, also called **silica,** is the major component of ordinary sand and quartz. Polymeric and insoluble in water, its acid-base properties can be judged from its reaction with strong bases and strong acids. The latter have no effect, showing the absence of basicity. Strong bases dissolve silicon dioxide to form silicates. Silicates are more commonly formed by heating basic metal oxides with sand.

Phosphorus. Phosphorus is widely used in incendiary bombs and tracer bullets because of its vigorous and easily initiated reaction with oxygen. From the electronic configuration 2-8-5, we could predict that the outermost shell has the capacity to form only three covalent bonds, because the fourth orbital must already contain a pair of electrons. On the basis of the information presented up to now, a formula of P_2O_3 could be predicted for the oxide. Since phosphorus has a higher electronegativity (2.2) than silicon, the partial charge on oxygen in this compound must be lower than in silicon dioxide, which was already weakly acidic. Our prediction for P_2O_3 must be that it is at least more acidic than silica. Because no obviously vacant orbitals are present on either atom, we have no basis for predicting coordinated polymerization. Yet since phosphorus, like silicon, would be expected to be relatively unable to form ordinary double bonds to oxygen, we might predict polymerization, with each oxygen atom acting as a bridge between two phosphorus atoms. Unless such polymers were extremely stable, and certainly if they do not form, phosphorus oxide would be predicted to be molecular and volatile.

At this point the examination of oxides across the periodic table must be delayed to go back and pick up something bypassed in the earlier discussion of chemical bonding. Up to now the concept of each atom having four outer orbitals which might or might not be available for covalent bonding, depending on whether or not they already contain electrons, has been quite satisfactory. Nitrogen, for example, although commonly assigned the formal oxidation number of +5, has only four orbitals in its outer shell and therefore could not possibly form more than four bonds of any kind. When the atomic structure builds up to the third principal quantum level, however, the capacity increases to 18 electrons, by the addition of five d orbitals to the original four of s and three p. Ordinarily, these d orbitals, when they have no electrons at all, have too much energy to participate in the bonding. However, as the atom becomes progressively more positive, the picture may change. When a given atom has outer d orbitals that are not normally available in bonding, this is because the effective nuclear charge is not strong enough to hold electrons in the d orbitals. The shielding of the nuclear charge by the intervening electrons is too great. If this atom now becomes attached to more electronegative atoms which draw electronic charge from it, the remaining electrons are less able to shield the nuclear charge. Its effect is then more strongly felt in the d orbitals.

Under such conditions, the d orbitals may participate in bonding in either of two ways. First, they may accept electron pairs from donor atoms of other molecules, in coordination. Indeed, they may accept electron pairs from an atom to which their own atom is already bonded. This strengthens the single covalent bonding by addition of a sort of double bonding. For example, in silicon dioxide, each oxygen atom is attached to two silicon atoms by single covalent bonds. But these bonds are actually shorter and stronger than expected for single covalent bonds, and have a much wider bond angle (150° instead of 109°). These facts suggest that the single bonds between silicon and oxygen are being strengthened by additional electron sharing. The lone pairs of the oxygen are apparently accommodated partially by the outer d orbitals of the silicon.

The second way in which d orbitals of a positively charged atom may participate in bonding is by accepting one electron from a lone pair in the underlying s and p orbitals. For example, phosphorus atoms have three half-filled orbitals for bonding and one lone pair for electrons. This restricts them normally to three covalent bonds, but if a d orbital becomes available, one electron from the lone pair may be promoted out to it. Notice that this creates simultaneously two half-filled orbitals, and therefore the ability to form two additional covalent bonds. With chlorine, phosphorus can form PCl_3 as predictable, but it can also react with additional chlorine to form PCl_5. The phosphorus atom now has ten electrons around it instead of the customary eight. Hence the term, **expanding the octet.**

Can you account for the existence of PCl_3 and PCl_5 but only PH_3 and no PH_5?

Although phosphorus does unite with oxygen to form the compound of empirical formula P_2O_3, having properties as predicted, it readily reacts further to form an oxide of empirical formula P_2O_5. This is the anhydride of phosphoric acid (H_3PO_4), which is a moderately strong acid. The molecular structures of P_2O_3 and P_2O_5 are quite complex and show that the true molecular formulas are P_4O_6 and P_4O_{10}.

Sulfur.   With sulfur, the expansion of the octet seems to become the rule in the combination with oxygen. We might predict that because the outer shell structure of sulfur is just like that of oxygen, the two should unite readily to form a compound of formula SO. No such compound is stable at ordinary temperatures. When sulfur is burned in air, the chief product is sulfur dioxide, SO_2. This may or may not represent an expansion of the octet. There is some evidence that on the average sulfur forms a double bond with one oxygen and donates a pair of electrons to the other in a coordinate covalent bond. This would not require use of the *d* orbitals. However, if an electron were promoted from a lone pair on sulfur to an outer *d* orbital, this would provide the means of forming a double bond with the second oxygen, and would involve expanding the octet. This question remains imperfectly answered.

Further combination of SO_2 with O_2, aided by a catalyst, produces SO_3. Again, it is uncertain whether the octet is expanded by promotion of an electron from the final lone pair on sulfur, to an outer *d* orbital, or whether this pair is simply donated to the third oxygen in coordination. Both oxides can be predicted to be molecular and acidic. Sulfur dioxide is a gas that reacts only very slightly with water to form the hypothetical **sulfurous acid** (H_2SO_3). This acid has never been isolated although its salts are well known and quite stable. It is a moderately weak acid. Sulfur trioxide is very soluble; in fact, it is completely miscible with water. It polymerizes weakly to form both solid and liquid, but the polymers readily dissociate to give the gaseous molecules of SO_3, which is the anhydride of sulfuric acid (H_2SO_4), a very strong acid.

Chlorine.   There is not time here to consider all the chemistry of oxygen with chlorine. Let us consider what could form if each of the three lone pairs on chlorine could be promoted to an outer *d* orbital in the reaction with oxygen. This would give chlorine the capacity to form seven covalent bonds or their equivalent. With oxygen we would predict the formula Cl_2O_7. This can readily be predicted to be molecular, volatile, unstable, highly acidic, and strongly oxidizing because of the low polarity of its bonds. The compound does indeed exist, as an unstable, oily liquid, volatile and strongly oxidizing. It is the anhydride of the strongest known aqueous acid, **perchloric acid** ($HClO_4$). This is so strong an acid that even when only one molecule of water is present per molecule of acid, almost all the protons of the perchloric acid are transferred to the water molecule. Crystals of **hydronium perchlorate** ($H_3O^+ClO_4^-$) can thus be isolated.

Incidentally, chlorine forms an interesting series of oxygen acids that illustrate very nicely the effect of increasing the electron withdrawal on the acid strength of the hydroxide. $HOClO_3$ is an extremely strong acid as just mentioned ($HClO_4$ is $HOClO_3$), **chloric** acid ($HOClO_2$) is a strong acid,

chlorous acid (HOClO) is a weak acid, and **hypochlorous** acid (HOCl) is an extremely weak acid.

Let us summarize our observations on this second trip across the periodic table. The first oxide we discussed was Na_2O, a stable, strongly basic, non-volatile solid having no oxidizing power. From sodium to the right, as the elements become more electronegative and have higher valence, the oxygen becomes less and less negative. This change in the condition of oxygen causes

Table 23.1.   Some Properties of Oxides of Periods 2 and 3

Compound	Partial charge on oxygen	Melting point	Boiling point	Acid-base properties	Oxidizing power
Li_2O	-0.80	1727	high	strong base	none
BeO	-0.35	2547	high	amphoteric	none
B_2O_3	-0.24	450	high	very weak acid	none
CO_2	-0.11	-56.6 (under P)	-78.5 (subl.)	weak acid	low
N_2O_5	-0.05	30	45–50	strong acid	good
Na_2O	-0.81	920	high	strong base	none
MgO	-0.42	2802	high	weak base	none
Al_2O_3	-0.31	2027	high	amphoteric	none
SiO_2	-0.23	1700	high	very weak acid	none
P_4O_{10}	-0.13	422	——	moderate acid	almost none
SO_3	-0.06	16.9 (form)	44.8	strong acid	moderate
Cl_2O_7	-0.01	-91.5	83	very strong acid	good

a change in chemical properties from stable, strongly basic, nonoxidizing, nonvolatile solid at one extreme to unstable, strongly acidic, highly oxidizing, volatile molecular compound at the other. Does this seem familiar? It should, because this second road parallels the first, not very far removed from it. The oxygen chemistry we observed in traveling from lithium toward fluorine was not very different from the progression from sodium to chlorine. If we were to travel from one element to the next higher in atomic number, through the entire periodic system, studying the chemistry with oxygen all along the way, we would recognize a periodic variation from one extreme to another and then back again. **The properties of the oxides of the chemical elements are a periodic function of their atomic number.**

A comparison of the two routes across the periodic table step by step can also be informative. In group M1, lithium and sodium form oxides that

Figure 23.3.   Relative Size and Partial Charge on Combined Oxygen in Some Oxides.

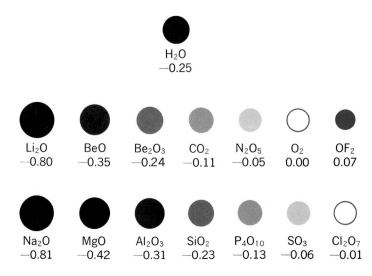

are very similar, having the formulas M_2O and being solid nonmolecular substances that are stable and nonvolatile. They are alike in reacting with water to form hydroxides that are very strong bases, and in lacking oxidizing power. But with increasing size and ease of electron loss by sodium, we observed that oxygen behaves differently with sodium than with lithium.

In group M2, beryllium oxide is amphoteric but the moderately basic magnesium oxide is not acidic at all. This is the result of differences between magnesium and beryllium atoms. The magnesium atoms are bigger, less electronegative, and better suppliers of electrons to the oxygen. Yet the formulas are very similar: BeO, MgO, $Be(OH)_2$, $Mg(OH)_2$. The products that form when these hydroxides or oxides act only as bases are likewise very similar: $BeCl_2$, $MgCl_2$, and so on.

The first member in group M3, boron, forms an oxide B_2O_3 and a hydroxide $B(OH)_3$ that are not basic at all, only very weakly acidic. The second member, aluminum, forms an oxide and hydroxide of similar formulas. However, the aluminum, being somewhat less electronegative and larger, allows the oxygen to become more negative, causing the compounds to acquire slight basicity in addition to their slight acidity.

In group M4, we observed a significant change in physical properties for compounds of similar formula, CO_2 and SiO_2. This change was attributed largely to the tendency of carbon to favor double bonds to oxygen. Chemically we saw a weakening of the acidity from CO_2 to SiO_2 that corresponds to the lower electronegativity of the silicon and the larger size of its atoms, but no basicity is shown.

In group M5 nitrogen and phosphorus are able to form oxides of similar empirical formula, N_2O_5 and P_2O_5, although these are quite different in nature.

The nitrogen oxide is more acidic, and much stronger as an oxidizing agent. Although acidic, the phosphorus oxide is not an oxidizing agent under ordinary circumstances.

In summary, down each group was observed a small tendency toward greater basicity or reduced acidity, or both.

Test Your Memory

1. a) Describe the result of combination of lithium with oxygen and explain.
   b) What feature of lithium oxide makes it basic?
2. What are the formula and structure of beryllium oxide?
3. What is boric acid?
4. What kind of bonding makes CO_2 a gas rather than a solid?
5. What oxide of nitrogen is the anhydride of HNO_3?
6. What compound do fluorine and oxygen form?
7. What is the formula for sodium peroxide?
8. For what two reasons are the bonds in MgO less polar than in Na_2O?
9. What are the acid-base properties of aluminum oxide?
10. How do we decide SiO_2 is acidic when it is insoluble in water?
11. What is meant by *expanding the octet?*
12. To what oxide formulas does expansion of the sulfur octet possibly lead?
13. How do oxides of similar formula compare within the same periodic group?
14. What is the series of oxygen acids of chlorine?

Test Your Understanding

1. Why would a single molecule of Li_2O be expected to have a bent structure?
2. Predict some of the physical and chemical properties of K_2O.
3. Why is BeO less basic than Li_2O?
4. Predict the general nature of an oxide of calcium.
5. Why do oxides tend toward greater volatility from left to right across the periodic table?
6. Why are the trends in oxide properties similar for periods 2 and 3?
7. What can be said about an element whose monoxide is very high melting and basic?
8. Why is oxygen assigned an oxidation number of -1 in certain compounds?
9. What differences cause CO_2 to be gaseous but SiO_2 solid?
10. What likelihood is there of expanding the octet of nitrogen? Why?
11. Why does expansion of the octet always produce two new bonds at once?
12. In CO_2 the two double bonds are linear but in SO_2 they are not. Can you suggest the reason for the difference?
13. Predict some properties of SnO_2 and TeO_2.

24

ACID-BASE EQUILIBRIA IN AQUEOUS SOLUTION

ACID IONIZATION CONSTANTS

In dilute aqueous solution, all very strong acids ionize completely to form hydronium ion and the appropriate anion. But there are many acids that are only incompletely ionized in water. Solutions of these involve equilibria among the various species present. If we consider a hypothetical weak acid to have the formula HA, then the equation for the ionization is:

$$HA + H_2O \rightleftharpoons H_3O^+ + A^-$$

Since this does not occur to completion in the forward direction as written, the system reaches equilibrium. The expression for the equilibrium constant is:

$$K = \frac{[H^+][A^-]}{[HA]}$$

The magnitude of K really depends upon a competitive reaction. This occurs between the water molecules, which in a dilute solution are present in vastly superior numbers, and the anion from the acid A^-. The competition is for the proton that originally was part of the acid molecule HA. Whether the proton is attached to the anion in HA or to the oxygen of the water molecule in H_3O^+, it sits on a pair of electrons. The "more comfortable" seat will be on the pair of electrons that is more readily available, that is most freely donated to it. This is where the proton is more likely to become attached.

If the anion A^- is stingy with its electron pair, scarcely making it available to the proton, the proton will find a more available electron pair at the very first opportunity. When HA is dissolved in water, the proton finds a great abundance of electron pairs available to it on each of the oxygen atoms of the water molecules. All of the protons will transfer to water. The solution is then described as strongly acidic, and HA as a strong acid.

But if the anion A^- is reasonably generous with its electron pair, protons will not so readily transfer to the electron pairs on water, even though the latter are much more abundant. They will tend to stay with A^-, as HA. This is another way of saying that the ionic dissociation of HA will be limited. HA is then a weak acid. If A^- has an electron pair that is extremely easily available to a proton, HA will hardly ionize at all. Such a compound must be classified as a very weak acid. K is large for a strong acid, small for a weak acid, and very small for a very weak acid. K may be referred to as either the **ionization constant** or the **dissociation constant** of the acid. Some typical ionization constants of common weak acids are given in Table 24.1.

H_2CO_3	2×10^{-4}	
HCN	4×10^{-10}	
CH_3COOH	1.8×10^{-5}	**Table 24.1. Some Acid Ionization Constants** (at 25°C) (first, second, third)
HNO_2	4.5×10^{-4}	
H_3PO_4	$7.5 \times 10^{-3}, 6.2 \times 10^{-8}, 10^{-12}$	
H_2S	$1.1 \times 10^{-7}, 1.0 \times 10^{-14}$	
H_2SO_3	$1.2 \times 10^{-2}, 1 \times 10^{-7}$	
HOCl	3.2×10^{-8}	

The distinction among differences in acid strength is this: An acid is a strong acid if its anion, compared to water, is a poor donor of an electron pair to a proton. An acid is a weak acid if its anion, compared to water, is a good donor of an electron pair to a proton.

For example, hydrofluoric acid is a weak acid but hydrochloric acid, hydrobromic acid, and hydriodic acid are all strong acids. The principal reason for this difference is that the fluoride ion F^-, being smaller and having its electron pairs packed more closely together, is a much better electron donor to a proton than are any of the larger halide ions. In fact, it is comparable to water itself. Therefore, the transfer of protons from HF to H_2O is quite incomplete. But the larger halide ions such as chloride, Cl^-, have their electrons spread out over the surface more extensively, and cannot supply them so readily to a proton. In the presence of excess water molecules, water gains practically all of the protons. If the solution of hydrogen halide becomes more concentrated, however, so that the water molecules do not so greatly outnumber the halide ions, the competition becomes more even. The hydrogen halides are not completely ionized in concentrated solutions. This is evidenced by the immediate loss of some hydrogen halide gas as soon as the stopper is removed from a reagent bottle containing any concentrated hydrogen halide solution, such as hydrochloric acid.

In general, among oxygen acids, if the partial negative charge on the oxygen of the anion is relatively high, making it a good donor, then the acid is very weak. But if the partial negative charge on the oxygen of the anion is

Figure 24.1. Competition for Protons in Aqueous Acids.

Every acid molecule (HA) can be thought of as an anion (A⁻) acting as an electron donor to a proton (H⁺):

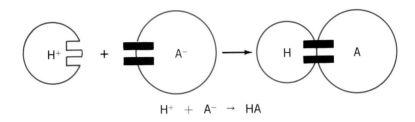

$$H^+ \ + \ A^- \ \rightarrow \ HA$$

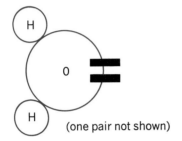

(one pair not shown)

Water is also an electron donor, able to act through one of the lone pairs on its negatively charged oxygen atom.

Therefore any solution of HA in H_2O presents a competition between donors for the same proton:

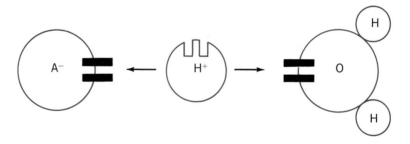

Possessing the proton first offers no advantage. In the competition, the proton will tend to end up on the most effective donor.

In a dilute solution of HA, water molecules far outnumber HA molecules. Therefore H_2O may be expected to acquire at least some of the protons from HA, just as they do from other water molecules.

If the anion A⁻ is not a very effective electron donor to the proton, H_2O molecules will acquire essentially all protons from the HA molecules. We say that HA *ionizes (or dissociates) completely*, or is a **strong acid.** The anion of a strong acid is a poor donor to the proton.

If the anion A⁻ still holds its proton fairly successfully, even though A⁻ is outnumbered, we say that HA *ionizes (or dissociates) incompletely*, or is a **weak acid.** The anion of a weak acid is a good donor to the proton.

280 Acid-Base Equilibria in Aqueous Solution

Figure 24.2. The Condition of Combined Oxygen in Anions of Strong and Weak Acids.

IN ANIONS OF STRONG ACIDS:

IN ANIONS OF WEAK ACIDS:

OXYGEN

bears relatively low negative charge, is smaller, a poor donor, and is likely to be an oxidizing agent.

OXYGEN

bears a relatively high negative charge, is larger, a good donor, and not a very effective oxidizing agent.

Examples:

ClO_4^-
NO_3^-
HSO_4^-
CCl_3COO^-

Examples:

$CO_3^=$
$PO_4^\equiv$
OH^-
CH_3COO^-

not very high, then it cannot be a very good donor and the acid is strong. Anything that decreases the negative charge on oxygen in the anion, such as the addition of competitive oxygen atoms, increases the strength of the acid. Already noted are the examples of HOCl as an extremely weak acid but $HOClO_3$ as an extremely strong one. The negative charge on oxygen in ClO_4^- is only -0.21 whereas in ClO^- it is -0.52.

There are numerous acids which contain more than one replaceable proton. Such acids, including sulfuric acid (H_2SO_4) and phosphoric acid (H_3PO_4), are called **polyprotic** or sometimes **polybasic** acids. These ionize by steps. For each step there is a different ionization constant. As one might expect, each departing proton leaves its electron behind. As the anion becomes more and more negative, it becomes a better and better electron donor. Therefore the successive ionizations of a polyprotic acid are almost invariably weaker and weaker, with each constant only about $1/100,000$ as large as the preceding one. Some examples are given in Table 24.1.

Notice that we have been talking about anions as electron donors, and in this sense basic. A concept of acids and bases developed by Bronsted and Lowry defines **acids as proton donors and bases as proton acceptors.** By this concept, all anions from the ionization of an acid are called bases. All proton suppliers such as the acid molecules themselves are called acids. The relationship between any acid and the anion left when it has lost a proton is recognized by

	Acid	Base
	NH_4^+	NH_3
	H_2O	OH^-
	H_3O^+	H_2O
	H_2S	HS^-
	H_2SO_4	HSO_4^-
Table 24.2. Conjugate Acids and Bases	HSO_4^-	$SO_4^=$
	HCl	Cl^-
	HNO_3	NO_3^-
	H_3PO_4	$H_2PO_4^-$
	$H_2PO_4^-$	$HPO_4^=$
	HPO_4^-	$PO_4^\equiv$
	H_2CO_3	HCO_3^-
	HCO_3^-	$CO_3^=$

calling these pairs **conjugate.** Nitrate ion (NO_3^-) is thus the **conjugate base** of nitric acid (HNO_3). Nitric acid is similarly the **conjugate acid** of the nitrate ion. Water is the conjugate base of the hydronium ion and the conjugate acid of the hydroxide ion.

What would be the conjugate base of the hydroxide ion? When this base is placed in water, what do you predict would happen?

As demonstrated above, it is very important to recognize that no molecule tends to split into separate ions all by itself. Rather, some other species must take one of the ions to itself. In this sense, the Bronsted-Lowry concept of acids and bases is useful in helping us to appreciate that neutralization is merely a transfer of a proton from one species to another. It may, therefore, go in either direction.

But there are other concepts of acids and bases also. We must not confuse the concepts with the facts. The nature of a substance is not changed by changing its name in the chemistry books or by changing the term by which it is classified. If we decided to call sodium hydroxide a strong acid, our definition and our concept would have to be changed, but sodium hydroxide would go on having exactly the same properties it always has had.

In the reversible ionization of a weak acid such as hydrocyanic acid (HCN), we can change the concentrations of the individual ions without changing the total amount of hydrogen cyanide (HCN) in the water. Hydrocyanic acid ionizes very weakly, as follows:

$$HCN + H_2O \rightleftharpoons H_3O^+ + CN^-$$

If a strong acid, such as hydrochloric acid, is added to a solution of hydrogen cyanide, the rate of the reverse reaction will become much greater than the rate of the forward reaction due to the increased concentration of hydrogen ion. This will greatly increase the probability that hydrogen ion and cyanide ion will meet and form molecular hydrogen cyanide. A new equilibrium will be reached, in which the concentration of cyanide ions is greatly reduced and the concentration of undissociated hydrogen cyanide is practically equal to the total amount of hydrogen cyanide originally added. In other words, the addition of the common ion, here the hydrogen ion, suppresses the ionization of hydrogen cyanide almost completely.

A similar effect could be achieved by adding sodium cyanide. Although weak acids themselves are incompletely ionized, their salts are considered to be completely ionized in dilute aqueous solution. Any sodium cyanide that we add will therefore dissolve as sodium ions and cyanide ions. The chances of cyanide ions and hydrogen ions meeting to form undissociated hydrogen cyanide molecules is now greatly enhanced because of the higher concentration of cyanide ions. Therefore, the equilibrium is temporarily upset because the reverse reaction is greatly speeded. Soon a new equilibrium is reached, at which the concentration of hydrogen ion is very small and the hydrogen cyanide molecules are again almost completely undissociated. **The common ion,** here the cyanide ion, **represses the ionization of the weak acid,** here hydrocyanic acid.

> How would NH_4Cl affect the ionization of ammonia in water? What would be the effect of the OH^- ion?

HYDROLYSIS OF SALTS OF WEAK ACIDS OR BASES

If a given anion of a weak acid is a good electron donor in the solution of the weak acid, it will also be a good electron donor in any solution in which it occurs, such as the solution of any of its salts. Placed in water, it will then attract, to a very limited extent, some of the protons from water, leaving behind hydroxide ions. Since hydroxide ions are very strong bases, well able to acquire protons, the concentration of these built up in the solution cannot become very great, because as soon as they have the opportunity, they will tend to reclaim their lost proton. Nevertheless, the action of the anion on the pure water is sufficient to change it from neutral to appreciably basic, by creating the excess of hydroxide ions.

For example, suppose we add sodium cyanide (NaCN) to pure water. The cyanide ion is the ion of the very weak hydrocyanic acid. The acid weakness tells us that the cyanide ion is an excellent donor of an electron pair to a proton. That is why hydrocyanic acid is weak. In contact with water, the cyanide ion can occasionally acquire a proton from the water, leaving behind a hydroxide ion. You may wonder how this is possible, since hydroxide ion tends to combine so strongly with a proton. But after all, if one water molecule can acquire a proton from the hydroxide ion of another water molecule, as it does in the autoionization of water, then many species should be expected to be able to accomplish the same thing to a greater or lesser degree. The chemical reaction is:

$$CN^- + H_2O \rightleftharpoons HCN + OH^-$$

Such a reaction is called the **hydrolysis** of the cyanide ion.

In a similar manner, the cation of a weak base, which is a weak base because the cation holds the hydroxide ion strongly, can acquire a hydroxide ion from neutral water. This leaves behind a hydrogen ion, which, of course, becomes attached to a water molecule. For example, zinc hydroxide is a weak base, which means that zinc ions hold hydroxide ions fairly strongly. If a zinc salt is dissolved in water, the zinc ions may acquire hydroxide ions from the water, causing it to become slightly acidic:

$$Zn^{++} + H_2O \rightleftharpoons Zn(OH)^+ + H^+$$

This is called hydrolysis of the zinc ion.

The anion of a strong acid has little attraction for a proton and, therefore, will have no tendency to acquire one from water. Such an anion will not hydrolyze at all. The cation of a strong base has little attraction for a hydroxide ion and therefore will have no tendency to acquire one from water. Such a cation will not hydrolyze either.

When we talk about the hydrolysis of salts, we really mean the hydrolysis of one or both of their ions. From the above discussion, it should be apparent that salts resulting from neutralizing strong acids and strong bases do not hydrolyze. Salts of strong acids and weak bases must hydrolyze through the action of water on the cation of the base. Salts of weak acids and strong bases must hydrolyze through the anion of the acid. If the salt was formed from both a weak base and a weak acid, then both ions must be expected to hydrolyze.

For example, a solution of sodium chloride will be neither acidic nor basic because this is a salt of a strong base and a strong acid. A solution of sodium carbonate will be basic. The sodium ion, being that of a strong base, will not hydrolyze; however, carbonic acid, and especially the monoprotonic species, bicarbonate ion, are very weak acids. Carbonate ion will hydrolyze leaving an excess of hydroxide ions:

$$CO_3^= + H_2O \rightleftharpoons HCO_3^- + OH^-$$

A solution of aluminum chloride will be acidic. The chloride ion is that of a strong acid and will not hydrolyze. The aluminum ion is that of a weak base (amphoteric). It will tend to acquire hydroxide ions from the water, leaving an excess of hydrogen ions:

$$Al^{+++} + H_2O \rightleftharpoons Al(OH)^{++} + H^+$$

Finally, ammonium hydroxide is a weak base and acetic acid is a weak acid. In a solution of their salt, ammonium acetate, both ions will hydrolyze, and as a result the solution contains molecules of ammonia and acetic acid (CH_3COOH) as well as the original ammonium and acetate ions:

$$NH_4^+ + H_2O \rightleftharpoons NH_4OH + H^+ \rightleftharpoons NH_3 + H_3O^+$$
$$CH_3COO^- + H_2O \rightleftharpoons CH_3COOH + OH^-$$

Whether such a solution will be basic or acidic depends on the relative extents of the two hydrolyses. In this case they are practically alike. The water will still remain essentially neutral, for the hydronium ion from hydrolysis of the ammonium ion will combine with the hydroxide ion from hydrolysis of the acetate ion. But a salt of a weak acid and a weaker base will hydrolyze to give an acidic solution. A salt of a weak base and a weaker acid will hydrolyze to give a basic solution.

pH

Although concentrations of ions in solutions are usually expressed in moles per liter of solution, the hydrogen ion concentration is frequently expressed as a pH. This is defined as the negative logarithm of the hydrogen ion concentration in moles per liter.

A very brief review of logarithms may be helpful here, but you may need further information if you have not studied them at all. The logarithm of a number to the base 10 is the power to which 10 must be raised to be equal to that number. If the number is X, then $10^{\log X} = X$. Thus, if the number is 1, the logarithm of that number is 0, since $10^0 = 1$. If the number is 10, the logarithm of the number is 1, since $10^1 = 10$. If the number is 100, the logarithm of the number is 2, since $10^2 = 100$. If the number is 1000, the logarithm is 3 because $10^3 = 1000$. Tables have been computed and compiled for logarithms of all numbers between 0 and 1, 1 and 10, 10 and 100, and so on. Their utility comes from the fact that when a given number raised to a certain power is multiplied by the same number raised to a different power, the product is the same number raised to the sum of these powers. In other words, $A^m \times A^n = A^{m+n}$. Similarly, to divide, subtract exponents. Since a

Table 24.3.   Hydrolysis of Salts and pH of Salt Solutions

Salt	of	Acid	and	Base	pH of solution
NH_4Cl		HCl strong		NH_3 weak	<7
$ZnCl_2$		HCl strong		$Zn(OH)_2$ weak (amphoteric)	<7
$Al_2(SO_4)_3$		H_2SO_4 strong		$Al(OH)_3$ weak (amphoteric)	<7
NaCl		HCl strong		NaOH strong	7 (no hydrolysis)
$Ba(NO_3)_2$		HNO_3 strong		$Ba(OH)_2$ strong	7 (no hydrolysis)
K_2CO_3		H_2CO_3 weak		KOH strong	>7
$NaOOCCH_3$		$HOOCCH_3$ weak		NaOH strong	>7
$Ca(CN)_2$		HCN weak		$Ca(OH)_2$ strong	>7
NH_4OOCCH_3		$HOOCCH_3$ weak		NH_3 weak	7
MA		HA weak		MOH very weak	<7
MA		HA very weak		MOH weak	>7

logarithm is an exponent of the same number, ten, to multiply two or more numbers, simply add their logarithms and then look up in the tables that number (antilogarithm) that corresponds to that sum.

Concentrations of hydrogen ion are usually less than one molar. This means that their logarithms are negative. If the concentration of hydrogen ion is 10^{-1} the logarithm is obviously -1, since this is the power to which 10 must be raised to equal 10^{-1}. The negative of -1 is $+1$, which is therefore the pH of that solution. If the concentration of hydrogen ion is 10^{-7} mole per liter, the logarithm is -7 and the negative of that logarithm is $+7$, so the pH is 7. This is the concentration of hydrogen ion in pure water, where it equals the concentration of hydroxide ion. Any solution of pH less than 7 is therefore acidic. Any solution of pH more than 7 is basic. When the hydrogen ion concentration is between 1 and 10 times 10 raised to a whole number power, then the pH is also intermediate. For example, a pH of 4.7 represents a hydrogen ion concentration that is between 10^{-5} and 10^{-4} mole per liter. These are between a hundred and a thousand times *greater* than 10^{-7}, so the solution is clearly acidic.

The effects of hydrolysis of a neutral salt are often indicated by saying that the pH of a solution of a salt of a strong base and weak acid must be greater than 7; the pH of a solution of a salt of a strong acid and weak base must be less than 7.

Name some strong acids and strong bases.

Predict the approximate pH of solutions of each of the following: $ZnSO_4$, $BaCl_2$, K_2CO_3, NH_4Br, $AlCl_3$.

Buffers

Buffers are substances that help to keep the pH of a solution from undergoing drastic change when small quantities of acid or base are added. A typical buffer can be a solution of a weak acid and one of its salts. For example, a solution of a desired pH may be made by adding a little acetic acid and sodium acetate together. If an attempt is made to change this pH by adding a little acid, which in plain water would have a large effect, the following reaction absorbs the added hydrogen ion, keeping its concentration from rising unduly:

$$CH_3COO^- + H^+ \rightleftharpoons CH_3COOH$$

But if an attempt is made to change the pH in the opposite direction, by adding a little base, the extra hydroxide ion will be used up in the following reaction:

$$CH_3COOH + OH^- \rightleftharpoons CH_3COO^- + H_2O$$

In summary, when a solution contains both a weak acid and its salt, the solution is buffered against change in pH resulting from addition of further acid or base. The weak acid takes up the added hydroxide ion, forming an anion and water. The anion takes up the added hydrogen ion, forming undissociated weak acid.

The pH is extremely important in most biological fluid systems. Usually such natural systems are protected against the catastrophe of sudden influxes of acid or base by built-in buffering agents that keep the pH relatively constant. Control of the hydrogen ion concentration within rather narrow limits is also very desirable in many laboratory experimental procedures. This can be accomplished by deliberately adding an appropriate buffer to the solution.

INDICATORS AND ACID-BASE TITRATIONS

There are many substances that change color with changes in the pH of a solution. Such substances are known as **indicators.** Usually their color change is associated with the indicator's function as a very weak acid where the color of the molecular form differs from the color of the anion. Three of the more common indicators are **methyl red,** which changes from red to yellow when the pH changes from about 4.2 to 6.3, **litmus,** which changes from red to blue when the pH changes from about 5.6 to 8.0, and **phenolphthalein,** which changes from colorless to red or pink while the pH is changing from 8.2 to 9.8. Litmus is commonly used in the laboratory in the form of porous paper which has absorbed it. Red litmus is used for testing for bases, since alkaline solutions color it blue. Blue litmus is used for testing for acids, since acidic solutions color it red or pink.

Often it is useful to be able to neutralize an acidic or basic solution. The only real problem in this is to know when neutralization has been accomplished. Usually the acid, base, and salt are all colorless in solution and you cannot tell the difference by looking. If a small amount of indicator is added, however, the color and the color change corresponding to the appropriate pH change are easily visible. In the slow, carefully measured addition of an acid to a base, or vice versa, the point at which neutralization has been achieved can be determined quite precisely. If the exact quantity of acid per milliliter of added solution is known, and the exact volume of solution required to neutralize the unknown base is measured, then the exact total amount of acid added can be calculated. From this, the equivalent amount of base that must have been neutralized is easily determined. Such a procedure, common in analytical chemistry, is called the **titration** of a base by an acid. A titration, in general, is the slow addition of measured quantities of one reagent solution to another, with some means of knowing when the correct amount has been added. By using a combination of indicators, whose color changes cover a wide range of pH, it is possible to determine the approximate pH of any solution from the color.

If no buffer is present, a very small quantity—a drop or two—of a dilute solution of acid or base will have a large effect on the pH. Therefore, in the titration of a strong acid with a strong base or vice versa, the exact pH at which the indicator changes color is not very critical. One drop more or less at the neutralization point will cause the pH to change several integers. However, if we wish to determine quantitatively the concentration of a weak acid or a weak base, we must take into account that when the acid or base is exactly neutralized, the solution will not be exactly neutral (i.e., have a pH of 7). This is because of hydrolysis.

For example, suppose we wish to determine the amount of acetic acid in vinegar by titrating it with a standard sodium hydroxide solution. Remember that what we want to do is add enough sodium hydroxide so that the solution becomes exactly the same as if the correct quantity of sodium acetate had been added to pure water. A solution of pure sodium acetate is not neutral, because the acetate ion hydrolyzes to leave an excess of hydroxide ions:

$$CH_3COO^- + H_2O \rightleftharpoons CH_3COOH + OH^-$$

In other words, we wish to add sodium hydroxide not until the solution becomes exactly neutral, but rather, until the solution becomes exactly as alkaline as it would be if we had only pure sodium acetate present. This calls for the addition of the standard sodium hydroxide beyond pH 7 to a somewhat higher value. We therefore choose an indicator that changes color not at pH 7 but at a higher pH. Phenolphthalein serves very nicely in this case.

Similarly, ammonium hydroxide, which is really a solution of ammonia in water, is weakly basic:

$$NH_3 + H_2O \rightleftharpoons NH_4^+ + OH^-$$

To determine the amount of ammonia in a solution, we can titrate it with a strong standard acid such as hydrochloric acid. The product, ammonium chloride, would not give an exactly neutral solution in pure water because of the hydrolysis of the ammonium ion:

$$NH_4^+ + H_2O \rightleftharpoons H^+ + (NH_4OH \rightleftharpoons NH_3 + H_2O)$$

We should therefore try to add exactly enough hydrochloric acid to make the solution slightly acidic to correspond to complete neutralization of the ammonia and hydrolysis of the ammonium ion. Here an indicator that changes color in the acid range, like methyl red, is more suitable.

Test Your Memory

1. a) Write an equation for the ionization of an acid in water.
   b) Write an expression for the equilibrium constant for that ionization.
2. What properties of an anion determine the extent of ionization?
3. What is meant by *ionization constant?*
4. What does the partial charge on oxygen have to do with acid strength?
5. a) What is a *conjugate acid?*
   b) What is a *conjugate base?*
6. What is the *Bronsted-Lowry concept* of acids and bases?
7. What is meant by *common ion effect* in acid ionization?
8. What is meant by *hydrolysis of a salt?*
9. Write equations showing how hydrolysis of ions can change the hydrogen ion concentration in both directions.
10. Why doesn't sodium chloride hydrolyze?
11. Define pH.
12. a) What does a buffer do? b) How does it function?
13. What is an indicator?
14. How is a titration carried out?
15. What is a polyprotic acid?
16. What is a strong acid?

Test Your Understanding

1. Write an expression for the equilibrium constant for the ionization of $H_2PO_4^-$.
2. Why don't molecules separate into ions without help?

3. What are the conjugate bases corresponding to H_2O, HCN, H_2S, HCl, and HNO_3?

4. What are the conjugate acids corresponding to $CO_3^=$, $SO_4^=$, NH_3, Cl^-, I^-?

5. Write equations for the hydrolysis of Al^{+++}, Cd^{++}, NH_4^+, Ac^-, CN^-, $CO_3^=$.

6. How would the pH of water be changed by the addition of (a) NaAc, (b) KCN, (c) NH_4Cl, (d) Na_2CO_3, (e) K_2SO_4, (f) LiBr?

7. What pH corresponds to H^+ concentrations of 10^{-3}, 10^{-9}, 10^{-2}, 10^{-12}?

8. What is the OH^- concentration in solutions of pH 4, 6, 8, 10, and 12?

9. Write equations showing how a solution containing $H_2PO_4^-$ would be buffered.

25

ELECTROCHEMISTRY: THE USE OF ELECTRICAL ENERGY TO PRODUCE CHEMICAL CHANGE

OXIDATION-REDUCTION BY ELECTRICITY

The production of fluorine from fluoride ion, hydrogen from hydrogen ion, and sodium hydroxide in solution from sodium chloride are all examples of the use of electrical energy to bring about chemical change. Since chemical change frequently involves a shifting of electrons, and since electricity is a flow of electrons, it is not surprising that a close relationship between electricity and chemical change has long been recognized. The most extensive studies were made more than a century ago by a brilliant experimenter named Michael Faraday (1791–1867). His work gave results of great practical importance to us today.

If certain electrically neutral materials are rubbed together, electrons from one become attached to the other, giving the one a negative charge and leaving the original source of the electrons positively charged. By various mechanical devices it is possible to build up a considerable charge and a considerable difference in potential between the two materials. Studies of such **electrostatic charges** produced the earliest information about electricity. Later it was found that certain chemical reactions could be carried out in such a way as to produce a flow of electrons through a wire or other conductor. We shall examine this phenomenon in some detail in Chapter 26. Then it was observed that when a conductor is passed through a magnetic field, there is induced within it a flow of electrons. This is the basis of the modern electromagnetic generator, or "electron pump."

We have seen in a general way that highly positive ions have a strong attraction for electrons and tend to acquire them, acting as oxidizing agents. Similarly, highly negative ions hold electrons relatively weakly, and can lose them, acting as reducing agents. By means of a generator or electron pump of some kind, electrons can be pumped out of one piece of metal and into another. The metal having the surplus of electrons (and thus a negative charge) takes on the qualities of a reducing agent. It can readily supply electrons from its surplus to some electron-attracting chemical species like a positive ion. The metal that has the deficiency of electrons (and thus a positive charge) takes on the qualities of an oxidizing agent. It removes electrons from chemical reducing agents in an attempt to eliminate the deficiency.

QUALITATIVE ASPECTS OF ELECTROLYSIS

If an electrical potential is created across two such pieces of metal partially submerged in a liquid, they are called **electrodes.** Electrons may or may not flow off the negative electrode, called the **cathode,** into the liquid, and out of the liquid into the positive electrode, called the **anode.** If there is no such flow of electrons, the liquid is called a nonelectrolyte. If such a flow occurs, it is called an **electrolyte.**

As previously noted, the difference between an electrolyte and a non-electrolyte arises from the presence or absence of mobile ions. If ions are present and can move in the electrical field, then conduction takes place. The mechanism for **electrolytic** conduction is *not* the same as for metallic conduction. If two electrodes are simply connected by a metal wire, in addition to their connection through the electron source, electrons will flow from electron source to the cathode, then into the wire, through the wire to the anode, into the anode, and back to the electron source (dry cell or generator). These electrons comprise the valence electrons of the conducting system. The same electrons that leave the cathode to enter the wire soon find their way out of the wire again to enter the anode. This is metallic conduction.

In electrolytic conduction, the electrons that leave the cathode to enter the electrolyte are taken out of the "circuit" permanently. The only reason there appears to be a circuit is this: For every electron that permanently leaves the cathode, *another* electron, a different one from a different source, leaves the electrolyte to join the anode. Electrons are removed from the cathode by positive ions in the electrolyte which thus become neutral atoms and separate from the electrolyte. Electrons are supplied to the anode by negative ions in the electrolyte which lose their surplus of electrons to the anode, thus becoming neutral atoms and separating from the electrolyte. The electrons which join the cations and leave the anions cannot be the same ones, yet we cannot tell the difference.

If six seemingly identical basketballs per second enter one door of a dark room, and simultaneously six identical basketballs per second come bounding out a second door to that room, there is a steady flow of basketballs through that room. For all we know, somebody may be in the room secretly throwing the incoming basketballs into the basement, while a manufacturer may be delivering the same number of new basketballs at the same time

Figure 25.1. Comparison of Metallic and Electrolytic Conduction.

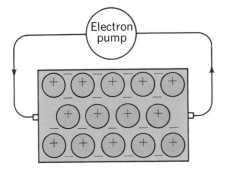

In **metallic conduction,** electrons flowing in at one side of the metal circuit simply displace by repulsion the electrons originally there as delocalized valence electrons. Thus the *identical* electrons can travel through the complete circuit. (Remember that a metal can be pictured as a collection of cations held together by the cloud of valence electrons in which they are imbedded.)

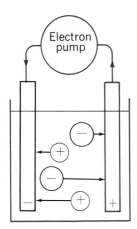

On the other hand, in **electrolytic conduction,** the *same* electrons do not pass from cathode to anode. It *seems* that they do because for every electron that leaves the cathode, discharging a cation, *another* electron simultaneously leaves an anion to join the anode. The current that only *appears* to flow through the electrolyte is completely absorbed by cations at the cathode, which thereby become neutral atoms. The anions are a new source of current at the anode, where they give up their surplus of electrons, thereby also becoming neutral atoms. This is the basis for stating that the current is carried by *ions* in electrolytic conduction. If ions are absent, current does not flow.

through an unseen window, to be rolled out the second door. This would be similar in principle to the fate of electrons in electrolytic conduction, or **electrolysis.** The ones that go in are not the same as the ones that come out.

In electrolysis, however, we are able to observe what happens, to a limited extent. We can usually see chemical change occurring at both electrodes. Usually either bubbles of gas are escaping or some new solid is appearing at each electrode.

Molten Salts

Two types of electrolytes may be used in electrolysis. One is simply a fused salt. Since salts are usually strongly held together, a high temperature is commonly needed for the melting. This magnifies the problem of keeping the electrode materials from combining with the products of electrolysis as they are formed at the electrode surface. Let us assume that inert electrodes are dipped in a melt of sodium chloride. First consider a solid crystal of sodium chloride between the two electrodes: only a very high potential difference between the electrodes could cause electrons to pass through this crystal. The separate atoms, usually considered to be present essentially as charged ions, are held too rigidly for them to move toward the electrodes. Therefore, at any ordinary potential difference, the sodium chloride crystal would be a nonelectrolyte or nonconductor. If, however, the crystal lattice is broken down by melting, the ions are free to move. The positive ions will be attracted toward the cathode while the negative ions will be attracted toward the anode. For this reason, positive ions are called **cations,** and negative ions, **anions.** At the cathode, sodium ions each remove an electron to become sodium atoms, which form droplets of molten sodium that rise to the surface. At the same time, chloride ions at the anode surface each lose an electron to become chlorine atoms. These join in Cl_2 molecules that form bubbles that rise to the surface.

We really do not know whether all of the molten sodium chloride is in the form of free ions. Possibly relatively few free ions are present. Nor can we

Figure 25.2. Diagram of Electrolysis of Molten NaCl.

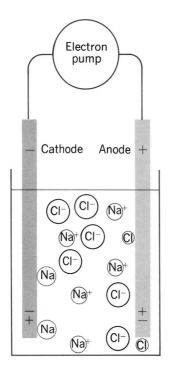

Molten NaCl appears to contain free Na+ and Cl- ions. When electrons are pumped from one of two electrodes immersed in the molten salt (making it an anode) into the other electrode (making it a cathode), these charges attract ions of opposite charge and repel ions of like charge. Positive sodium ions migrate toward the negatively charged cathode, from which they take one electron each, becoming sodium atoms. The sodium, being liquid at the high temperature of the molten salt, and less dense, rises to the surface. Negative chloride ions migrate toward the positively charged anode, to which they give up their extra electrons, becoming chlorine atoms. These atoms form Cl_2 molecules, which rise to the surface and escape as a gas. In this manner the electrical energy reverses the normal combination of sodium and chlorine to form sodium chloride. In electrolysis, oxidation always occurs at the anode and reduction at the cathode, as long as the current flows. Here chloride ions are oxidized to chlorine atoms and sodium ions are reduced to sodium atoms.

see exactly what goes on at each electrode. All we do know is that electrons leave the cathode to go into the melt, and that sodium atoms form there. Electrons do come out on the anode, and chlorine gas does form there. The simplest explanation, although not necessarily the fully correct one, is that sodium chloride is a collection of ions in the melt and that these are discharged at the respective electrodes. We also know that there must be some mechanism by which the ions can discharge around each electrode without producing an excess of the oppositely charged ion in that region. Such an excess would, in effect, reduce the potential difference between electrodes. In a melt of ions, such an excess is prevented by migration of more cations to replace those discharged at the cathode, and the migration of more anions to replace those discharged at the anode.

In general, any molten binary compound that will conduct an electric current can be decomposed by electrolysis into its component elements.

Which products would be found at the cathode, and which at the anode, in electrolysis of each of the following fused salts: KBr, CaO, Na_2S, $CuCl_2$.

Solutions

The second type of electrolyte that can be used in electrolysis is an ionic solution. Pure water is practically a nonelectrolyte, but when ions of solute are present in significant concentrations, the water solution conducts quite well. This conduction is electrolytic. Chemical change occurs at each electrode. Water can be decomposed by electrolysis into its components, hydrogen and oxygen, if the ions present are either like those of water itself or ions more difficult to discharge than the ions of water.

For instance, the electrolytic substance added to the water can be sulfuric acid, sodium hydroxide, or sodium sulfate. If it is sulfuric acid, the ions are hydrogen ions and sulfate ions. The hydrogen ions are attracted to the cathode and discharged, producing elemental hydrogen. The sulfate ions are attracted to the anode but oxygen is produced. The exact mechanism by which this occurs is not known. If we imagine sulfate ions ($SO_4^=$) to be discharged, the product would be SO_4. This would be very unstable, losing oxygen and forming SO_3. This SO_3 would react with the water forming sulfuric acid again. More likely, it is the water molecules themselves which are reacting:

$$4 H_2O \rightarrow 4 e^- + 4 H^+ + 4 (OH)$$

$$4 (OH) \rightarrow O_2 + 2 H_2O$$

Probably the actual reactions are more complex than this. Whatever the mechanism, oxygen is produced, a constant concentration of sulfate ion remains in the solution, and new hydrogen ions are produced to replace those discharged at the cathode.

When sodium hydroxide is the electrolyte, the hydroxide ions can be pictured as being discharged at the anode:

$$4 \, OH^- \rightarrow 4 \, e^- + 4 \, (OH)$$

$$4 \, (OH) \rightarrow O_2 + 2 \, H_2O$$

Meanwhile at the cathode hydrogen ions are being discharged in preference to sodium ions. It is convenient to consider that hydronium ions are being discharged at the cathode and hydroxide ions at the anode. Yet in the sulfuric acid solution the hydroxide ion concentration would be extremely small. In the sodium hydroxide solution the hydronium ion concentration would be extremely small. It seems possible that the actual reaction is between the electrode electrons and water molecules at the cathode:

$$4 \, e^- + 4 \, H_2O \rightarrow 2 \, H_2 + 4 \, OH^-$$

In part, at least, these mechanisms are supported by the electrolysis of water containing sodium sulfate. Here, as before, hydrogen is released at the cathode and oxygen at the anode. By adding some indicator to the solution, it can be demonstrated that hydroxide ions tend to accumulate around the cathode, and hydrogen ions around the anode.

If water molecules themselves are capable of being discharged at the electrodes, why does water require additional ions in solution before it can be electrolyzed? This is a difficult question to answer. It can be observed that the accumulation of hydroxide ions around the cathode and hydrogen ions around the anode would tend to stop the electrolytic decomposition in pure water because the excessive buildup of charge in the solution would counteract and reduce the potential between the electrodes. When an ionic solute is present, its ions can migrate into the electrode regions to neutralize the charge buildup. Thus, sodium ions can move to the cathode region to offset the hydroxide ion accumulation, and sulfate ions can move to the anode region to offset the hydrogen ion accumulation.

If the solute furnishes cations that are more easily discharged than hydrogen ions, or anions that are more easily discharged than hydroxide ions, the electrolysis products will consist of the solute atoms rather than hydrogen and oxygen. For example, if the cation is silver or copper, it is more easily discharged than hydrogen ion, and silver or copper will be plated out on the cathode. If the anion is chloride, chlorine instead of oxygen will be liberated at the anode.

On a commercial scale, electrolysis is used to isolate or purify many metals. If the metal ion is easier to discharge than water or its ions, an aqueous solution is electrolyzed. If the metal ion is not as easy to discharge as water or its ions, the presence of water must be avoided. Usually an anhydrous salt of the metal is fused and electrolyzed. A *mixture* of fused salts, which melts at a lower temperature, is always desirable because at high temperatures such anode products as chlorine become extremely corrosive to the electrode material. In addition, a few metal salts can be dissolved in certain nonaqueous solvents in which they provide high enough ion concentrations for successful electrolysis.

QUANTITATIVE ELECTROLYSIS

A very fundamental fact about electrical circuits is that the number of electrons passing each point in the circuit during the same period of time must be equal. The number flowing into the generator must exactly equal the number flowing out of the generator. The number flowing out of the cathode must exactly equal the number flowing into the anode. Therefore, the number of electrons used to discharge cations must equal exactly the number of electrons obtained by the discharge of anions. Michael Faraday first observed this electrochemical equivalence. The chemical change occurring at the cathode must be "equivalent" to the chemical change occurring at the anode: The quantity of an element formed at the cathode must be exactly the right amount to react completely with the element formed at the anode, with none of either left over.

The unit called the *mole,* which has become so useful in chemistry, is applied to the number of electrons involved in an electrolysis. One mole of electrons, which is Avogadro's number of electrons, is called a **faraday.** The amount of chemical change brought about by the passage of one faraday of electrons through an electrolytic cell is determined as the quantity of substance formed at an electrode, which is called a **chemical equivalent.** The **equivalent weight,** which we have already considered previously, is the amount of any substance measured in grams that could be formed at an electrode by one faraday of electrons. For the discharge of ions of unit charge, one equivalent weight and one mole are exactly the same, but when the ion bears more than one charge, the equivalent weight is found by dividing the weight of one mole of atoms by the charge. One faraday is sufficient to deposit one mole of sodium atoms from Na^+, but only one-half mole of magnesium atoms from Mg^{++}, since each ion requires two electrons. Similarly, each ion of aluminum, Al^{+++}, requires three electrons for discharge; one faraday is enough to deposit only one-third of a mole of aluminum. The weights of one mole in grams are: sodium 23 g, magnesium 24 g, and aluminum 27 g. The equivalent weights are sodium 23 g, magnesium 12 g (24/2), and aluminum 9 g (27/3).

Similarly, one mole of chloride ions would supply one faraday of electrons to the anode, so one mole equals one equivalent weight. (Since electrons are negligible in mass, negative and positive ions are considered to be identical in mass to their neutral atoms.) One mole of oxide ion, $O^=$, would supply two faradays of electrons to the anode. Since an equivalent weight is the amount that would supply only one faraday, one equivalent weight of oxide ion is one-half the weight of one mole of atoms, or $16/2 = 8$ g. One equivalent weight of chloride ion would be about 35.5 g. If it were possible to electrolyze some fused salt of a trinegative ion, the equivalent weight of this would be one-third the weight of one mole of atoms. Each anion would furnish three electrons, and each mole, three faradays of electrons, to the anode.

In electrolysis of a substance such as Al_2O_3, every faraday would produce one-third mole of aluminum at the cathode and one-fourth mole of O_2 at the anode. These quantities are one equivalent of aluminum and one equivalent of oxygen. They are exactly the correct amounts to react with one another leaving no unreacted atoms of either kind. Furthermore, they are exactly equivalent to one equivalent of any other substance. Using the weight in grams that corresponds to each equivalent weight, we can observe that, if the equivalent weight of magnesium is 12 g and the equivalent weight of oxygen is 8 g, 12 g of magnesium is exactly the correct quantity to be oxidized by 8 g of oxygen. Since the atomic weight ratio is 24:16 and the combination is 1:1 in atoms, the 12:8 is quite correct. Also, 23 g of sodium should be oxidized by 8 g of oxygen. This is consistent with the formula, Na_2O, and the weight contributions: sodium 46 and oxygen 16, since 46:16 equals 23:8. The equivalent weight of any cation is the exact quantity needed to react with the equivalent weight of any anion to form a neutral salt.

Quantity of electricity is usually measured in the arbitrary unit called the **coulomb.** One faraday is approximately 96,500 coulombs. An **ampere** is defined as a unit of electric current equal to the flow of one coulomb per second. Given the amperage of a current used for electrolysis and the length of time current flows, the exact quantities of substances formed at each electrode can be calculated easily.

Example 25.1. *In the production of hydrogen and oxygen by electrolysis of water, a current of 5 amps is allowed to flow through the solution for one hour. What weight of products forms?*

One hour contains 60 minutes of 60 seconds each, or a total of 3600 seconds. A current of 5 amps means 5 coulombs per second, and $5 \times 3600 = 18,000$ coulombs per hour. If one faraday is 96,500 coulombs, the total quantity of current used in the electrolysis is $18,000/96,500$, or 0.187 faraday. The quantity of hydrogen must be 0.187 equivalent weight, or $0.187 \times 1 = 0.187$ g. The quantity of oxygen must also be 0.187 equivalent weight, since exactly the same number of electrons must be involved in the anode reaction as in the cathode reaction. The weight of oxygen formed is therefore 0.187×8 or 1.495 g.

To check this result, remember that water has a molecular weight of 18. Therefore, the percentage of oxygen is close to $16/18 \times 100$, or 88.9%. The total weight of electrolysis products is $0.187 + 1.495$, or 1.682 g. Taking

88.9% of 1.682 g we find the oxygen produced should weigh 1.495 g, which agrees with what we calculated above.

Example 25.2. *In a carefully designed apparatus called the* silver coulometer, *the quantity of an electric current flow can be determined experimentally by weighing the silver deposited by the current upon a cathode. Suppose the cathode weighed 120.056 g before the experiment and 278.944 g after the flow of current. How many coulombs flowed?*

Silver forms Ag^+ ions, and one equivalent weight is the same as the weight of one mole of atoms: 107.870 g. The weight gain of the cathode was $278.944 - 120.056$ or 158.888 g. The number of faradays is therefore equal to $158.888/107.870$ or 1.47, from which the number of coulombs is obtained by multiplying by 96,500. The answer is about 142,000 coulombs.

Test Your Memory

1. Who was Michael Faraday?
2. How can a piece of metal be caused to act as a reducing agent? An oxidizing agent?
3. Identify the cathode and the anode.
4. Compare metallic conduction with electrolytic conduction.
5. What two types of material conduct a current by transport of ions?
6. What is a cation? An anion?
7. What are the products of electrolysis of water?
8. What is meant by *"electrochemical equivalence"*?
9. Why is an equivalent weight the same as a mole for sodium, but not for aluminum?
10. How many coulombs are there in one faraday?
11. a) Define *ampere.* b) What is an ampere in faradays per second?

Test Your Understanding

1. If a fused salt contains unit-charged cations and tricharged anions, how many anions would be discharged during an electrolysis that produces 10^{15} atoms from the cations?
2. How many electrons are in one coulomb?
3. How many coulombs flow by a given point in a circuit if a current of 0.1 amp flows for 16 hours?
4. How many seconds are in one day? One week?
5. a) How many weeks would be required for a current of one amp to electrolyze 10 liters of water?
   b) What volume of hydrogen would be obtained?
   c) What volume of oxygen would be formed?

6. In the electroplating of silver, a current of 0.5 amp would deposit how many grams of silver in six hours? (Silver forms Ag^+.)
7. To measure a flow of electricity, the weight of copper deposited from a solution of $CuSO_4$ is found to be 2.5 g after 2.4 hrs. What was the amperage?

26

ELECTROCHEMISTRY: THE PRODUCTION OF ELECTRICAL ENERGY FROM CHEMICAL REACTIONS

METALS IN WATER

Metals were described earlier as consisting of cations held together by attraction to the relatively mobile and delocalized valence electrons. In addition, the dissolution of metal salts in water was pictured as involving, among other things, hydration of the cations. It is not unreasonable, therefore, to expect that if a metal is placed in contact with water, the metal cations at the surface of the metal will tend to become hydrated and dissolve. If this were a metal salt, the anion would also become hydrated and dissolve. Thus, the undissolved crystal would remain electrically neutral, as would the solution. But since there are only cations in the metal, and since the negative components are electrons themselves, dissolution of the cations leaves extra electrons behind on the metal, giving it a negative charge. The presence of cations but no anions in the solution gives a positive charge to the solution. Before this process can go very far, the potential difference between metal and solution becomes so great that no further dissolution of the metal can occur. Stated differently, an equilibrium is soon reached, at which the rate of return of cations to the metal crystal equals the rate at which they leave to join the solution:

$$M(s) + aq \rightleftharpoons M^+(aq) + M(s)^-$$

In this formal equation, $M(s)$ means the metal in the solid phase, aq means water of hydration, $M^+(aq)$ means the hydrated cation, and $M(s)^-$ indicates the fact that the electron that once belonged to the cation is now left behind on the solid metal, giving it an excess negative charge.

Figure 26.1. Representation of a Metal Electrode in Water.

A metal consists of cations held together by a cloud of valence electrons in which they are imbedded. In contact with water, the surface cations tend to become hydrated. A few leave the crystal to become hydrated ions in solution, leaving their valence electrons behind on the crystal (the electrode). Equilibrium is soon reached, with cations leaving and rejoining the metal at equal rates.

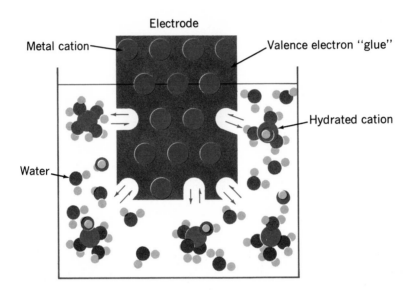

The *electrode potential* resulting from the excess of negative charge left on the electrode by the dissolved cations is proportional to the hydration energy of the cations and inversely proportional to the energies required to atomize the metal and remove its valence electrons.

The equilibrium constant for this reaction is different for each different metal. In other words, the concentration of excess electrons accumulating on a metal in contact with water is different for each different metal. Between any two different metals, then, both immersed in water, there will exist a potential difference. If the metals are dipped into the same solution and are then connected by an external wire, electrons will flow from the higher potential to the lower, as electrons always do when a potential difference exists and a conductor is available.

We have already seen that electrons are capable of reacting with water. Whether or not they react under circumstances such as those described depends on how densely they accumulate on the metal—in other words, on how extensively the cations tend to dissolve. Whether the metal reacts with the water, liberating hydrogen, depends in part on how great a tendency it has to dissolve as cations, for this determines how high a concentration of electrons can be built up on the metal remaining. Sodium ions leave solid sodium to dissolve in water very easily. The electron concentration they leave behind is ample to discharge positive hydrogen, forming H_2. Copper ions leave the metal much less readily. When equilibrium is reached, the concentration of electrons on the copper metal is too small to discharge the positive hydrogen of water. For these reasons, sodium reacts vigorously with water and copper does not react at all.

It is interesting to compare free electrons with negative ions. If a negative ion can become hydrated and dissolve, then why cannot a free electron become hydrated and dissolve? Recently it has been proven that under appropriate conditions hydrated electrons do exist in water. However, these electrons are extremely reactive because of the positive hydrogen of water, to which they presumably become attached in the hydration process. These hydrogens readily acquire the electrons for their own, forming hydrogen atoms. In other words, water is too strong an oxidizing agent to endure contact with free electrons without reacting with them. But, a solvent such as liquid ammonia is not nearly as strongly oxidizing as water. When sodium is placed in contact with liquid ammonia, sodium ions become solvated (attached to solvent molecules) and dissolve, *and* electrons also become solvated and dissolve. A solvated electron has a bright blue color in liquid ammonia. All the M1 and M2 metals dissolve in liquid ammonia giving the same blue color. Each electron is believed to occupy a cavity created by four ammonia molecules, directing their three hydrogen atoms each toward the electron, in a tetrahedral configuration of ammonia molecules.

THE VOLTAIC CELL

Consider a piece of zinc dipped in dilute hydrochloric acid. The tendency for zinc ions to become hydrated and dissolve in water is sufficient to build up an electron concentration on the zinc capable of reducing water, forming hydrogen. The accumulation of hydroxide ions as a byproduct must be avoided, however, since they quickly coat the zinc with insoluble and impervious zinc hydroxide, making impossible further dissolution of the zinc or evolution of hydrogen. This problem is solved by adding the hydrochloric acid, whose protons unite with the hydroxide ions as fast as they are formed, preventing the formation of insoluble zinc hydroxide.

If this is a piece of very pure zinc, what we will observe is an initial evolution of hydrogen which quickly slows down until it is almost imperceptible. This is partly explained by the accumulation of hydrogen on the surface of the zinc, which greatly reduces the ability of new zinc ions to dissolve. Also, the positive zinc ions entering the solution repel the positive hydrogen ions, hindering their approach. But it is the surplus electrons left behind on the zinc which discharge the hydrogen ions. These same electrons can perform in exactly the same way if they are made available somewhere other than on the zinc. Suppose a piece of copper is placed in the solution. Nothing visible happens to the copper, which is incapable of displacing hydrogen from the hydrochloric acid solution. But if the copper is moved so that it touches the zinc, we observe bubbles of hydrogen forming on the surface of the *copper*. Since copper in equilibrium with the solution accumulates a far smaller concentration of electrons than does zinc, the electron pressure on the zinc is much greater than on the copper. As soon as contact is made between

Figure 26.2.   Diagram of a Voltaic Cell Made by Combining Two Half Cells.

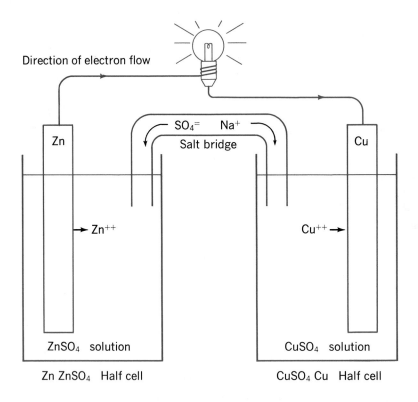

When the circuit is closed (completed), zinc ions (which tend to go into solution much more readily than copper ions, chiefly because of the much stronger metallic bonding in copper) dissolve continuously. They leave behind excess electrons on the zinc bar which flow through the external circuit to the copper. This negative charge on copper attracts Cu^{++} ions, which by taking electrons from the copper electrode become copper atoms plated onto this electrode. Migration of ions through the salt bridge prevents accumulation of an excess of like charged ions in the solutions, but the bridge inhibits thorough mixing.

the two metals, the electrons from the zinc spread out rapidly through the copper. No positive zinc ions are present next to the surface of the copper to impede the approach of the hydrogen ions, which readily approach the copper surface where they can easily acquire the electrons that came from the zinc. As long as the zinc continues to dissolve, electrons flow from it to the copper, and hydrogen is discharged at the copper.

Now, instead of placing the zinc and copper chunks in contact in the solution, suppose we connect them by a wire, under the surface of the liquid. The reaction, of course, proceeds just as when the contact was direct. If we connect the chunks by a wire that comes out of the liquid and goes back in again, part of the electrical circuit is external. The flow of electrons through this wire can be detected. We have gained electrical energy from the reaction, which is essentially:

$$Zn + 2 H^+ \rightarrow Zn^{++} + H_2$$

But the reaction has not involved a direct transfer of electrons from the zinc to the hydrogen ions. The electrons first flowed through a wire, and then into the hydrogen ions. An oxidation-reduction reaction, with the hydrogen ion as oxidant and the zinc metal as reductant, has been carried out without the oxidizing agent and the reducing agent coming into direct contact at all. They have been connected only through an external wire through which the electrons travel.

A device to harness chemical energy as electrical energy is called a **voltaic cell,** used in flashlights, storage batteries, and countless other devices for creating electrical currents without benefit of mechanical generators. In principle, any oxidation-reduction reaction can be conducted under conditions requiring the transfer of electrons to occur through an external conductor. In practice, great ingenuity is often required to set up practical conditions.

Half-Cell Potentials

The potential of a voltaic cell is the result of difference in potential between the two electrodes. Because of the difficulty in measuring the potential of one electrode, a relative scale has been established. The potential of a **hydrogen electrode** is taken arbitrarily as zero. A single electrode of a voltaic cell, together with the solution surrounding it, is called a **half-cell.** The hydrogen half-cell is constructed by using a platinum electrode with very finely divided platinum at the bottom, and bubbling a stream of hydrogen gas around it. The reaction is:

$$1/2 H_2 \rightleftharpoons H^+ (aq) + e^-$$

Because the potential of this or any electrode varies with a number of factors, such as temperature, concentration, and physical state, it is necessary to standardize the conditions carefully. The standard hydrogen electrode is one

Figure 26.3. Diagram of a Hydrogen Electrode.

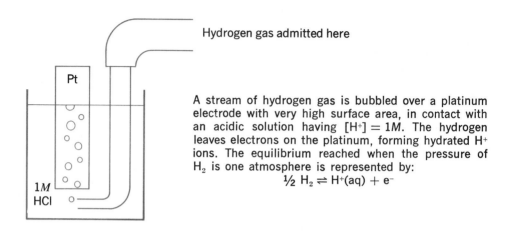

Hydrogen gas admitted here

A stream of hydrogen gas is bubbled over a platinum electrode with very high surface area, in contact with an acidic solution having $[H^+] = 1M$. The hydrogen leaves electrons on the platinum, forming hydrated H^+ ions. The equilibrium reached when the pressure of H_2 is one atmosphere is represented by:
$$\tfrac{1}{2}\ H_2 \rightleftharpoons H^+(aq) + e^-$$

in which: (1) the hydrogen gas is at one atmosphere of pressure; (2) the concentration of hydrogen ion in the solution around the platinum is 1 *M;* and (3) the temperature is 25°C.

Similarly, a standard zinc half-cell involves pure zinc metal in contact with a solution in which the concentration of zinc ion (Zn^{++}) is 1 *M* at 25°C.

A voltaic cell could consist of a zinc half-cell and a hydrogen half-cell. The electrodes could dip into the same solution, but to prevent free mixing of the electrode solutions it is better to contain them separately and connect them by a porous barrier or an inverted U-tube full of salt solution. The latter device is called a **salt bridge;** it allows electroneutrality to be preserved by migration of ions from one half-cell to the other, but it prevents free mixing. When the two half-cells are connected by an external wire, electrons flow from the zinc, through the wire, and into the platinum, where they serve to discharge hydrogen. If this potential is carefully balanced by an external source of current so that there is no net flow of electrons through the wire when the half-cells are connected, the potential can be measured accurately. (If current is allowed to flow, small temperature and concentration differences occur that may vary the potential somewhat.) The accurately measured potential difference between the standard half-cells of zinc and hydrogen is 0.76 volt. Remember that this is only a *difference.* Since the value of zero has been arbitrarily assigned to the hydrogen electrode, the value for zinc is taken as 0.76.

Consider a combination of half-cells of copper and hydrogen. The copper electrode would be a piece of copper metal immersed in a solution having a 1 *M* concentration of Cu^{++} ions. The tendency for copper to form copper ions is smaller than the tendency of hydrogen gas to form hydrogen ions. If the two half-cells are connected, electrons flow through the external wire from the hydrogen to the copper. The electrons on the copper attract copper ions which plate out on the copper surface. Meanwhile, at the other electrode, hydrogen gas is going into solution as hydrogen ion, leaving its electrons on the platinum. The voltage of the cell consisting of these two standard half-cells is 0.34 volt. Since this represents a potential in the opposite direction from that of the zinc-hydrogen couple, it is called −0.34 volt. Since the value for the hydrogen electrode is arbitrarily zero, the electrode potential of copper is −0.34 volt.

Redox Potentials

What would happen if a voltaic cell were constructed from a copper electrode and a zinc electrode? The potential of this cell should be the difference between the electrode potentials of the separate half-cells:

$$\text{Zinc } 0.76 - (-0.34) \text{ copper} = 1.10 \text{ volts}$$

When current is allowed to flow, the electron supply on the zinc is so much greater than the electron supply on the copper that the zinc electrons flow through the wire to the copper where they discharge copper ions. If we place a piece of zinc into a solution of copper ion, such as copper sulfate, we find it quickly becomes coated with a reddish layer which is copper metal. The zinc is said to displace the copper in solution. It reduces the copper ion to copper, becoming itself oxidized to zinc ion. The voltaic cell allows us to conduct this reaction under conditions where the zinc metal and copper ions never come into contact, but the electron exchange still takes place.

electrode	potential, volts
Li, Li$^+$	3.04
K, K$^+$	2.93
Ca, Ca^{++}	2.87
Na, Na$^+$	2.71
Mg, Mg^{++}	2.36
Al, Al^{+++}	1.66
Zn, Zn^{++}	0.76
Fe, Fe^{++}	0.44
Pb, Pb^{++}	0.13
H$_2$, H$^+$	0.00
Cu, Cu^{++}	−0.34
I$^-$, I$_2$	−0.54
Ag, Ag$^+$	−0.80
Hg, Hg^{++}	−0.85
Br$^-$, Br$_2$	−1.09
Cl$^-$, Cl$_2$	−1.38
F$^-$, F$_2$	−2.87

Table 26.1   Some Representative Electrode Potentials

This is the basis of what is sometimes called the **activity series** for metals. Elements that displace hydrogen from water and acids have electrode potentials above hydrogen. Those that cannot displace hydrogen but are displaced by hydrogen have electrode potentials below hydrogen and have a negative sign. The activity series will be discussed further in Chapter 29.

The farther above hydrogen in potential an electrode material is, the greater its reducing power, and vice versa. Therefore, a **redox potential** series can be tabulated which gives the order of decreasing reducing power and increasing oxidizing power. Table 26.1 gives some representative electrode or redox potentials. Such a table can be very useful in predicting which species will oxidize or reduce other species, in aqueous solutions.

PRACTICAL APPLICATIONS

The ordinary dry cell or "flashlight battery" is one of the most useful applications of the conversion of chemical to electrical energy. Strictly speaking, the word **cell** applies to one voltaic cell. The word **battery** describes an assemblage of two or more interconnected voltaic cells. The chief source of electrical energy in dry cells is the dissolution of zinc, but a complex set of reactions is involved in the complete operation. Cells of this type are intended to be discarded when used up since they are not reversible.

A reversible type, that can be recharged over and over again after it is discharged, is called an **accumulator cell,** a collection of which is known as a **storage battery.** In the familiar lead storage battery used in automobiles, one electrode varies between lead and lead sulfate and the other between lead sulfate and lead dioxide (PbO_2). The electrolyte is dilute sulfuric acid. When the battery has "run down," both electrodes are essentially lead sulfate ($PbSO_4$). Electricity from a charger is run through the cell in the opposite direction from that of the natural current, so that electrons are taken from one of the electrodes, oxidizing the lead from (II) to (IV) and converting the lead sulfate to lead dioxide. These electrons are supplied to the other electrode, reducing the Pb(II) to metallic lead, Pb(O). The reactions are shown by the following equations. Discharge of the battery accompanies the reactions from left to right as written. Charging the battery causes the reactions to proceed from right to left:

$$Pb + SO_4^= \rightleftharpoons PbSO_4 + 2\ e^-$$

$$PbO_2 + H_2SO_4 + 2\ H^+ + 2\ e^- \rightleftharpoons PbSO_4 + 2\ H_2O$$

Notice that water is a product of the discharge of the battery. This dilutes the sulfuric acid solution, causing it to have a lower specific gravity, since pure sulfuric acid is nearly twice as dense as water. By measuring the specific gravity (the density compared to that of water), a service station attendant can tell whether the battery needs charging or not. He uses a **hydrometer,** which consists of a rubber bulb to suck a sample of the electrolyte acid up

Figure 26.4. Diagram of a Common Dry Cell.

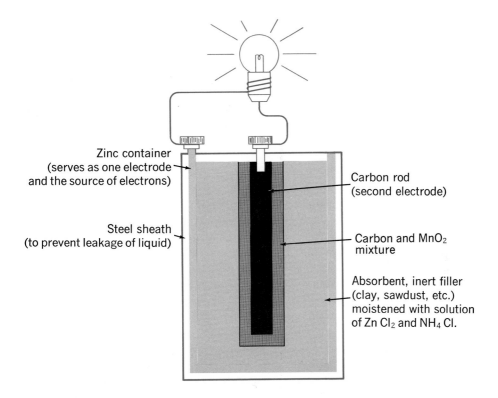

Zinc container
(serves as one electrode
and the source of electrons)

Carbon rod
(second electrode)

Steel sheath
(to prevent leakage of liquid)

Carbon and MnO_2
mixture

Absorbent, inert filler
(clay, sawdust, etc.)
moistened with solution
of $ZnCl_2$ and NH_4Cl.

When the circuit is closed, zinc ions dissolve from the zinc, releasing electrons to flow through the external circuit to the carbon. There they are absorbed by the MnO_2, which becomes reduced from Mn(IV) to Mn(III). Ammonium ions may also be reduced there, forming NH_3 and H. The H is oxidized to water by the MnO_2 and the NH_3 adds to zinc ion forming $[Zn(NH_3)_4]^{++}$ complex ion.

The cell is simple, but its chemistry is not.

into a glass tube containing a small float. The lower the specific gravity of the acid, the deeper the float will sink into the solution. Keeping the battery charged during the winter is very important to insure quick engine starting. It is also important because when the battery is run down, the acid is more dilute and freezes at a higher temperature.

A third type of cell, the fuel cell is a device for compelling heat-producing fuels like hydrocarbons to produce electrical energy when they are oxidized.

The corrosion of metals involves the oxidation of their atoms. The corrosion is frequently electrolytic in nature and is greatly accelerated by impurities in the metal in the form of tiny crystals of other conducting materials.

For example, pure zinc dissolves in acid solutions quite slowly. Impure zinc, which usually contains carbon from the reduction of zinc oxide, dissolves much more rapidly, just as it does when in contact with copper. When two connected metals or other conducting materials are subjected to corroding conditions, the more reactive substance tends to corrode preferentially, serving to protect the less reactive substance. Practical application of this principle is illustrated by the protection of iron pipelines or underground storage tanks, which can be connected to buried lumps of magnesium metal. The magnesium corrodes, thereby keeping the iron slightly negative, so that it can lose electrons without being corroded.

THE SIGNIFICANCE OF ELECTRODE POTENTIALS

When any system changes from an initial state to a final state, the net energy change is entirely independent of the pathway by which the change occurs. Often it is helpful, in trying to analyze a rather complex chemical change, to divide it up into individual steps which could in principle produce the final state from the initial state. It is not necessary that these individual steps be realistic. The actual mechanism of the change may well be entirely different. If the energy changes for the individual steps can be understood, they may shed some light on the nature of the overall change.

When a piece of zinc is placed in water, it tends to form hydrated ions in solution, leaving electrons on the metallic zinc. An arbitrary way of looking at this process is to imagine that the zinc first separates into gaseous atoms, which lose two electrons each to become gaseous zinc ions. The ions then dissolve in water to become hydrated ions. Of course, this is not what happens. But we do not know how to evaluate the direct movement from initial to final states, and we do know how to evaluate this indirectly. The energy required for zinc metal to change into gaseous atoms is called the **atomization energy.** The energy required to remove the two electrons from zinc atoms to form gaseous zinc ions is the sum of the first and second **ionization energies,** discussed previously. The **energy of hydration** of ions has also been estimated, from the measured heats of hydration of their salts. Hydration of the ions evolves energy, but the first two steps absorb it. The tendency of an electrode reaction to occur is directly proportional to the net result of these three energy steps. In other words, the ability of a metal to act as a reducing agent *increases* with *decreasing* atomization energy and ionization energy, and with *increasing* energy of hydration.

Compare zinc and copper in these respects. The atomization energy of zinc is about 23 kcal per mole, compared to 72 for copper. Zinc as a reducing agent is clearly favored here. The ionization energies needed to produce ions total 632 kcal per mole for zinc ion and 647 for copper ion, giving zinc a slight edge here, too. The hydration energy for zinc ions is about -484 kcal per mole compared to -497 for copper ions, the minus sign indicating that heat is evolved. The net energy for the total change is:

$$23 + 632 - 484 = 171 \text{ kcal per mole (zinc)}$$

$$72 + 647 - 497 = 222 \text{ kcal per mole (copper)}$$

Zinc is a much better reducing agent in aqueous solution, largely because copper atoms are held together much more tightly in the metal than are zinc atoms. It is more difficult for the copper ions to form, even though they are somewhat more strongly hydrated.

Both these metals can be contrasted with sodium. Sodium, with its large atoms and single valence electron per atom, is not very strongly held together in the metal, and requires only about 19 kcal per mole for atomization. The removal of an electron per atom also is relatively easy, requiring only 119 kcal per mole. The hydration energy is not very great, only -98 kcal per mole, but the net energy change for the total reaction is only about 40 kcal per mole compared to 171 for zinc and 222 for copper. No wonder, then, that sodium has such a high reduction potential: 2.71 volts compared to 0.76 volt for zinc and -0.34 for copper.

Test Your Memory

1. Write an equation for the reaction of a metal electrode with water.
2. How does ammonia differ from water in its action on sodium?
3. How can a chemical oxidation-reduction reaction be carried out to produce a useful current of electricity?
4. What is a *voltaic half-cell?*
5. What is taken as the standard half-cell? Why is a standard necessary?
6. What conditions are standardized for cell potential measurements?
7. What is a *salt bridge?* What is its purpose?
8. What is *redox potential?*
9. What is the significance of a position above or below hydrogen in the activity or electrode potential series?
10. What electrode reactions produce a current from a lead accumulator cell?
11. What is a storage battery?
12. Why does dilution of battery acid signify need for recharging?
13. How does a service station attendant test your car battery?
14. Why is zinc a better reducing agent than copper, in aqueous solutions?

Test Your Understanding

1. Consider the equilibrium between a metal electrode and its solution. What effect, if any, would you think might result from a change in concentration of the metal ion in solution?
2. To produce one faraday from a cell containing a zinc electrode, what weight of zinc would dissolve?
3. Do you see any relationship between the zinc and copper electrode potentials and the fact that hydrochloric acid will dissolve zinc but not copper?

4. What would you predict would happen if a piece of copper were placed in a solution of zinc sulfate? Zinc in copper sulfate?
5. What sign of charge kept on a metal should protect it against corrosion, and why?
6. Would you prefer to recover copper from solution by the action of potassium or iron? Why?

27

SOME CHEMISTRY OF THE HALOGEN FAMILY

ATOMIC STRUCTURE AND GENERAL NATURE

The halogens are the elements of Group M7 of the periodic table. Their location directly to the left of M8 elements indicates their electronic structure: each halogen has one electron less than a complete octet in its outer shell. Therefore, each halogen atom has one outer-shell, half-filled orbital, with which it can form a single covalent bond. Remember that as electrons are added to the outermost shell of atoms in the building up of elements, each outer-shell electron is only about one-third effective in shielding the surface from the additional positive charge of the nucleus. Consequently, each halogen represents the highest electronegativity in its period. As a group, M7 elements are the most electronegative in the periodic table. The one covalent bond that each halogen atom can form is therefore quite likely to be polar, with the halogen partially negative. The compounds in which halogen has the oxidation number of -1 are called **halides,** the most stable of which are those in which the bonds are most polar. This means, first, that the most stable halides are compounds with metals lowest in electronegativity. Second, fluorine is highest of all elements in electronegativity, chlorine is third highest and next in the halogens, and bromine and iodine follow in that order. The most stable halides are fluorides, followed by chlorides, then bromides, and last, iodides. This order is accentuated by the size relationships: the smaller the atoms, the stronger the bonds. Fluorine is not only the most electronegative halogen but, also, has the smallest atoms of the group.

OCCURRENCE AND LIBERATION

Because of their high electronegativity, we cannot expect to find any of the halogens free in nature. Most commonly, they are combined with other elements that provide them with electrons. The halides have two properties that tend to limit their natural occurrence. One is that of hydrolysis. This restricts the naturally occurring halides to those that do not react with water, since water may be regarded as being present at least as vapor nearly everywhere on the earth's surface. The other is that of solubility. With the exception of some fluorides and a few other metal halides, most halides, especially those that are immune to hydrolysis, are readily soluble in water. Therefore, naturally occurring, water-soluble halides cannot be expected in any place where rains could have leached them away. We can expect to find them concentrated in the sea, the final depository for all compounds that the rains leach out and the rivers carry away.

The chief sources of chlorides are the sea and salt deposits that have been protected naturally from leaching action of ground or rain waters. Fluorides occur chiefly in the form of calcium fluoride (CaF_2), an insoluble salt found with natural phosphates and other deposits. Bromides and iodides are much less abundant; very small concentrations of bromide and iodide ions are present in sea water.

To liberate the free halogen from its halide, it is necessary to take an electron away from each halide ion. In other words, the halide must be oxidized. Since fluorine is the most electronegative element of the whole periodic system, it should not be surprising that no chemical oxidizing agent is capable of removing an electron from a fluoride ion. For this reason, fluorine was isolated relatively late in the discovery of the elements. As we have seen in Chapter 25, powerful oxidizing agents can be created by pumping electrons out of any metallic conductor so that it becomes very positive. If an electrode is made positive enough, it can attract fluoride ions and remove their extra electrons, liberating fluorine atoms.

The electrode must be exceptionally resistant to chemical attack, for fluorine atoms will react violently with most substances. Carbon in the form of graphite, which is relatively resistant to fluorine, can be used as an electrode material. Fluoride ions in water would not suffice as the source of fluorine because as soon as they were discharged, the fluorine atoms would attack the water, removing its hydrogen as HF and liberating oxygen. The source of fluoride ions is therefore a liquid melt of potassium fluoride in anhydrous (water-free) hydrogen fluoride, having the approximate composition KFHF. If two electrodes are dipped into this fluoride melt and an electrical potential difference created between them, the fluoride ions will be attracted to the positively charged graphite electrode, where they will lose their electrons to become fluorine atoms. Positive potassium ions are attracted at the other, negatively charged electrode, but they cannot be supplied with electrons when hydrogen is present. The hydrogen acquires electrons from this electrode, becoming hydrogen atoms and then H_2 molecules. Through electrolysis, hydrogen fluoride is decomposed into hydrogen and fluorine. This is just the opposite of the reaction that would occur with great violence if these two elements were permitted to come together under ordinary conditions.

Chloride, bromide, or iodide ions could be discharged much more easily than the fluoride in a similar manner. However, usually there is no point in using electrolysis for this purpose since chemical oxidizing agents are available that may be cheaper and easier. Many strong chemical oxidizing agents are capable of oxidizing chloride ions to free chlorine atoms, as exemplified by the following equation:

$$4 \, HCl + MnO_2 \rightarrow Cl_2 + MnCl_2 + 2 \, H_2O$$

The more strongly an atom attracts an electron, the more reluctantly it will release it. Therefore, fluoride ion releases an electron least readily, chloride ion next, bromide next, and iodide ions relatively easily. Because of this difference, fluorine is able to oxidize bromide ion and iodide ion, and bromine can oxidize iodide ion. These oxidations illustrate that a stronger oxidizing element can usually displace a less strong oxidizing element from its compound. Stated another way, one element can displace another from its compound if it results in the formation of a stronger bond. As pointed out above, among the halogens, fluorine forms the strongest bonds to other elements, and iodine the weakest.

> Could you oxidize a NaCl solution by heating it with iodine? Why?

The preparation of elemental fluorine is electrolysis. In the laboratory a chemical oxidation of chloride ion is convenient for making small quantities of chlorine. Industrially, however, it is usually obtained by electrolysis because several useful products can thus be formed simultaneously. When aqueous sodium chloride is electrolyzed, chloride ions are attracted to the positively charged electrode and there discharged to become chlorine atoms. Sodium ions are attracted to the negatively charged electrode, but they cannot be discharged in the presence of water, since hydrogen has a lower oxidation potential and is much more readily discharged. Consequently, hydrogen atoms are formed at this electrode, leaving hydroxide ions behind in the water:

$$Cl^- \rightarrow Cl + e^-$$

$$e^- + H_2O \rightarrow H + OH^-$$

The total effect is the formation of a solution of sodium hydroxide, with hydrogen released at one electrode and chlorine at the other. Sodium hydroxide is a very important industrial base. The hydrogen and chlorine are either used for separate purposes or recombined to form hydrogen chloride which dissolves in water to give hydrochloric acid. Ordinarily, sodium hydroxide and hydrochloric acid neutralize one another to form sodium chloride and water. This electrolytic process, followed by the recombination of hydrogen and chlorine, makes sodium hydroxide and hydrochloric acid from sodium chloride and water. Again, electrical energy is used to reverse the usual direction of reaction.

The chief source of natural bromine is bromide ion found in very small concentrations in sea water, which is slightly alkaline. The halogens tend to react with alkaline solutions to form halides and oxyhalogen compounds. Thus they undergo their own type of oxidation-reduction reaction, acting as oxidizing and reducing agent. Only if the solution is slightly acidic can the free element be formed. To extract bromine from the sea, it is first necessary to add a little sulfuric acid to destroy the normal alkalinity of the sea water. The sea water is pumped into large tanks and acidified slightly. It is then treated with chlorine, which is far cheaper and more available than bromine. This oxidizes the bromide ion to free bromine. Bromine vapor can then be blown out of the water by bubbling air through it. The air containing bromine is then passed through absorbing solutions to extract the bromine. By this method it is commercially profitable to extract very small quantities of bromine from large quantities of sea water.

Although chemists and chemical engineers have solved the technical problems of extracting bromine from sea water, iodine is present in much smaller concentrations, and man is quite content to let Nature do the extracting for him. A giant variety of seaweed, called **kelp**, readily accomplishes what man cannot do so easily, absorbing iodine from the sea and concentrating it within itself. The kelp is harvested, dried, and burned, and the iodine recovered from the ash.

In the absence of some more attractive partner, all the halogens join with themselves through the half-filled orbital on each atom, forming diatomic molecules. Going down the group, the color deepens: F_2 is a yellowish gas, Cl_2 a greenish gas, Br_2 a deep red liquid, and I_2 a violet-brown or violet-gray solid. The differences in physical properties reflect the increase in van der

Table 27.1.   Some Properties of the Halogens

	F	Cl	Br	I
atomic number	9	17	35	53
electronic structure	2-7	2-8-7	2-8-18-7	2-8-18-18-7
or, one electron less than	Ne	Ar	Kr	Xe
atomic weight	19.00	35.45	79.91	126.90
formula	F_2	Cl_2	Br_2	I_2
color	yellow	greenish yellow	brown red	violet brown
melting point, °C	-219.6	-102.4	-7.2	113.6
boiling point, °C	-187.9	-34.0	58.2	184.5
1st ionization energy, kcal/g-atom	402	300	273	241
electronegativity	3.9	3.3	3.0	2.5
electrode potential, volts	-2.87	-1.360	-1.065	-0.536

Waals forces between the X_2 molecules that accompanies an increase in the total number of electrons. With only 18 electrons per molecule, these forces are very weak in fluorine. Consequently, it has a very low boiling point. In chlorine, with 34 electrons per molecule, intermolecular attractions are much greater, so that chlorine is easily liquefied under pressure at ordinary temperatures. It boils at about $-34°C$ at one atmosphere. Bromine, with 70 electrons per molecule, is a very volatile liquid giving a reddish-brown vapor. In iodine, with 106 electrons per molecule, the attractive forces are enough to hold the molecules together in a crystalline solid, in which the individual I_2 molecules are still the basic components and remain somewhat volatile. Iodine has an appreciable vapor tension well below its melting point, and therefore sublimes rather easily.

CHEMICAL PROPERTIES OF THE HALOGENS

All the halogens are oxidizing agents. Fluorine is so much more reactive in this respect that it is sometimes termed a "super halogen." Even at ordinary temperatures it reacts with almost everything with which it comes in contact. Frequently the reaction is so vigorous that the mixture inflames. Fluorine removes hydrogen from oxygen in water and silicon from oxygen in silicates. The reaction with water is almost explosive, forming HF and O_2. Materials normally thought of as completely fireproof, such as bricks, concrete, and other substances containing silicates, can actually burst into flame in fluorine. Researchers studying fluorine exercise the greatest caution to avoid bodily contact with it or with any explosive reactions it might undergo. Often their experiments are conducted by remote control from behind protective barricades, a precaution frequently proven wise. All the compounds of metals with other nonmetals are likely to react to form fluorides when heated with fluorine because it forms the strongest bonds of all. The only kinds of materials that resist fluorine are those that have already been fluorinated. A few metals, like copper and nickel, receive such an impervious coat of fluoride on first contact that the interior of the metal is protected from contact.

Chlorine is much less reactive than fluorine, but still powerfully corrosive toward any materials that can supply it with electrons. Like fluorine, it will react directly with most metals, forming stable chlorides. Many colored substances are made colorless by oxidation. For this reason, chlorine, and some of its compounds in which chlorine has a positive oxidation state enhancing its oxidizing power, are used as "bleaches." Chlorine reacts with carbon-hydrogen bonds to form carbon-chlorine bonds and hydrogen chloride:

$$\overset{|}{\underset{|}{-C}}-H + Cl_2 \rightarrow \overset{|}{\underset{|}{-C}}-Cl + HCl$$

The principal use of bromine is to react with ethylene (C_2H_4) to form

ethylene dibromide ($C_2H_4Br_2$), which is used in antiknock fluid for gasoline.

$$H_2C=CH_2 + Br_2 \rightarrow BrH_2C-CH_2Br$$

Antiknock agents are helpful in controlling the rate of fuel combustion in an internal combustion engine so that it burns smoothly to give maximum power output. Most effective are **tetramethyl lead,** $Pb(CH_3)_4$, and **tetraethyl lead,** $Pb(C_2H_5)_4$. However, these tend to form lead oxide residues that build up deposits in the engine. The function of the bromide is to volatilize the lead so that it blows out the exhaust as lead bromide, but this is a dangerous source of lead pollution of the environment.

Iodine, because of its milder oxidizing power, can be safely used for its antiseptic properties. For this purpose it is commonly dissolved in alcohol as **tincture of iodine.** All the halogens are corrosive to living tissue, but iodine is the least so. Chlorine was the first gas used in chemical warfare, because it is extremely irritating to the lungs. The German chemist Fritz Haber (1868–1934), whose chief fame rests on his development of the Haber process for the synthesis of ammonia, was also in charge of the chemical warfare development that led to the use of chlorine in battle in World War One. He favored the use of this horrible new weapon because he thought it would shorten the war. (His wife so bitterly opposed this that she became emotionally disturbed and killed herself. Later, when wartime resentment and hatred were still at a fever pitch, Haber was awarded a Nobel prize, but other winners refused to accept their prizes if it meant being in the same group with Haber.)

Bromine is also very corrosive, and can cause very bad, slow-healing burns. Like chlorine and fluorine, bromine and iodine also react rather readily with most of the chemical elements, forming bromides and iodides.

CHEMICAL PROPERTIES OF HALIDES

Hydrogen Halides

All the halogens will react with hydrogen to form hydrogen halides. Under almost all conditions, fluorine and hydrogen react explosively on contact. When the gases are scrupulously dried, the reaction may need to be initiated. As is true of almost all such reactions, tiny traces of water that are usually present serve to catalyze the initiation of the reaction. Hydrogen and chlorine, on the other hand, can be mixed without reaction until activation energy is supplied by a spark or a beam of sunlight. Then they, too, explode. Hydrogen and bromine must be heated together with a catalyst before reaction occurs, but even then the reaction is relatively mild. Hydrogen and iodine vapor react reversibly to form hydrogen iodide.

The hydrogen halides all have similar formulas, as expected from noting the univalence of both halogen and hydrogen: HF, HCl, HBr, and HI. They are all gaseous, as would be expected from the lack of vacant orbitals for further condensation. HF alone is able to form rather strong protonic bridges. It is therefore much less volatile than the others, boiling at 19°C. Even in vapor, up to about 100°, HF molecules are associated through protonic bridges. Experimental evidence exists for a species containing up to six HF molecules in one unit.

All the hydrogen halides are quite soluble in water, forming hydrofluoric, hydrochloric, hydrobromic and hydriodic acids. The last three are all strong acids in water solution, being completely ionized in dilute solution. Hydro-fluoric acid is exceptional, in that it is only weakly acidic, probably for the same fundamental reason that hydrogen fluoride is able to form protonic bridges. The relatively small size of the fluorine atom makes its electron pairs especially available to a proton. This causes protonic bridge formation and prevents protons from being removed completely by the water when it dissolves HF.

Hydrofluoric acid is exceptional in other ways, too. It is very corrosive to human tissue. Whereas the other hydrogen halides, in both gaseous and aqueous forms, are not exceptionally corrosive to the skin, both HF gas and hydrofluoric acid cause exceedingly painful burns that heal very slowly and require special sedation and treatment. Gaseous HF, if inhaled, is quite likely to be fatal. Indeed, some of the early workers in fluorine chemistry were unaware of its toxic properties, and died unnaturally early as a result.

Another of the exceptional properties of hydrofluoric acid arises from the fact that fluorine forms stronger bonds to silicon than does oxygen. HF will therefore react with silica or silicates, releasing gaseous silicon tetra-fluorides:

$$4\,HF + SiO_2 \rightarrow SiF_4 + 2\,H_2O$$

Glass, a mixture of silicates, is attacked by hydrofluoric acid, which must therefore be stored in plastic or wax bottles. When hydrogen fluoride is used to etch glass, the surface is first coated thinly with wax and the design to be etched is made by scratching away the wax at the proper places.

In general, the hydrohalic acids will dissolve metal oxides and hydroxides forming aqueous solutions of the corresponding halides:

$$MO + 2HX \rightarrow H_2O + MX_2$$

They will also dissolve the more reactive metals, liberating hydrogen and forming halide solutions. For example,

$$Mg + 2\,HCl \rightarrow H_2 + MgCl_2$$

Because hydrochloric acid is much cheaper than the others and just as useful as an acid, it is the one most commonly used. Hydrochloric acid is a standard, indispensable reagent in the chemical laboratory.

The hydrogen halides, with the exception occasionally of hydrogen chloride, are not usually made by direct synthesis from the elements. Rather, they are made by the reaction of some reagent such as water or another acid on a halogen compound of another element. The volatility of the hydrogen halides, compared to the much less volatile sulfuric acid, permits the use of sulfuric acid to liberate HF and HCl from their salts. The first proton comes more easily from the sulfuric acid. The second proton removal requires heat, so the total reaction requires two steps:

$$H_2SO_4 + NaF \rightarrow NaHSO_4 + HF$$

$$NaHSO_4 + NaF \rightarrow Na_2SO_4 + HF$$

The reactions with sodium chloride are of the same form. In concentrated form H_2SO_4 is a fair oxidizing agent, but it is not able to oxidize hydrogen chloride or chloride ion. Otherwise hydrogen chloride could not be made by this method. However, bromide ion and hydrogen bromide are better reducing agents than their chlorine analogs. If we try to get HBr by treatment of NaBr with H_2SO_4, the mixture darkens and SO_2 is given off. The reaction is:

$$2\ NaBr + 3\ H_2SO_4 \rightarrow Br_2 + SO_2 + 2\ NaHSO_4 + 2\ H_2O$$

Iodide ion and hydrogen iodide are even stronger reducing agents. Their reaction with sulfuric acid reduces it to sulfur and hydrogen sulfide. In summary, the action of concentrated sulfuric acid on a fluoride or chloride is very useful for making the hydrogen halide, but hydrogen bromide and iodide cannot be made this way.

To make HBr or HI, the halide of an element whose hydroxide is wholly acidic is treated with water. This generally means a nonmetal halide, which is irreversibly hydrolyzed by water:

$$PBr_3 + 3\ H_2O \rightarrow P(OH)_3 + 3\ HBr$$

$$PI_3 + 3\ H_2O \rightarrow P(OH)_3 + 3\ HI$$

If the hydroxide formed were able to ionize as a base, the reaction would be reversible, and good yields might be hard to obtain. When, as in the above examples, the hydroxide of the water attaches to an element from which a hydroxide ion cannot separate, the reaction is irreversible and goes to completion.

Other Halides

The principal reactions of the halides of the elements are hydrolysis, as described above, and halogenation, their reaction as oxidizing agents. When the hydroxide formed by hydrolysis is a strong base, no hydrolysis occurs. Sodium chloride, for example, does not react with water except to form completely ionized products which can only condense to sodium chloride and water again. But when the hydroxide formed ionizes weakly or not at all, extensive hydrolysis occurs. For example, anhydrous aluminum chloride cannot be prepared from aqueous solution. Once the hydroxyl group displaces the chlorine on the aluminum, it tends to remain there. Hydrogen chloride is vaporized with the water. Therefore, no hydrolysis is expected of the halides of metals that give strong bases. Halides that give weak and amphoteric hydroxides tend to hydrolyze partially and sometimes reversibly. Halides that form only acidic hydroxides hydrolyze completely and irreversibly.

Consider the nature of silica. Could hydrogen bromide be prepared from $SiBr_4$ by hydrolysis? Could you dissolve sand in hydrobromic acid?

Oxidizing power persists in highly electronegative elements when they are present in compounds in which they have not succeeded in acquiring very high negative charge. Therefore, most of the halides of other nonmetals, in which the partial charge on halogen cannot be very negative, can serve as halogenating agents toward elements that give up electrons more easily. However oxidizing power is expected of halides in which the partial charge on the halogen is fairly negative.

There is also a tendency for highly negative halogen atoms to act as electron donors. There is a large number of complex halides in which the halide ion from a compound such as sodium chloride acts as donor to another halide molecule which acts as acceptor. For example, BF_3 can accept an electron pair from a fluoride ion to form salts of the complex fluoroborate anion, BF_4^-. But we would not expect this donor ability of halogen to persist when the partial charge on the halogen is not very high.

Halides of elements that give up electrons fairly readily tend to be nonmolecular solids. This could be predicted because the simplest molecules that could form would still have unoccupied orbitals on the metal and lone pairs of electrons on the halogen. These simplest molecules therefore condense or polymerize to form crystalline solids. We expect these salts to be stable, relatively nonvolatile, and high-melting, which they are. Halides in which no vacant low-energy orbitals are left on the other atom remain molecular, relatively low-melting, and volatile, and often are not very stable.

Test Your Memory

1. What is the chief fundamental characteristic of the halogens?
2. What is the meaning of the word *halide?*
3. How is fluorine produced and why is this method necessary?
4. Discuss the relative ease of oxidation of the different halide ions.
5. What general procedures are used to isolate bromine from the sea?
6. How and where is iodine obtained?
7. What kind of material can best resist chemical attack by fluorine?
8. To what do the halogens owe their oxidizing power?
9. How does hydrofluoric acid differ from the other hydrohalic acids?

10. What are the differences in reactivity shown by hydrogen toward the individual halogens?
11. How is glass chemically etched? What precautions are important?
12. How is hydrogen chloride obtained from salt?
13. a) Why can HBr and HI *not* be prepared similarly to HCl?
    b) How can they be prepared?
14. What are the characteristics of negatively charged halogen?
15. Why are some halides much more volatile than others?
16. a) What is the purpose of adding a bromide to antiknock fuel additive?
    b) What problem does this create?

Test Your Understanding

1. How are the electronegativities of the halogens related to the ease of their liberation from halides?
2. On what basis can certain halogens be liberated by action of other halogens?
3. Why is iodide ion a reducing agent?
4. Why is iodine volatile, although solid?
5. a) What evidence is there that concentrated sulfuric acid can oxidize?
   b) Why does concentrated sulfuric acid not oxidize fluorides and chlorides?
6. Why are protonic bridges formed by hydrogen fluoride alone of the hydrogen halides?
7. How might SiO_2 be removed from a solid mixture?
8. a) Would hydrolysis of PF_3 and PCl_3 be possible sources of the corresponding hydrogen halides?
   b) Would halides of boron hydrolyze?
   c) What are the chances of hydrolysis of potassium halides?
   d) What products would be expected from hydrolysis of SF_6, SCl_4, $AsBr_3$, and SiI_4?
9. Write chemical equations for the reactions of each of the hydrohalic acids with CaO, $Ba(OH)_2$, Al, and Zn.

PERIODICITY OF HALIDE CHEMISTRY

CHLORINE FROM METAL TO NONMETAL

It may now be useful to traverse the periodic table once or twice to gain some idea of how the properties of halides correspond to their position in the periodic system. As examples, let us use compounds of the elements with chlorine, which is intermediate between fluorine and the other halogens. Chlorides will show us representative trends that generally hold well for all halides.

Period 2

Lithium. The first element of the second period is lithium. Its electronic configuration (2-1) clearly indicates univalence. Chlorine is also univalent, but for a different reason. While lithium has more than enough vacancies (seven) but a covalent bonding capacity limited by its number of outer-shell electrons (one), chlorine (2-8-7) has more than enough outer-shell electrons (seven) but a bonding capacity limited by its number of outer-shell vacancies (one). We predict a one-to-one combination with empirical formula LiCl. We would not expect this compound to exist as separate molecules, because of the strong tendency for all available orbitals and electrons to be utilized in bonding. Fuller use of these orbitals and electrons is made by condensation of the LiCl molecules to a nonmolecular solid. Since chlorine is much more electronegative than lithium, the covalent bonding can be predicted as very polar. Lithium should be positive and chlorine negative; such a compound should be very stable and nonoxidizing. It should also be nonhydrolyzable because it is the salt of LiOH, a strong base, and HCl, a strong acid. Both ionize completely in aqueous solution. LiCl should have some ability as an electron donor through the chlorine.

These predictions are amply verified by experiment. Lithium reacts readily with chlorine. The product, lithium chloride, has indeed the empirical formula LiCl. It crystallizes in the nonmolecular form shown by NaCl. Each lithium atom is surrounded by six equidistant chlorine atoms. Each chlorine atom is surrounded by six equidistant lithium atoms. The compound has a high melting point and is nonvolatile. Its chlorine can act as electron donor in the formation of complex chlorides. Since the chlorine is already highly negative, it has no further attraction for electrons. LiCl is not a chlorinating agent.

Beryllium. Beryllium atoms have two outer-shell electrons. Therefore they each can form two covalent bonds. $BeCl_2$ may be predicted for the formula of the chloride. Here the bonds cannot be nearly as polar as in LiCl since beryllium is more electronegative than lithium, and two chlorine atoms must compete for the electrons of only one beryllium atom. The simplest molecule would leave two vacant orbitals on the beryllium atom and three lone pairs on each chlorine. Interaction of these molecules would be expected to lead to condensation to a nonmolecular solid, but this solid would be lower melting and more volatile than LiCl. It should be less able to act as an electron donor and more susceptible to hydrolysis because $Be(OH)_2$ is only weakly basic. Again the experimental facts verify the predictions.

Boron. Boron atoms have the capacity to form three covalent bonds. The formula for boron chloride should be BCl_3. In the simplest molecule, this would still leave one vacant orbital on boron as well as the lone pairs on the chlorine atoms. According to the general principle, we should therefore expect further condensation. In fact, however, the boron halides provide the single known apparent exception to the rule of making maximum use of available orbitals and electrons. They are molecular compounds consisting of

Figure 28.1. Molecule of Boron Trichloride.

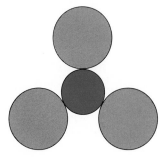

BCl_3 consists of planar, triangular molecules which do not polymerize despite the potential availability of a fourth orbital on the boron. Presumably the negative charge on Cl is too small to permit it to act effectively as an electron donor. BCl_3 is a gas easily condensed to a liquid and is rapidly and completely hydrolyzed to boric acid [$B(OH)_3$] and HCl.

planar, triangular, single molecules with boron at the center and the three halogen atoms making bond angles of 120°. This structure would be predicted for three bonds that use all available electrons. In part, at least, this exceptional behavior may be the result of partial use of the fourth boron orbital by electron pairs from the halogen atoms, leading to partial multiplicity of the bonding. This is in agreement with the bond lengths, which tend to be shorter than expected of single covalent bonds, and with the bond energies, which tend to be higher than expected of single covalent bonds.

Boric acid, or boron trihydroxide, $B(OH)_3$, is acidic only, giving no hydroxide ions in solution. It follows that hydrolysis of a boron halide would be irreversible. In general fluorides, and BF_3 in particular, resist hydrolysis much more than the other halides because fluorine is more strongly bonded. The chloride, bromide, and iodide of boron hydrolyze immediately and irreversibly:

$$BCl_3 + 3 H_2O \rightarrow 3 HCl + B(OH)_3$$

The flat, triangular, symmetrical trihalide molecules would be expected to be held together only by weak van der Waals forces. Thus, BCl_3 is a gas.

Carbon. Carbon atoms have the ability to form four covalent bonds. CCl_4 is the predicted formula for the chloride. It should be tetrahedral, with the four chlorine atoms, much larger than the carbon atom, effectively shielding the carbon from outside attack. In theory, CCl_4 should hydrolyze irreversibly with water since carbonic acid has no basicity at all. In practice, water does not attack carbon tetrachloride under ordinary conditions. Presumably this is because the water molecule has no way of getting at the carbon or the carbon-chlorine bond. Remember that before reaction can occur, contact between reagents must be made. This contact must be of the kind that can result in rearrangement of the atoms.

With its symmetrical molecular structure, carbon tetrachloride would

Figure 28.2. Molecule of Carbon Tetrachloride.

In the tetrahedral CCl_4 molecule, the carbon atom is so effectively covered by the 4 chlorine atoms that the compound is very difficult to hydrolyze, even though in principle it should hydrolyze completely to CO_2 and HCl. The molecule is also quite unreactive at ordinary temperatures, although the low negative charge on chlorine clearly reveals it as a potential chlorinating agent, which it is at higher temperatures. For this reason it is hazardous to mix it with substances which are susceptible to chlorination, even at 25°C. Both vapor and liquid are toxic.

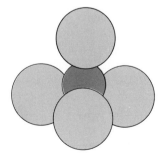

have little intermolecular attraction except for van der Waals forces, which appear to be strong enough to hold the compound in the liquid state. The liquid is quite volatile and easily separates into gaseous molecules. With four chlorine atoms trying to remove electrons from the same carbon atom, which itself is not very low in electronegativity, no one chlorine atom can be expected to acquire much of a negative charge. Therefore, CCl_4 should be a chlorinating agent. At ordinary temperatures, however, carbon tetrachloride is an excellent solvent but otherwise inert.

Its reluctance to act as a chlorinating agent resembles its resistance to hydrolysis. Apparently, although the ability is not lacking, the mechanical means is not available. Some years ago, two men died in an explosion that occurred when they were rinsing traces of grease from powdered aluminum, using carbon tetrachloride as a solvent. This was a standard practice which had never been recognized as dangerous. In fact, however, chlorine can become attached much more strongly to aluminum than to carbon. Given an opportunity, it will leave the carbon to join the aluminum, with the release of substantial energy. Normally the structure of carbon tetrachloride does not permit such an opportunity, and no one knows exactly what happened on that fatal occasion. It certainly demonstrated that any compound in which an active nonmetal has not been able to acquire a very high negative charge is potentially capable of acting as an oxidizing agent. An oxidation process may produce large amounts of energy rapidly, and thus be dangerous if uncontrolled. At higher temperatures, carbon tetrachloride is well known to be an effective chlorinating agent. It is used in the production of many different anhydrous metal chlorides.

Carbon tetrachloride is such a good solvent for grease that it is often found in the household for use as spot remover for fabrics. It is also used as fire-extinguishing fluid. In light of these common applications, it is especially important to be aware that the compound is highly toxic. Either absorption through the skin or inhalation of the vapors may cause serious or fatal poisoning, with permanent damage to the liver. CCl_4 should never be used without excellent ventilation, and even then only with caution.

Nitrogen. The next element in this period is nitrogen. We predict here the formula NCl_3 for a molecular compound with only weak intermolecular attractions. The bonds could not be very polar, so it should be a powerful chlorinating agent. In fact, nitrogen trichloride can be prepared as a volatile oily liquid, but it is exceedingly unstable and very highly explosive. In a recent experiment, only 10 ml (2 teaspoonsful) of NCl_3, dissolved in a solvent in which it was presumed to be stable, was stored inside a refrigerator. Suddenly it exploded, blowing open the door and wrecking the refrigerator. Part of the reason for this instability is that large chlorine atoms do not form very strong bonds to small nitrogen atoms, especially since the polarity must be very low. The chief source of the energy produced by the decomposition, however, arises from the formation of the very stable N_2 molecule. This decomposition reaction is very easily initiated, even by shock or impact. Once started, it

Figure 28.3. Molecule of Nitrogen Trichloride.

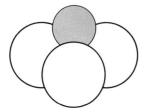

NCl_3 forms a low pyramid in which the N sits on a triangular base of 3 Cl atoms. Both elements are highly electronegative, so this is not a satisfactory combination for either. The compound is a dangerously unstable liquid capable of violent explosion without warning. A major part of the energy released results from formation of the extremely stable molecules of N_2 as a product.

goes explosively fast, evolving a great deal of energy and forming gaseous products.

The special features of almost any chemical explosion are that a highly condensed state, solid or liquid, changes extremely rapidly to gases, with the evolution of much energy. This energy heats the gases, giving them tremendous pressure.

(Another nitrogen halide that can be made is nitrogen iodide, a very unstable solid that can detonate even when touched with a feather. Lest you think it would be fun to prepare one of these unstable compounds, let me tell you of a student who came to see me after a lecture on nitrogen compounds. He said he wished he had heard that lecture a few years earlier. When I asked what he meant, he showed me his hand from which the ends of three fingers were missing. He had been having fun with nitrogen halides and was lucky to have gotten off so lightly.)

Oxygen. From here to the end of the second period we have Cl_2O and ClF, but in these compounds the chlorine bears partial positive charge. They therefore are not closely comparable with the chlorides. The trend across period 2 chlorides is from a very stable, high-melting, nonvolatile crystalline salt having electron donating but no electron accepting properties and no oxidizing power, toward less stable, more volatile chlorides having increasing susceptibility to hydrolysis and decreasing donating power, to less stable, volatile chlorides easily hydrolyzed and having strong chlorinating power.

Figure 28.4. Molecule of Chlorine(I) Oxide.

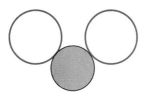

Cl_2O, an unstable oxide, combines two highly electronegative elements. It is therefore a powerful oxidizing agent, because within it neither element has acquired satisfactory negative charge.

Figure 28.5. Molecule of Chlorine Fluoride.

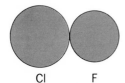

Cl   F

Only in combination with F or O does Cl acquire a partial positive charge. Chlorine is more electronegative than any other element. Chlorine also forms a useful fluorinating agent, ClF_3.

Period 3

Sodium. A brief survey of the next period on the table should now be useful, beginning with sodium chloride. So much has been said here about this compound that it should hardly be necessary to point out how its properties could be predicted from the nature of its atoms. Here is a nonmolecular solid of high stability that does not hydrolyze and can act as an electron donor but not as a chlorinating agent.

Magnesium. The next element in this period is magnesium, with its two valence electrons and an easily predicted formula of $MgCl_2$ for the chloride. Again we expect, and find, that this is a nonmolecular solid: stable, relatively high-melting, and very low in volatility. Still, it is not the same as the NaCl it follows. The chlorine is much less negative here. Hydrolysis can occur to some extent, because magnesium hydroxide is not a strong base. If an attempt is made to recover $MgCl_2$ from its aqueous solution by evaporating off the water, some HCl is lost. Some $Mg(OH)Cl$, basic magnesium chloride, is left with the $MgCl_2$ in the residue:

$$MgCl_2 + H_2O \rightarrow MgClOH + HCl$$

Aluminum. The simplest molecule of aluminum and chloride would be $AlCl_3$. This would be planar and triangular like the BCl_3. Here the aluminum, although more electronegative than the magnesium, is much less electronegative than boron. The chlorine is therefore more negative, with the aluminum more positive. These higher charges, plus the larger size of the aluminum atom, make it possible for one molecule of $AlCl_3$ to act as donor to the vacant orbital of another. What happens is that on each of two $AlCl_3$ molecules, one chlorine serves as donor to the vacant orbital of the aluminum of the other molecule. A dimer forms of formula Al_2Cl_6, in which the two aluminum atoms are bridged by two chlorine atoms. However, the dimer is not a very large molecule, so it is relatively low-melting and volatile. Hydrolysis is extensive because $Al(OH)_3$ is amphoteric, and therefore very weakly basic.

Silicon. Silicon is the next element in this period. Like carbon, it can form four covalent bonds. We correctly predict the formula $SiCl_4$ for the chloride.

Figure 28.6. Molecule of Aluminum Chloride Dimer.

Chlorine bridge

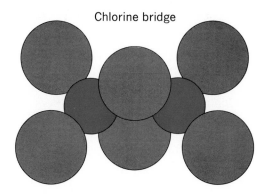

In $AlCl_3$, the chlorine is fairly negative and therefore (through its lone pairs) is a good donor. The aluminum is quite positive and its fourth valence orbital is unoccupied. Therefore, each Al accepts a lone pair from the chlorine of another $AlCl_3$ molecule. Two $AlCl_3$ molecules hold together as the dimer, Al_2Cl_6, bridged from Al to Al by two chlorine atoms. Each aluminum atom now has a completed octet and is at the center of a tetrahedron of chlorine atoms. The dimer bridge is readily broken by better electron pair donors than the chlorine in $AlCl_3$, forming $AlCl_3$-donor complexes. Aluminum chloride, perhaps for this reason, is one of the most valuable of industrial and laboratory catalysts.

This is a molecular compound. Van der Waals forces between molecules cause it to be a liquid. Silicon dioxide is acidic only, not basic; hydrolysis of $SiCl_4$ is therefore irreversible and complete. Here, unlike in CCl_4, water seems to encounter no difficulty finding a site for attack, as $SiCl_4$ reacts vigorously with water, and is completely converted to hydrated silica and HCl:

$$SiCl_4 + 4\,H_2O \rightarrow SiO_2 \cdot 2\,H_2O + 4\,HCl$$

Figure 28.7. Molecule of Silicon Tetrachloride.

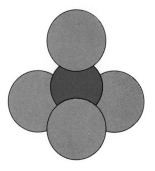

$SiCl_4$, a tetrahedral molecule, hydrolyzes with much greater ease and speed than does CCl_4, partly because four Cl atoms do not shield the Si nearly as effectively as they cover up the C atom, and partly because Si has low-lying d orbitals, absent in C, which are capable of coordinating with water molecules as a possible intermediate step in the hydrolysis. $SiCl_4$ is a liquid which fumes in moist air through formation of SiO_2 and HCl.

Silicon is less electronegative than carbon, however. We therefore would not expect its tetrachloride to be as effective a chlorinating agent, and in fact, it is not.

Phosphorus. Phosphorus can form only three bonds if the octet is to be preserved. As was observed in an earlier chapter, chlorine can attract away the shielding electrons on phosphorus enough to allow the outer-shell *d* orbitals to become involved in bonding. Thus, the octet can be expanded to allow five covalent bonds. PCl_3 and PCl_5 are known compounds, both of which are volatile and molecular. The first is a liquid, the second a solid whose atoms are arranged in the crystal as $PCl_4^+ PCl_6^-$. Both are potential chlorinating agents, but the latter is a much more effective one. This would be expected with five chlorine atoms competing for electrons instead of only three. One of five cannot be as successful in gaining negative charge as one of three.

Sulfur. Sulfur reacts with chlorine in a somewhat unexpected manner to form S_2Cl_2. In this twisted molecule each sulfur forms the two covalent bonds predicted for it. One is to the other sulfur and one to a chlorine atom. The compound is molecular, unstable, and volatile, with strong chlorinating power. It is, of course, easily hydrolyzed, since sulfur hydroxides are exclusively acidic.

Figure 28.8.   Molecules of Phosphorus Trichloride and Phosphorus Pentachloride.

In **phosphorus(III) chloride** (phosphorus trichloride), the P atom is the apex of a low pyramid with the three Cl atoms as the base. A lone pair of electrons on the P completes an octet of electrons in the outer shell.

In **phosphorus(V) chloride** (phosphorus pentachloride), a triangle of three chlorine atoms surrounds the P atom, another Cl sits above and a fifth below, forming the trigonal bipyramid most common for a coordination number of 5. To form bonds to the two extra chlorine atoms, one of the lone pair of electrons on P is promoted to an outer *d* orbital, forming two new half-filled orbitals. The phosphorus atom now has 10 valence electrons around it, a result of *expanding the octet*. By making the P positive, the chlorine helps to stabilize the outer *d* orbital so it can be used this way.

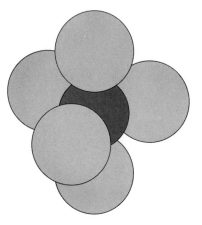

Figure 28.9. Molecule of Sulfur Monochloride (S_2Cl_2).

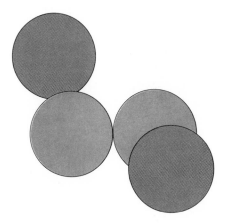

The trend through this third period is thus quite similar to that observed in studying the progression across the second period. The chlorides change from stable, high-melting salts, low in volatility, and nonhydrolyzed, nonoxidizing electron donors, to unstable, volatile, molecular substances that are easily hydrolyzed and act as strong oxidizing (chlorinating) agents.

SUMMARY

It should be clear from these descriptions that if we consider the chlorides, or any of the other halides, of the elements in order of steadily increasing atomic number, we find their properties changing in a periodic manner. They change from one extreme to another and then back to the first again. The periodicity of the chemical elements shows up just as clearly in the chlorides, or other halides, as it does in the elements themselves. In this respect, it is very similar to the previously discussed periodicity of oxide chemistry.

Generalizing, we can point out that the binary chemistry of the elements with *any* nonmetal at all will tend to follow a periodic pattern when the elements are considered in order of increasing atomic number. The halides, or the nonmetal salts in general, including the oxides, may be expected to change from stable, high-melting solids of low volatility at the left side of the periodic table, to unstable, volatile molecular compounds at the right side of the table. Their chemical properties will change from nonoxidizing, electron donating, to oxidizing and acidic. Within each *group,* the physical and chemical properties will tend to be quite *similar* but never *exactly* the same.

Figure 28.10. Relative Radius and Charge of Chlorine in Some Chlorides Across the Periodic Table.

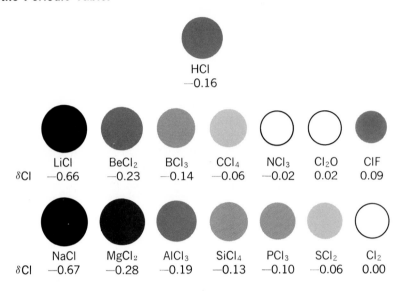

	HCl						
	−0.16						
	LiCl	BeCl$_2$	BCl$_3$	CCl$_4$	NCl$_3$	Cl$_2$O	ClF
δCl	−0.66	−0.23	−0.14	−0.06	−0.02	0.02	0.09
	NaCl	MgCl$_2$	AlCl$_3$	SiCl$_4$	PCl$_3$	SCl$_2$	Cl$_2$
δCl	−0.67	−0.28	−0.19	−0.13	−0.10	−0.06	0.00

Table 28.1. Some Properties of Chlorides of Periods 2 and 3

Compound	Partial charge on chlorine	Melting point	Boiling point	Hydrolysis	Chlorinating power
LiCl	−0.66	610	1382	none	none
BeCl$_2$	−0.23	405	547	extensive	none
BCl$_3$	−0.14	−107	12.4	complete	poor
CCl$_4$	−0.06	−22.9	76.7	(complete but extremely slow)	good at high T.
NCl$_3$	−0.02	. . . .	71	(complete but slow)	good
Cl$_2$O	0.02	−116	3	. . . . . .	good
NaCl	−0.67	808	1465	none	none
MgCl$_2$	−0.28	714	1418	slight	none
Al$_2$Cl$_6$	−0.19	192	180.1 (subl.)	extensive	poor
SiCl$_4$	−0.13	−68	57.0	complete	poor
PCl$_3$	−0.10	−92	76	complete	fair
PCl$_5$	−0.07	. . . .	159	complete	good
S$_2$Cl$_2$	−0.09	−76.5	138	complete	good
Cl$_2$	0.0	−101.0	−34.1	. . . . . .	good

Test Your Memory

1. What are the predicted properties of LiCl? How do they compare with those actually observed?
2. What is the structure of BCl_3 and how is it dependent on the atomic structure of boron?
3. Why do CCl_4 and water not react under ordinary conditions?
4. Why is NCl_3 unstable?
5. a) What trends in physical properties of binary chlorine compounds are observed from left to right across the periodic table? Explain.
   b) Explain the trend in chloride chemical properties across the periodic table.
6. In what ways do period 3 chlorides differ from those of period 2?
7. What permits the molecular formula of aluminum chloride to be Al_2Cl_6?
8. What compounds of chlorine are formed by phosphorus?

Test Your Understanding

1. What should be the structure of NCl_3?
2. Why should $SiCl_4$ hydrolyze so much more readily than CCl_4?
3. Why should PCl_5 be a better chlorinating agent than PCl_3?
4. Why is sulfur chloride easily hydrolyzed?
5. Which would you predict to be more volatile, PBr_3 or $CaBr_2$? Why?
6. Which would you predict to be higher melting, $SiCl_4$ or $BaCl_2$? Why?
7. Which would be a better chlorinating agent, S_2Cl_2 or $SnCl_2$? Why?
8. Which would be a better brominating agent, $NaBr$ or PBr_3? Why?
9. If element B combines with chlorine to form a stable salt of high melting point, on which side of the periodic table would you predict it would be located?
10. A certain element X forms a chloride XCl_2 that is a stable solid and not a chlorinating agent or susceptible to hydrolysis. What formula and basicity would you predict for the oxide of X?
11. A certain element Y forms a fluoride of formula YF which is volatile and a strong fluorinating agent. Predict the physical and chemical nature (a) of its chloride, and (b) of its oxide.

29

SOME CHEMISTRY OF HYDROGEN

HYDROGEN IN THE PERIODIC TABLE

There just isn't any obvious position for hydrogen in the periodic table. Since hydrogen and helium form the first, very short period, hydrogen ought to be at the top and to the left of helium. Some authors place hydrogen in the M1 group with the alkali metals because, like them, it has only one outer-shell electron. Some place hydrogen in the M7 group with the halogens because it, like them, has only one outer-shell vacancy. In reality it doesn't belong in either place. In order to resemble the alkali metals it would need outer-shell vacant orbitals, which it does not have. In order to resemble the halogens it would need outer-shell lone pairs, which it does not have.

In this book hydrogen is placed above and slightly to the left of carbon, group M4. The justification for this is that hydrogen and carbon have two important qualities in common. One is that they are very similar in electronegativity (H 2.31, C 2.47), and occupy an intermediate position in the periodic table in this respect. The other is a property possessed by these two elements alone: When a hydrogen atom or carbon atom has formed the maximum number of covalent bonds that it can, it has neither electrons nor low-energy orbital vacancies left over. We may also observe that although hydrogen is halfway through its period just as carbon is halfway through its period, since it doesn't have a covalence of four, it does not quite qualify for a position in group M4. A special position for it in the table is still required.

Hydrogen atoms, with their intermediate electronegativity and their ability to form a single, covalent bond, form a wide variety of compounds across the periodic table. The partial charge on hydrogen ranges from highly negative to somewhat highly positive. Hydrogen chemisty is, therefore, somewhat more interesting in this respect than that of most of the other nonmetals, the chemistry of which is governed largely by the properties of the negative oxidation state. Two principal kinds of binary hydrogen compounds are known, those with the major group elements and those with the transitional elements. The compounds of the latter are very different in nature from those of the former. They do not have predictable or very definite compositions. They are all solids which appear to be more like alloys or metals whose lattices are contaminated by absorption of an indefinite amount of hydrogen within the interstitial spaces—the holes and crevices between the layers of metal atoms. In fact, the difference in hydrogen chemistry is one of the most significant reasons for considering the transitional elements and the major group elements separately. In this chapter only the chemistry of hydrogen with the major group elements will be emphasized.

The dual nature of hydrogen is clearly shown by its compounds with the other elements. When it unites with an element that is less electronegative than itself, it acquires partial negative charge at the expense of the other element. It thus acts as an oxidizing agent, attaining the oxidation state of -1. When it unites with an element that is more electronegative than itself, it loses part of the control of its electron to the other element. Thus it acquires partial positive charge and acts as a reducing agent, attaining the oxidation state of $+1$. The difference between negative hydrogen and positive hydrogen is in some respects even more striking than the difference between highly negative and slightly negative oxygen in the oxides.

LIBERATION OF HYDROGEN

Hydrogen gas can be formed very easily from partially negative hydrogen by simply allowing it to react with partially positive hydrogen. For example, sodium is much less electronegative than hydrogen. When it reacts with hydrogen it forms **sodium hydride** (NaH), in which the hydrogen bears high negative charge. The most common example of a compound of partially positive hydrogen is water. If sodium hydride and water come together, hydrogen is vigorously evolved:

$$NaH + H_2O \rightarrow NaOH + H_2$$

This is perhaps the most familiar example of a very general kind of reaction: **Practically any compound of negative hydrogen and any compound of positive hydrogen will react to release molecular hydrogen** and form whatever new compound the residual parts can compose.

Write equations for the reactions, if any, between the following pairs of compounds: NaH and H_2S, HCl and HBr, NH_3 and CH_4, MgH_2 and HCl.

Action of Water on Metals

A more common way of preparing hydrogen in the laboratory is to liberate it from water or an acid by the action of a metal. Consider first the action of a metal on water. First of all, what is a metal? It is a collection of cations held together by a cloud of mutually held electrons. What is a metallic cathode? It is also a collection of cations held together by a cloud of mutually held electrons, but it has an excess of electrons. Notice the close similarity between a metal and a cathode. If a negatively charged cathode is placed in water, hydrogen ions are discharged and hydrogen gas is liberated. If a neutral piece of metal is placed in water, the same kind of thing may happen, provided the electrons are held loosely enough. Sodium is such a metal. If it comes in contact with water, hydrogen is immediately and very rapidly evolved, often with enough vigor to ignite the hydrogen and the sodium. Sodium ions and hydroxide ions remain in the water. The reaction may be written:

$$2\,Na + 2\,H_2O \rightarrow 2\,NaOH + H_2$$

One way of thinking of this reaction is as a competition between a sodium ion and a hydrogen ion for an electron. It does not matter that the sodium already has the electron, before the hydrogen ion has a chance at it. All that matters is that the electron will be acquired by the ion attracting it more strongly. Evidently the hydrogen ion attracts an electron, under the prevailing conditions, more strongly than does the sodium ion. The hydrogen ion takes the electron away from the sodium atom leaving a sodium ion and forming a hydrogen atom. In the next chapter, we will consider the fact that this picture is quite oversimplified but it is useful for the present.

Consider some metal that does not release its electrons quite as easily as does sodium. Place magnesium in water and what happens? Nothing. Nothing that we can see, that is. It seems probable, however, that reaction does occur, at first. Positive hydrogen from the water takes electrons from the magnesium, becoming molecular hydrogen and leaving magnesium ions and hydroxide ions. However, magnesium hydroxide is an exceedingly insoluble compound. Its formation on the surface of the magnesium would almost instantly prevent any further reaction with the water. The apparent unreactivity of magnesium with water might lead us to suppose that in a competition between magnesium ions and hydrogen ions for the same electrons, the magnesium would win. Other types of experiments show that this is not true at all. Given a chance, the hydrogen ion would win.

How do we know this? Simply acidify the water. The reaction then proceeds vigorously: hydrogen bubbles madly around the magnesium metal as the latter dissolves as magnesium ions. What did the acid do? It increased the concentration of hydrogen ions over what was present in pure water, but its chief function was to remove the hydroxide ions as fast as they were formed. If the hydroxide ions almost immediately encounter hydrogen ions, forming water, they cannot coat the metal surface with magnesium hydroxide. Then the metal surface cannot be protected from the positive hydrogen, and reaction continues as long as all the necessary reagents are present.

You are probably aware of the great utility of magnesium as a structural metal for such applications as ladders and aircraft, where strength and light weight are both important. How far would you ride in a magnesium canoe, however, if the magnesium were continually dissolving, liberating hydrogen from the water? Most natural waters are somewhat alkaline and able to attack magnesium only superficially. Many metals resist corrosion in a similar way: the initial corrosion occurs very readily but prevents continuance by coating the metal with an impervious, sometimes invisible, layer of corrosion product. Very few metals yield corrosion products like that of sodium, which is so highly soluble.

What about aluminum? Aluminum is used for teakettles, saucepans, baking dishes, canoes, ladders, aircraft, roofing, siding, and in hundreds of other applications where contact between aluminum and water is not prevented and is often encouraged. This seems to indicate that aluminum is impervious to chemical attack by water, but is it really? One way to find out is to dissolve aluminum in mercury. Most metals, with the notable exception of iron, dissolve in mercury to some extent, forming **amalgams.** Mercury itself is unaffected by water. If an aluminum amalgam is placed in water, hydrogen bubbles up around it quite rapidly. This shows that under conditions where protection by a coating of aluminum hydroxide cannot be provided, aluminum rapidly gives up its valence electrons to water, and hydrogen gas is liberated.

If the unreactivity of ordinary aluminum to water is the result of a protective coating of oxide or hydroxide on the aluminum surface, how could it be removed? Remember that aluminum hydroxide is amphoteric and can therefore dissolve in either an acid or a base. If the water is made alkaline, aluminum dissolves in it by acting acidic, and liberating hydrogen. If the water is made acidic, aluminum dissolves in it by acting basic, and liberating hydrogen:

$$2\,Al + 6\,H_2O \rightarrow 3\,H_2 + 2\,Al(OH)_3$$

$$Al(OH)_3 + OH^- \rightleftharpoons [Al(OH)_4]^- \text{ (in solution)}$$

$$Al(OH)_3 + 3H^+ \rightarrow 3\,H_2O + Al^{+++} \text{ (in solution)}$$

You may paddle your aluminum canoe for a long time in ordinary lakes and streams, but keep it out of sodium hydroxide solution or hydrochloric acid if you wish to remain afloat.

Differences Among Metals: The Activity Series

It has just been pointed out that the differences in reactivity among sodium, magnesium, and aluminum toward positive hydrogen are not nearly as great as they seem under ordinary conditions. Nevertheless, even discounting the effects of protective coatings of corrosion products, differences still exist. Sodium is the most reactive, with magnesium next. These differences were discussed earlier in Chapter 26. As pointed out there, all metals differ in reactivity. Their differences are sufficiently consistent that they can be arranged in an order known as the **activity series.** A partial list is: sodium, magnesium, aluminum, zinc, iron, tin, *hydrogen,* copper, silver, mercury. Remember that metals ahead of or more reactive than hydrogen can displace it from water and acids.

To prepare hydrogen in the laboratory, the action of a metal on an acid is usually employed. Zinc or iron are usually used because the more reactive metals are inclined to react too vigorously.

Other Methods of Liberating Hydrogen

Other methods are more practical for large-scale industrial preparation of hydrogen. These include thermal decomposition of hydrocarbons, electrolysis of water, and the **water gas** reaction. The last is a means of obtaining hydrogen from water by passing steam over heated coke. Carbon (the chief constituent of coke) removes the oxygen from the water:

$$C + H_2O \rightarrow CO + H_2$$

Both carbon monoxide and hydrogen are good fuel gases, and this water-gas mixture is usually used as such. However, hydrogen can be separated out if the carbon monoxide is first catalytically oxidized to carbon dioxide. Carbon dioxide is sufficiently soluble in water, under high pressure, to be separable from the hydrogen gas, which is very insoluble.

SYNTHESIS OF HYDROGEN COMPOUNDS

Many hydrogen compounds can be prepared by direct synthesis from the elements. These include most of the compounds in which hydrogen has acted as oxidizing agent, and, therefore, bears partial negative charge. The alkali and alkaline earth metals, groups M1 and M2, combine readily with hydrogen gas when heated with it. Hydrogen also reacts readily with many of the nonmetals that are more electronegative and cause the hydrogen to become partially positive. Hydrogen can burn in oxygen, fluorine, or chlorine, forming the corresponding binary compounds H_2O, HF, and HCl. One of the most important compounds of positive hydrogen, ammonia, is more difficult to prepare because of the great stability of the triple bond between the two nitrogen atoms in N_2. But even this will react with hydrogen when heated under pressure with the help of a catalyst:

$$N_2 + 3\,H_2 \rightleftharpoons 2\,NH_3$$

Less stable hydrogen compounds, such as those of aluminum and zinc, can be made by double decomposition reactions using lithium hydride and the chloride of the other metal:

$$3\,LiH + AlCl_3 \rightarrow AlH_3 + 3\,LiCl$$

Such reactions depend on the greater bond strength between the halogen and the alkali metal.

A very general method of synthesis of hydrogen compounds that are not attacked by water—in other words, compounds of neutral or positive hydrogen but not of negative hydrogen—is the hydrolysis of a binary compound of two other elements. The hydroxide from the water tends to become attached to the less electronegative of the other two elements. The hydrogen becomes attached to the more electronegative element. For example, hydrolysis of aluminum carbide (Al_4C_3) gives methane:

$$Al_4C_3 + 12\,H_2O \rightarrow 4\,Al(OH)_3 + 3\,CH_4$$

Phosphine (PH_3) can be formed by hydrolysis of calcium phosphide (Ca_3P_2):

$$Ca_3P_2 + 6\,H_2O \rightarrow 3\,Ca(OH)_2 + 2\,PH_3$$

We have already considered the similar example of the preparation of hydrogen bromide:

$$PBr_3 + 3\,H_2O \rightarrow P(OH)_3 + 3\,HBr$$

PHYSICAL PROPERTIES OF HYDROGEN COMPOUNDS

Compounds of highly negative hydrogen are nonvolatile solids. Most of these decompose before they reach a melting temperature, but are stable over a range of several hundred degrees. The bonding in these solids is generally considered to be ionic, with hydride ions (H^-) and metal cations. However, a negatively charged hydrogen ion would hold the largest excess of negative charge by far of any anion, having double the original number of electrons. The next closest, fluorine, only gains in electrons by about eleven per cent when it forms fluoride ion. Consequently the hydride ion would be extremely susceptible to sharing its electrons with all neighboring cations. Evidently, the electron is capable of partially occupying vacant orbitals of several cations at once. The apparent size of the hydride ion in the crystal is remarkable, for it seems to fill about as much space as a potassium ion.

When the hydrogen is less negative, it seems capable of acting as a bridge even though it supposedly can form but one covalent bond. Such a bridge is called a **hydridic bridge** because it is a partially negative hydrogen holding two positively charged atoms together. Hydrides of beryllium, magnesium, boron, and aluminum, and perhaps others, are polymers or solids that appear to be held together by hydridic bridging.

When the hydrogen is not negative at all, but is either neutral or positive, the hydrogen compounds should no longer be called *hydrides*. The *-ide* ending signifies the negative charge. Compounds of neutral or positive hydrogen are molecular, volatile, low-melting substances. Three of them—ammonia, water, and hydrogen fluoride—can be associated by protonic bridges, but the rest are very volatile gases. They include methane (CH_4), silane (SiH_4, in which the hydrogen does have small negative charge), germane (GeH_4), stannane (SnH_4), phosphine (PH_3), arsine (AsH_3), hydrogen sulfide (H_2S), and the hydrogen halides, among others. Most of them are highly toxic.

CHEMICAL PROPERTIES OF HYDROGEN COMPOUNDS

The reactions of compounds of negative hydrogen with compounds of positive hydrogen to liberate molecular hydrogen have already been mentioned. Negative hydrogen tends to be quite the opposite of positive hydrogen in every way.

Remember that neutral hydrogen itself can act either as oxidizing agent or reducing agent. To the extent that it acts as an oxidizing agent, it is expected to lose its capacity to act as an oxidizing agent, and vice versa. But hydrogen which has already acted as oxidizing agent, thus becoming negative, acquires reducing power greater than it had as elemental hydrogen. Compounds of negative hydrogen are very useful as reducing agents in a great variety of chemical syntheses.

Hydrogen which has acted as reducing agent has become better able to oxidize than before, by virtue of its positive charge. The most positive hydrogen in chemical combination is only about half as positive as the most negative hydrogen is negative. This is the result of hydrogen having an electronegativity a little higher than the median value for the elements. Consequently, we cannot expect positive hydrogen to have acquired as much oxidizing power as negative hydrogen can acquire reducing power. Nevertheless, good reducing agents—such as the more reactive metals—are easily oxidized by positive hydrogen compounds. Sodium, for example, is not only oxidized by water, giving sodium hydroxide, but it can also be oxidized by ammonia, giving hydrogen and sodium amide ($NaNH_2$), or by hydrogen fluoride, giving hydrogen and sodium fluoride:

$$2\,Na + 2\,NH_3 \rightarrow H_2 + 2\,NaNH_2$$

$$2\,Na + 2\,HF \rightarrow H_2 + 2\,NaF$$

The special characteristics of positive hydrogen are usually described in terms of acidity rather than oxidizing power, although acidity and oxidizing power are closely related and frequently go hand in hand. All compounds containing positive hydrogen are acidic, including even those that also can be basic. For example, ammonia is usually thought of as basic because the lone pair of electrons on the nitrogen can acquire an outside proton. The acidity of ammonia is shown by the reaction with sodium, in which hydrogen is released and sodium amide formed.

The characteristics of negative hydrogen that give it reducing power also give it the ability to act as electron donor and, in this sense, to be basic. In fact, the combination of a hydride ion with a proton to form molecular hydrogen is an example of negative hydrogen acting as an electron donor to a proton:

$$H:^- + H^+ \rightarrow H:H \text{ (or, } H_2)$$

It is well known that complex hydrogen ions result when a compound of positive hydrogen acquires a proton by acting as an electron donor. For example:

$$NH_3 + H^+ \rightarrow NH_4^+$$

$$H_2O + H^+ \rightarrow H_3O^+$$

It is likewise possible for a hydrogen compound that is an electron acceptor to form a complex hydrogen ion by taking on a hydride ion:

$$AlH_3 + H^- \rightarrow AlH_4^-$$

$LiAlH_4$, formed from lithium hydride acting as donor and aluminum hydride acting as acceptor, is a very valuable reducing agent.

Test Your Memory

1. a) Where should hydrogen be placed in the periodic table?
    b) Why is hydrogen misplaced in Group M1? In Group M7?
2. What unique characteristic do hydrogen and carbon have in common?
3. Write an equation for the action of water on sodium.
4. How can a coating of insoluble metal hydroxide be prevented or removed?
5. Why doesn't a magnesium canoe dissolve in water?
6. What is meant by *activity series?* List a few common elements in their proper order.
7. a) Write an equation for the *water-gas* reaction.
    b) Write equations for the burning of water gas.
8. Write an equation for the synthesis of ammonia from its elements.
9. Write an equation for a preparation of AlH_3 by double decomposition.
10. Write an equation for the formation of a binary hydrogen compound by hydrolysis.

11. What is a *hydridic bridge?*
12. How does partial charge affect the oxidizing and reducing properties of hydrogen?
13. Write an equation illustrating the acidic nature of ammonia.
14. Discuss possible complexes of (a) negative hydrogen; (b) positive hydrogen.

Test Your Understanding

1. How does the nature of a metal hydroxide affect the action of the metal on water?
2. Under what conditions can hydrogen act as an oxidizing agent?
3. a) What are some compounds of negative hydrogen?
   b) Write equations showing how one of the compounds of negative hydrogen would be predicted to react with water and with hydrogen chloride.
4. a) What, if anything, would happen if Mg_3P_2 were treated with aqueous acid?
   b) Why would acid be preferable to plain water here?
5. Predict what reaction if any would result between the following pairs of compounds: (a) NaH and LiH; (b) AlH_3 and H_2O; (c) HBr and CaH_2; (d) H_2O and SiH_4; (e) CH_4 and H_2O; (f) H_2S and BaH_2; (g) H_2S and HF.

30

THE PERIODICITY OF HYDROGEN CHEMISTRY

PERIOD 2

We have already crossed the periodic table several times in considering the elements, their oxides, and their chlorides, but another trip or two may still prove useful. The periodic system serves remarkably well as a basis for organization of chemical knowledge.

Lithium. The first element of period 2, lithium, with its single, outer-shell electron is clearly able to unite one to one with hydrogen to form LiH:

$$2\,Li + H_2 \rightarrow 2\,LiH$$

The hydrogen is much more electronegative than lithium, indicating that the bonds must be polar, with hydrogen negative and lithium positive. Lithium hydride is not expected to remain as separate molecules because of the ease of

Figure 30.1. Molecule and Crystal of Lithium Hydride.

Electrolysis of molten LiH discharges H_2 at the *anode*, showing that H is negative in the melt.

LiH molecule

LiH crystal

The highly negative hydrogen appears to occupy an extraordinarily large volume within the crystal (about as large as a K^+ ion). This is probably the result of the large excess of negative charge which the nuclear proton cannot control in the face of the competition by six surrounding lithium atoms of high positive charge.

sharing the electrons on the highly negative hydrogen and the vacant orbitals that would otherwise be left on the lithium. We predict that the negative hydrogen of this nonmolecular solid will act as electron donor in the formation of complex hydrides or as a reducing agent in the presence of oxidizing agents. It will also combine with positive hydrogen to liberate molecular hydrogen. We can confidently predict all these properties from our knowledge of the nature of the component atoms. And these properties are, in fact, observed experimentally.

Beryllium. Beryllium is the next element in this period. With two outer-shell electrons it can form two covalent bonds to hydrogen. Its electronegativity is higher than that of lithium but still much lower than that of hydrogen. The two bonds in BeH_2 must be quite polar. Intermediate negative charge on hydrogen seems to lead to polymerization through hydridic bridging. Such bridging is predicted for BeH_2. It can also be predicted that BeH_2 should be very easily oxidized and very susceptible to hydrolysis. These are the properties observed for beryllium hydride.

Figure 30.2. Molecule of Beryllium Hydride.

A single molecule of BeH_2 would be linear as shown. The compound exists as a highly polymeric solid, believed to be held together by hydride bridges, which use the two otherwise vacant outer orbitals on the beryllium atom and the negative charge on hydrogen which is attracted by positive charge on beryllium.

Boron. The next element is boron. Here is the classic example of the hydridic bridge. From the three outer-shell electrons of boron and its general ability to form three covalent bonds, we should think it would unite with hydrogen to form BH_3. Indeed, this was the formula given in earlier textbooks. Later it was discovered, however, that BH_3 never occurs alone. It is always dimerized in **diborane** (B_2H_6). Here two BH_2 groups appear to be bound together by two hydridic bridges. Since no additional bridging is possible with only two boron atoms, this is a molecular substance. In fact, it is a very low-melting, low-boiling gas. Boron is more electronegative than beryllium but still less so than hydrogen. The hydrogen in diborane can be predicted to have small but appreciable negative charge. It should therefore be susceptible to oxidation and hydrolysis.

These are in fact the properties of diborane. A number of other boron hydrogen compounds are now known that we would not have been able to predict without understanding much more about boron than is now known.

Figure 30.3.   Molecule of Diborane.

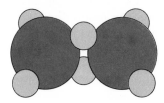

In B_2H_6, two BH_2 groups are bridged together by two hydrogen atoms, each of which shares an orbital from each boron. The bridge is at right angles to the two BH_2 groups which are in the same plane. Each bridging hydrogen is held equally to two boron atoms, so that two electrons are holding three atoms together. This very unusual situation is called *electron deficient bonding*.

Boron is quite unusual among the chemical elements. Its compounds with hydrogen stand in a distinct class by themselves.

It may be of passing interest to note here that, since boron is lower in electronegativity than carbon, its bonds to oxygen should be more polar and, therefore, stronger. Thus, more heat should be obtained per mole by burning boron than carbon. The most common fuels for aircraft consist of hydrocarbons, which produce energy by combination with oxygen to give carbon dioxide and water. Similarly, boron-hydrogen compounds should burn to give boric oxide and water, but with greater evolution of energy. Great interest has been shown in the possibilities of the boron hydrides as high-energy fuels for aircraft and rocket propulsion, because their burning liberates more energy per pound of fuel.

Carbon.   The next element in this period, carbon, can form four covalent bonds per atom and therefore should form CH_4. As we shall consider in much greater detail later in this book, carbon and hydrogen can form countless other compounds also. Carbon is only a little more electronegative than hydrogen (2.47 compared to 2.31). Therefore, the carbon atom should become only very slightly negative in methane (CH_4), at the expense of the hydrogen atoms which are left just slightly positive. There is no apparent way by which methane could act as electron donor. Its hydrogen is not very positive, so its acidic properties are practically nonexistent. Without negative hydrogen it can be much more resistant to oxidation. Although methane burns well when ignited, it is unreactive in oxygen under ordinary conditions. With no possibility of either hydridic or protonic bridging, we expect methane to be strictly unassociated and a very low-melting, low-boiling gas. Methane has just the properties expected of it.

Nitrogen.   Nitrogen is more electronegative than carbon. With five outer-shell electrons per atom, it can only become joined by ordinary covalent bonds to three hydrogen atoms. For these reasons, we expect the hydrogen in ammonia to be appreciably more positive than that in methane. The combination of a lone pair on nitrogen and positive hydrogen should permit formation of protonic bridges, causing ammonia to have higher melting and boiling points than would otherwise be expected. The negative nitrogen with its lone pair of electrons should also be able to act as electron donor to many acceptors besides a proton. The positive hydrogen should have acidic properties. All these properties are observed for ammonia.

Figure 30.4.   Molecules of Methane, Ammonia, and Hydrogen Fluoride.

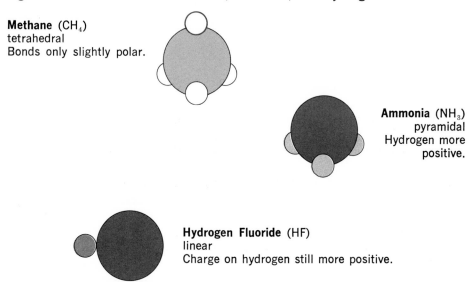

Methane (CH$_4$)
tetrahedral
Bonds only slightly polar.

Ammonia (NH$_3$)
pyramidal
Hydrogen more
positive.

Hydrogen Fluoride (HF)
linear
Charge on hydrogen still more positive.

Oxygen.   The next element is oxygen. Water has already been discussed extensively. Note that the oxygen might be expected to be a donor, but less so than the nitrogen in ammonia, and the hydrogen should be acidic, more so than in ammonia. These differences do exist.

Fluorine.   Finally, with fluorine, hydrogen forms a compound in which the partial charge on hydrogen is 0.25. This is the largest positive charge on hydrogen for any binary hydrogen compound. HF is strongly acidic (although in aqueous solution it does not ionize completely), and associates through protonic bridging.

Once more a trend has been seen in crossing the periodic table from left to right. From a nonvolatile solid having reducing and electron donor properties but no oxidizing power, we progressed to a volatile molecular compound having acidic, oxidizing properties. The chief difference between the trend for hydrogen compounds and those for oxygen and chlorine is that highly electronegative elements, such as the latter two, do not become good reducing agents merely by acquiring high negative charge. **Elements which initially attract electrons strongly do not then give them up easily.** On the other hand, the intermediate electronegativity of hydrogen means that the electrons acquired by hydrogen in its more negative state are not held very securely, and can rather easily be removed by an oxidizing agent. Negative hydrogen is an effective reducing agent whereas negative oxygen is not. Negative chlorine is only effective when under attack by very strong oxidizing agents.

PERIOD 3

Sodium. Moving across period 3 of the periodic table in the study of hydrogen compounds discloses the expected similarities but also some important differences. The first element of period three, sodium, has one loosely held, outer-shell electron. Sodium joins hydrogen by a single covalent bond that is quite polar, with hydrogen negative. In order to make maximum use of the vacant orbitals on sodium, the simplest molecules of NaH should condense to give a nonmolecular solid. This we predict to be a reducing agent and to react with compounds of positive hydrogen to liberate H_2. Sodium hydride is just as we have predicted.

The three chemicals that have been commonly used for extinguishing fires—water, carbon tetrachloride, and carbon dioxide—are not useful for sodium hydride fires.

Sodium hydride is so easily oxidized that if it catches fire it burns very vigorously. Smothering the fire with an inert material, such as sand, is about all that can be done to prevent further burning. Water would produce a hydrogen explosion; the hydride would go right on burning in carbon tetrachloride, taking the chlorine away from the carbon to form sodium chloride; the reaction would also continue in carbon dioxide. In a chemical laboratory or industrial plant, it is a good idea to find out what is burning before trying to put out the fire.

Magnesium. The next element in this period is magnesium. Here the formula is easy to predict: MgH_2. The bonds, although planar, cannot be nearly as polar as in sodium hydride. Bonding more in the nature of hydridic bridging can be expected to hold MgH_2 together in solid form. Again, strong reducing power, high reactivity with water and other hydrogen compounds, and basicity would be predicted. All these are observed properties of magnesium hydride.

Aluminum. Aluminum, with its three outer-shell electrons, should be able to form AlH_3. This should have less polar bonds, although with hydrogen still appreciably negative. AlH_3 should show the properties by now almost automatically associated with negative hydrogen: reducing power, reactivity with water and other protonic reagents, and association through hydridic bridging.

In fact, aluminum hydride is a white solid polymerized through hydridic bridging. It is extremely reactive, inflaming in air, and hydrolyzes practically explosively.

The reactivity of compounds is associated not only with the condition of the combined atoms with respect to charge, but also with the strength of the bonds. With reduced polarity, bonds tend to become weaker. We may ascribe the high reactivity of aluminum hydride to its inherent instability. There is also the fourth orbital of each aluminum atom, which probably participates in hydridic bridging but also is a point of attack for oxygen, water, or similar reagents.

Silicon. The next element, silicon, with its four outer-shell electrons per atom, should form tetrahedral molecules of SiH_4. Here the bonds should still be somewhat polar, with hydrogen appreciably negative, but not sufficiently negative to activate the outer d orbitals. No hydridic bridges can form. The molecules are so symmetrical that they attract one another only very weakly. Hence silane (SiH_4) is a gas, having the predictable properties of a compound of negative hydrogen. It is spontaneously inflammable, and easily hydrolyzed.

Phosphorus. A phosphorus atom has five outer-shell electrons. With only three vacancies it should be able to combine with only three hydrogen atoms. The electronegativity of phosphorus is only a little less than that of hydrogen (2.16 to 2.31), and hydrogen cannot be expected to activate the outer d orbitals of phosphorus the way that chlorine can. Therefore, no compound PH_5 can be expected, although phosphine (PH_3) is well known. With the lone pair of electrons on the phosphorus atom, one might be tempted to predict good electron donor properties for phosphine akin to those of ammonia. Two facts operate against this, however. One is the larger size of the phosphorus atom: The lone pair spreads out so that it is not sufficiently concentrated to attract protonic hydrogen and form protonic bridges as ammonia can. More important, however, is that here the charge on phosphorus is slightly positive, rather than negative as on the nitrogen of ammonia. Therefore, the electron pair is much less available. Phosphine forms only very unstable phosphonium salts PH_4X, in contrast to ammonium salts which are quite stable. In general, phosphine is a much weaker donor than ammonia. Since both phosphorus and hydrogen burn very readily, it is not surprising that phosphine is very inflammable. As usually prepared, small amounts of spontaneously inflammable impurities cause it to ignite in air. Bubbles of phosphine formed under water cause a flash of light when they reach the surface and burn. Phosphine is generally effective as a reducing agent.

Sulfur. With sulfur, two hydrogen atoms can form covalent bonds to give hydrogen sulfide (H_2S). Sulfur cannot be expected to show a higher valence here. The hydrogen, rather than activating the d orbitals of sulfur by withdrawing electrons from it, is less electronegative, and becomes positive with sulfur negative. The positive hydrogen should impart reducing properties only to the extent that both elements burn easily. Its chief influence, associated with its charge, is to make hydrogen sulfide weakly acidic. The only way in which the molecular H_2S could associate with other molecules is through protonic bridging, but this does not occur, partly because of the relatively small bond polarity. The hydrogen has only a small positive charge and the sulfur only small negative charge. Also, the sulfur is large enough for its lone pairs to spread out. In this condition an electron pair is relatively unattractive to protonic hydrogen. Unlike water, hydrogen sulfide is unassociated, and a low-melting, low-boiling gas. Incidentally, also unlike water, it is extremely toxic. Its powerful, nauseating odor discloses its presence in traces.

Chlorine. Hydrogen chloride has already been mentioned several times. It is strongly acidic because, in excess of water, the chloride ion only very weakly attracts the proton in comparison to the oxygen of the water molecule.

Figure 30.5. Relative Size and Charge of Hydrogen in Binary Compounds Across the Periodic Table.

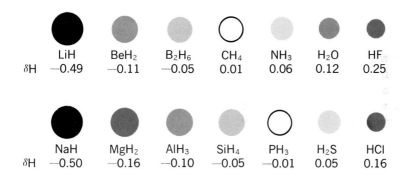

	LiH	BeH$_2$	B$_2$H$_6$	CH$_4$	NH$_3$	H$_2$O	HF
δH	−0.49	−0.11	−0.05	0.01	0.06	0.12	0.25

	NaH	MgH$_2$	AlH$_3$	SiH$_4$	PH$_3$	H$_2$S	HCl
δH	−0.50	−0.16	−0.10	−0.05	−0.01	0.05	0.16

Once more a crossing of the periodic table from left to right has revealed a dramatic change from solid, nonmolecular compounds of strongly reducing, electron-donating, and basic properties, to molecular, low-melting, low-boiling compounds exhibiting acceptor properties through the protonic hydrogen and being acidic and oxidizing. The periodicity of the chemical elements is just as evident in their hydrogen chemistry as in any other aspect of their properties.

Table 30.1. Some Properties of Hydrogen Compounds of Periods 2 and 3

Compound	Partial charge on hydrogen	Melting point	Boiling point	Acid-base*	Oxidizing or reducing*	Hydrolysis
LiH	-0.49	680	....	basic	reducing	complete
BeH$_2$	-0.11	decomp.	....	basic	reducing	complete
B$_2$H$_6$	-0.05	-165.5	-92.5	basic	reducing	complete
CH$_4$	0.01	-182.5	-161.5	neither at 25°	neither at 25°	none
NH$_3$	0.06	-77.7	-33.4	extremely weak acid	very weakly oxidizing	none
H$_2$O	0.12	0.0	100.0	amphoteric	weakly oxidizing	none
HF	0.25	-83.1	19.9	acidic	oxidizing	none
NaH	-0.50	d	....	basic	reducing	complete
MgH$_2$	-0.16	....	....	basic	reducing	complete
AlH$_3$	-0.10	d	....	basic	reducing	complete
SiH$_4$	-0.05	-184.7	-111.4	basic	reducing	complete
PH$_3$	-0.01	-133.8	-87.7	neither at 25°	reducing	none
H$_2$S	0.05	-85.5	-60.3	weakly acidic	weakly oxidizing	none
HCl	0.16	-114.2	-85.0	strongly acidic	oxidizing	none

* refers only to the property of the combined hydrogen atoms. For instance, boron in B$_2$H$_6$ is acidic and nitrogen in NH$_3$ is basic.

Test Your Memory

1. a) What compound is formed when lithium reacts with hydrogen?
   b) Why is lithium hydride a solid?
2. Why is diborane not a solid?
3. What is the formula of the beryllium compound with hydrogen?
4. Why are boron hydrides of interest as high-energy fuels?
5. Why are methane molecules unassociated?
6. Write an equation for the synthesis of water.
7. Why is negative hydrogen a much better reducing agent than negative chlorine or negative oxygen?
8. Why is phosphine quite different from ammonia?
9. What is meant by *periodicity of hydrogen chemistry?* Explain in detail.

Test Your Understanding

1. What properties of lithium and hydrogen predetermine the nature of their compound?
2. What do LiH, BeH_2, and B_2H_6 have in common?
3. a) Write equations for the burning of LiH, BeH_2, B_2H_6, and CH_4.
   b) Write an equation for the action of water on each of the preceding compounds.
4. Why doesn't nitrogen form NH_5?
5. What molecular structures would you predict for SbH_3, H_2S, H_2Se, H_2Te, AsH_3, and SnH_4?
6. Indicate which of the following pairs of compounds would be higher melting: (a) LiH, SiH_4; (b) H_2S, NH_3; (c) H_2O, H_2Te; (d) HI, NaI; (e) CH_4, BaH_2.
7. Which of the following compounds would you predict to have some acidity: BeH_2, NaH, HBr, H_2S, PH_3, H_2O?

Part 4

Chemical Practice and Description

31

PRINCIPLES OF ANALYSIS

ANALYTICAL CHEMISTRY

Very few chemical substances that are useful to man are found lying around. Most occur in nature in complex mixtures or otherwise combined in materials that have very little practical application. Usually in such conditions the useful substances are not easily recognized. Who but a trained chemist would expect to find mercury in a red dust, oil for milady's perfume in the scent glands of a buck, or vitamin A in the liver of a shark? The material civilization of man received an enormous boost indeed when he began to discover that beneath the appearance of things as they are lay valuable products within the power of his ingenuity to extract. But before he could plan a way of extraction, he had to learn how to identify what was there. This is the origin of that essential part of chemical science known as **analytical chemistry.** Knowledge of the nature of chemistry requires at least some understanding of the more general principles of analytical procedures.

GAS ANALYSIS

With the exception of the M8 elements, all the gases we know, both elemental and compound, are capable of undergoing a variety of chemical changes dependent on their composition: different compositions undergo different changes. By choosing appropriate chemical reagents, it is possible to convert certain components of a mixture of gases to nonvolatile substances, without affecting the remaining components. For example, acids, in general, will absorb ammonia to form relatively nonvolatile ammonium salts. Bases, in general, will absorb carbon dioxide, sulfur dioxide, hydrogen sulfide, sulfur trioxide; in fact, any nonmetal oxide. Heated active metals will absorb hydrogen, oxygen, and sometimes nitrogen gas. In all of these examples, the gas changes chemically into a nonvolatile substance when it is absorbed.

The general principle involved in chemical analysis of gaseous mixtures is the selective absorption of certain specific gases by certain specific solutions or solid reagents. To consider a very simple example, suppose we had a sample of gas containing unknown quantities of ammonia, carbon dioxide, and oxygen. After careful measurement of the total volume, the sample could be forced through some pellets of solid sodium hydroxide, or some absorbent solid coated with sodium hydroxide. This would remove the carbon dioxide as the bicarbonate or carbonate, allowing the ammonia to pass through unchanged along with the oxygen. We could then measure the volume again to determine by difference the amount of carbon dioxide absorbed. Then we could pass the residual gas through an acidic solution such as dilute sulfuric acid, which would take out all the ammonia as $(NH_4)_2SO_4$. The final volume of gas would be oxygen.

It is also possible to carry out physical separations of the components of gas mixtures, identifying each individual component by its physical properties without resorting to any chemical reactions at all. We normally think of distillations as involving liquids. All gases become liquids if cooled and/or compressed sufficiently. Thus, they can be handled as liquids at low temperatures or at high pressures if they are below their critical temperatures. The **critical temperature** of a gas is the temperature above which no amount of pressure can liquefy it. The so-called permanent gases—including oxygen, nitrogen, hydrogen, carbon monoxide, methane, and ethane—have critical temperatures well below 25°C and cannot be liquefied under pressure at ordinary temperatures. Gases having critical temperatures above 25°, such as ammonia, chlorine, and sulfur dioxide, can be liquefied by pressure without any cooling.

Very efficient apparatus has been devised for carrying out distillation of liquefied gas mixtures in such a way as to take fullest advantage of relatively minor differences in volatility. Such devices center around a vertical column called a **fractionating column** within which vapors constantly rise and condense. The less volatile components tend to run back down into the distillation pot, there to be reheated, while the more volatile components climb higher in the column to cooler temperatures before they condense. At the top of the column a **distillation head** accepts part of the most volatile components that reach it, continuously or intermittently allowing this part to condense and drain into a receiving vessel. Portions having different temperature ranges of volatility are called **fractions.** The separation procedure is called **fractional distillation.** Although it has been described here in relation to liquefied gases, it is a general process for the separation of any mixture of liquids.

When the components of a gas mixture are sufficiently different in volatility and when the distillation apparatus is efficient enough, different gaseous compounds can be separated very effectively. Once separated, they can then be identified by such physical properties as vapor tension, melting point, refractive index, and density.

A complete analysis of a gaseous mixture is likely to involve both physical and chemical procedures. Once a good analytical procedure has been developed, it is sometimes adapted for large-scale separation of the gases involved.

LIQUID ANALYSIS

A mixture of liquids is usually analyzed by first separating it into its components by fractional distillation. Each component is then identified individually by physical or chemical means. The apparatus is the same as that used for liquefied gases, except that cooling below ordinary temperatures is ordinarily unnecessary, and there is no need for operating at pressures above one atmosphere. Often, however, one or more components of the liquid mixture may be unstable at high temperatures and involatile at low temperatures. Such components can be separated without decomposition if the temperature requirement for distillation is lowered by reducing the pressure of the atmosphere over the liquid. Distillation at subatmospheric pressures is usually termed **vacuum distillation.** It requires vacuum pumps to produce the low pressures, and gas-tight apparatus to maintain the low pressure without leakage from the external atmosphere. Vacuum distillations may be carried out at pressures as low as a fraction of one millimeter, which allows volatilization at the lowest possible temperatures.

To minimize still further the temperature required for distillation, vacuum distillation is sometimes carried out in apparatus providing a very short path between liquid surface and condenser. Thus the time that the substance must remain in the vapor state and at the volatilizing temperature is kept to a minimum. This very low-pressure, short-path procedure is called a **molecular distillation.** Although its operation is usually very slow, it permits separations of many compounds by distillation that would decompose thermally under ordinary conditions in ordinary stills.

Distillations may also be conducted in an atmosphere of some unreactive gas if the vapors would react too readily with the oxygen or moisture in the air. Vacuum distillations at an extremely low pressure, about a millionth of a millimeter, also serve to protect easily oxidizable substances during their distillation, both by removing oxygen and by reducing the temperature required.

Some liquid compounds that are too unstable to be distilled without decomposing can be separated by **fractional crystallization.** Here the difference in melting point is exploited. Crystals of a pure substance often form when a liquid mixture containing that substance is cooled.

Solvent extraction, described below, can also be used for liquids.

ANALYSIS OF SOLIDS

If a solid substance can be volatilized without decomposition, distillation procedures can be used to separate them from mixtures. More commonly they are not sufficiently volatile at reasonable temperatures, even if stable to heat.

Then some other properties must be used for separation. Often it is the differences in solubility in different solvents. If a liquid can be found which can dissolve one or more of the compounds of a solid mixture but not the others without reacting chemically with them, the soluble substances can be extracted away from the insoluble ones. This is called **solvent extraction.** It can be used for separating solids, or extracting liquids or solids from mixtures with other liquids. If a given substance is somewhat soluble in both of two immiscible liquids, and is shaken with a mixture of the two, it will become distributed between the two solvents in proportion to its relative solubility in each. If, for example, the solute is nine times as soluble in solvent A as in solvent B, it can be extracted from its solution in solvent B by use of solvent A (assuming A and B are immiscible). However, an equal volume of A will only take out 90 per cent of the solute from the solvent B. A fresh volume of A will then take out 90 per cent of the 10 per cent that remained after the first extraction. By successive batches of fresh solvent, essentially all of the solute can be extracted from B. Often the apparatus and procedure involve some sort of continuous extraction to avoid the relative clumsiness of repeated batch extractions.

Most commonly, especially for an unknown mineral mixture, the first step in preparing for analysis of a solid is to dissolve it. The techniques for analysis of solutions have been developed to a high degree of sophistication. Many minerals are extremely difficult to force into solution. Very powerful reagents—such as hydrofluoric acid, strong oxidizing agents, or fused sodium carbonate—are needed to bring about the chemical changes required to obtain soluble components. Once the mixture has been dissolved, very elaborate procedures are available to determine the nature of the individual ions and molecules in solution.

Solubility and Solubility Product

Remember that a saturated solution was defined as one in which the dissolved solute and the undissolved solute are at equilibrium. That is, the rate of dissolution and the rate of recrystallization are exactly equal. One of the most valuable techniques for the separation and identification of substances from solutions is that of **precipitation,** causing the separation of an insoluble substance. Obviously such a separation requires that the solubility of the substance be exceeded; a situation must be created in which the rate of recrystallization exceeds the rate of dissolution.

Consider the salt, sodium chloride, which is quite soluble in water. When an excess of salt is added to a sample of water, the crystalline NaCl dissolves as Na^+ and Cl^- ions. As the concentration of these increases, their rate of recrystallization increases until finally the crystal is dissolving and reforming at the same rate; we have a saturated solution. When a solute dissolves as ions, it is possible to change the concentration of one or the other ion by adding some different compound that furnishes the same ion. For instance, to the saturated sodium chloride solution could be added hydrochloric acid. In concentrated hydrochloric acid, the chloride ion concentration is greater than in a saturated sodium chloride solution, because hydrogen chloride is more soluble. If concentrated hydrochloric acid is added, the concentration of chloride ion is now made higher than the equilibrium concentration. Therefore, the rate of recrystallization of sodium chloride is speeded up, because the probability is greater in the presence of a higher chloride concentration. This upsets the equilibrium of the dissolution of sodium chloride. Sodium ions are used up faster than before, until they are so reduced in concentration that even with the higher concentration of chloride ion, the probability of both rejoining the crystal once more equals the probability of the ions leaving the crystal to become hydrated and dissolved. A new state of dynamic equilibrium has been reached.

At this new equilibrium, however, the concentration of sodium chloride in solution, as measured by the sodium ion, is lower than when only pure water and sodium chloride were present. In other words, the addition of concentrated hydrochloric acid to a saturated solution of sodium chloride causes precipitation of sodium chloride until less is dissolved than before. Or, stated differently, the solubility of sodium chloride is greater in pure water than it is in concentrated hydrochloric acid.

In our study of weak acids it was shown that the common ion, hydrogen ion, suppresses the ionization of weak acids. In a similar way, the common ion, chloride ion, suppresses the "ionization" (actually the dissolution) of sodium chloride. In both examples, the effect is called the **common ion effect.**

If this effect is valid, changing the concentration of sodium ions should cause a similar result. Adding sodium hydroxide, which is much more soluble in water than sodium chloride, increases the sodium ion concentration and does speed up the recrystallization process without changing the dissolution rate. Consequently some of the dissolved sodium chloride is required to rejoin the crystal before the chloride ion concentration can be reduced to where the probability of encounter with a sodium ion to recrystallize is the same as before. Sodium hydroxide will precipitate sodium chloride from its saturated solution in pure water. Sodium chloride is less soluble in concentrated sodium hydroxide solution than in pure water.

For the dissolution of sodium chloride and its recrystallization, the equation may be written:

$$NaCl(s) \rightleftharpoons Na^+ + Cl^-$$

and for the equilibrium the expression can be written:

$$K = \frac{[Na^+]\,[Cl^-]}{[NaCl]}$$

Recognizing that the denominator is unchangeable because the concentration of a solid phase is constant, we omit it, leaving only what is known as the **solubility product:** $K_{sp} = [Na^+]\,[Cl^-]$. To evaluate K_{sp}, we need to know the solubility of sodium chloride in moles per liter. Since all of it is in the solution in the form of ions, the concentration of each ion in a saturated solution in pure water is exactly the same as the solubility. In this particular example, the solubility product happens to be equal to the square of the solubility. On the basis of the equilibrium constant, we recognize that the effect of increasing the chloride ion concentration is to **exceed the solubility product.** The effect of increasing the sodium ion concentration was similar. A precipitate forms whenever the solubility product is exceeded, if equilibrium is reached.

For most analytical purposes, we are not interested in changing the solubility of such substances as sodium chloride, for we usually wish to separate essentially *all* of a substance by precipitation. This must involve substances having much smaller solubility products. Table 31.1 lists a number of relatively insoluble compounds with their solubility products. From such small values, we can see that these compounds have extremely small solubilities. The following examples illustrate how the solubility can be calculated from the solubility product.

Example 31.1. *The solubility product of ZnS is 10^{-24}. What is the concentration of zinc ion in a saturated solution of ZnS?*

$$K_{sp} = 10^{-24} = [Zn^{++}] [S^=]$$

Every zinc ion that dissolves is accompanied by a sulfide ion that also enters the solution. All the ZnS in solution is considered to be present in the form of ions, since the solution must be extremely dilute. Therefore, if the solubility of ZnS = x, then $[Zn^{++}] = [S^=] = x$; $x_2 = 10^{-24}$; $x = 10^{-12}$ mole per liter.

Table 31.1.   Some Solubility Products

AgCl	1.6×10^{-10}
$PbCl_2$	1.7×10^{-5}
AgBr	5×10^{-13}
AgI	1×10^{-16}
PbI_2	9×10^{-9}
$Al(OH)_3$	1×10^{-33}
$Ca(OH)_2$	8×10^{-6}
$M_g(OH)_2$	6×10^{-12}
$Zn(OH)_2$	1×10^{-15}
$CaCO_3$	4.8×10^{-9}
$PbCO_3$	1×10^{-13}
Ag_2CrO_4	1×10^{-12}
$PbCrO_4$	2×10^{-14}
$PbSO_4$	2×10^{-8}
$BaSO_4$	1×10^{-10}
FeS	10^{-22}
ZnS	10^{-24}
PbS	10^{-28}
CuS	10^{-40}
HgS	10^{-54}

Example 31.2. *The solubility product of* PbI_2 *is* 9×10^{-9} *What is its solubility?*

$$K_{sp} = 9 \times 10^{-9} = [Pb^{++}]\,[I^-]^2$$

If x = solubility, then $[Pb^{++}] = x$ and $[I^-] = 2x$, since two iodide ions dissolve for each lead ion.

$$9 \times 10^{-9} = x(2x)^2 = 4x^3$$

$$x^3 = 2.25 \times 10^{-9}$$

$$x = \sqrt[3]{2.25} \times 10^{-3} = 1.3 \times 10^{-3} \text{ mole per liter.}$$

Solubility Equilibria in Analysis

Whenever the mixing of solutions or addition of reagents produces a system in which any two kinds of ions are present in concentrations that exceed the solubility product of their compound, the compound will precipitate until the excess has come out of solution. By choosing precipitating ions that form insoluble salts with only some but not all of the components of a solution, it is possible to remove these particular components from the solution. The very formation of a precipitate gives a useful clue to the possible identity of the ions. Then the precipitate can be subjected to further tests, away from the ions remaining in solution which might have interfered by giving reactions of their own.

Qualitative Analysis. For example, of all the common chlorides, only those of silver, lead, and mercury(I) are insoluble in water. If chloride ion is added to a solution of unknown substances, the appearance of a precipitate suggests that at least one of these metals must be present. The absence of a precipitate suggests that none of them is present. Suppose enough chloride solution is added to bring about essentially complete precipitation of whatever forms insoluble chlorides. This point is indicated when an additional amount of chloride solution shows no visible effect. The chloride precipitate is filtered from the remaining solution and washed free of residues from the solution. Since $AgCl$, $PbCl_2$, and Hg_2Cl_2 are all white, we cannot tell by looking at the precipitate which of them might be present.

Of the three, the most soluble happens to be $PbCl_2$. This is soluble enough to be leached out of a solid mixture with hot water. The precipitate is therefore washed thoroughly with hot water. If any remains undissolved, it must be either $AgCl$ or Hg_2Cl_2, or both. Perhaps it is not clear from inspection whether or not anything has dissolved in the hot water. This calls for some further testing of the hot filtrate. For instance, sodium chromate solution will form a bright yellow precipitate with lead that is much less soluble than the chloride. If the chromate is added to the filtrate and no such precipitate appears, it can be concluded that no lead was in the original chloride precipitate.

After removing any lead chloride, we can test whether the residue is silver or mercury chloride by adding ammonium hydroxide. Although silver chloride is an extremely insoluble compound, it gives a few silver ions and chloride ions in solution at equilibrium. If the concentration of any ion of an insoluble compound can be reduced, it will then dissolve faster than it recrystallizes. By this means the entire sample of compound might be caused to dissolve. It happens that silver ions react with ammonia molecules to form very stable soluble complex ions:

$$Ag^+ + 2\ NH_3 \rightleftharpoons Ag(NH_3)_2{}^+$$

Ammonium hydroxide is just a solution of ammonia in water, so it provides the ammonia molecules in abundance for the formation of this complex ion. Furthermore, although the solubility of AgCl is very low, the complex salt $Ag(NH_3)_2Cl$ is quite soluble. Therefore, the equilibrium between the silver and chloride ions and the undissolved AgCl is upset by the removal of silver ions to form the soluble complex. Since the solubility product is never reached, all the AgCl dissolves. Silver chloride, although insoluble in water, dissolves in water containing ammonia.

We may not be able to tell by inspection whether anything really was dissolved by the ammonia. To check on this, we recognize that although the silver **diammine** complex is quite stable, it too is in equilibrium with silver ions and ammonia molecules:

$$Ag(NH_3)_2{}^+ \rightleftharpoons Ag^+ + 2\ NH_3$$

If one of the components could be removed as fast as it is formed, even though it is present in very minute traces, the complex could be decomposed and the silver ion could be brought back into solution. With the chloride ions still there, the solubility product of silver chloride would again be exceeded, and silver chloride would be reprecipitated. One good way to decompose the ammine complex is to take advantage of the fact that, although ammonia forms a strong complex with silver ion, it forms a stronger one with a hydrogen ion, namely, the ammonium ion, $NH_4{}^+$. Thus, if nitric acid is added to the filtrate from washing the precipitate with ammonia solution, and a white precipitate appears again, we conclude that silver ion was present. The dissolution of the silver in ammonia, followed by its reprecipitation with nitric acid, provides strong evidence of this. Nitric acid is chosen because silver nitrate is very soluble. The reaction with nitric acid is:

$$NH_3 + H^+ \rightleftharpoons NH_4{}^+$$

If Hg_2Cl_2 were also present in the solid when ammonia was added, it would have been changed at the same time the silver chloride was extracted. One of the products of the complex reaction of ammonia with mercury(I) chloride is metallic mercury, which appears dark gray or black when finely divided. If darkening of the filter paper holding silver or mercury chlorides results from extraction with aqueous ammonia, the presence of mercury(I) in the original unknown mixture is thereby indicated.

Qualitative analysis makes extensive use of this kind of reaction and manipulation illustrated by the chlorides. The identification of each element present in the original material being analyzed is accomplished by careful control of conditions of precipitation, and dissolution of precipitates to assure that only one specific element could behave in the manner observed. The identification of anions is similarly achieved, by carefully noting which metal ions cause precipitation and which do not, and what are the properties of the precipitate. For example, if either carbonate, sulfite, or sulfate ions are present, the addition of barium ion would result in separation of a white precipitate of $BaCO_3$, $BaSO_3$, or $BaSO_4$. But while barium sulfate remains insoluble under practically all conditions, barium sulfite or carbonate produces ions of a weak acid and hence good electron donors to a proton. Thus, if an acid is added to a precipitate of barium sulfate, nothing will happen, but a precipitate of barium sulfite or carbonate will dissolve, often with the visible evolution of gas:

$$CO_3^= + H^+ \rightleftharpoons HCO_3^- \text{ (bicarbonates and other acid salts}$$
$$\text{are soluble)}$$

$$HCO_3^- + H^+ \rightleftharpoons (H_2CO_3) \rightleftharpoons CO_2 + H_2O$$

This reaction serves to distinguish barium carbonate or sulfite from the sulfate. Furthermore, if the solution is made acidic before the addition of barium ion, any carbonate or sulfite ions present will be destroyed by the acid. In this case, a substance precipitated by barium ions must be a sulfate.

Quantitative Analysis. Quantitative analysis makes use of many of the same reactions and methods used in qualitative analysis. Usually the qualitative composition of the material is known. Such knowledge permits special conditions and shortcuts in the procedures directed toward a more speedy analytical result. For example, the insolubility of silver chloride is often used not only to recognize the presence of silver ion, but also to measure *quantitatively* the amount of *chloride* ion. Here there is no need to worry about the possible presence of lead or mercury, for if they were present with the chloride in the solution a precipitate would already have formed. The solution is made slightly acidic with nitric acid. Silver nitrate solution is added, and the silver chloride precipitates and is filtered. The filtrate is tested with more silver nitrate to make sure the chloride has been precipitated. After the precipitate is washed to remove any other ions present in the solution, the silver chloride is carefully dried and weighed. The amount of chlorine is calculated in exactly the same way you would calculate the weight of any other element from the formula of its compound and the weight of a sample of the compound.

As another example, although determination of barium is relatively seldom needed, an analysis for sulfate is often wanted. The addition of barium ion to the solution will precipitate any sulfate ion as barium sulfate. It is important to acidify the solution before adding the barium ion, in order to prevent the precipitation of any barium carbonate or sulfite which might otherwise occur. This acidification must be with hydrochloric, not sulfuric, acid. Why? The barium sulfate precipitate is filtered, dried, and weighed, and the amount of sulfate is calculated.

Combustion Analysis

Organic compounds—which contain carbon and hydrogen atoms joined together, and possibly various other elements, too—are usually analyzed by burning. A weighed sample is heated in oxygen, which converts the hydrogen to water and the carbon to carbon dioxide. The stream of oxygen which leaves the heated zone carries these combustion products with it into two tubes in succession. One is a previously weighed tube which absorbs the water quantitatively. The other, also previously weighed, contains a substance capable of absorbing the carbon dioxide. These tubes are then reweighed to determine the amount of water and carbon dioxide formed by the combustion. From these quantities the amount of hydrogen and carbon are easily calculated. If they do not add up to the weight of the original sample, the compound must have contained more than just carbon and hydrogen. The difference may represent oxygen which would have gone through this procedure unnoticed. The difference between the weight of the original sample and the weights of carbon and hydrogen in it is usually taken as the amount of oxygen, unless preliminary qualitative tests have revealed the presence of other elements such as halogens, sulfur, or nitrogen.

INSTRUMENTAL METHODS OF ANALYSIS

A generation ago, most chemists used the type of chemical analysis briefly described above. The past few decades, however, have brought the development of numerous ingenious mechanical and electrical devices that are extremely helpful in analytical chemistry. A relatively simple one is the automatic titrating machine that runs a solution of standardized acid or base into an unknown sample and measures exactly the neutralization point.

Most of them, however, make use of electronic and structural differences among the atoms and molecules under analysis to reveal their identity. The interaction of matter with electromagnetic radiation has a large number of very important applications. For example, each element is capable of being excited by the absorption of a precise amount of heat, light, or electrical energy to promote electrons to higher energy orbitals. These electrons return almost immediately to more stable orbitals, emitting specific quanta of light that serve to identify the element by their measured frequency. The analysis of such spectral lines emitted by excited matter is called **emission spectroscopy.** It has been perfected to the point of being quantitative as well as qualitative. In a few minutes **spectrochemical analyses** of substances can now be made that would have taken hours of expert laboratory chemistry to analyze without the help of the spectrometer.

Electronic transitions in *molecules* can also be very revealing. These are usually brought about by the absorption at certain specific frequencies of ultraviolet light. By continuously varying the frequencies and measuring the intensity of the light coming through the sample, usually in solution, it is possible to obtain **absorption spectra** that can be very helpful in identifying the substances present.

Many molecules, in their natural twisting, bending, and stretching vibrations that account for part of their energy, momentarily change in polarity during these vibrations. Such vibrational energy corresponds to certain frequencies in the infrared range of the spectrum. Many specific groups of atoms in molecules or ions exhibit absorption of **infrared radiation (IR)** at certain characteristic frequencies. These help to identify the presence of groups such as ^-OH, $^-NH_2$, ^-SH, and so on. This kind of information can be extremely valuable to chemists trying to find out the molecular structure of a very complicated polyatomic molecule.

Indeed, almost every measurable physical property has been utilized at one time or another in the analysis and identification of one or more different compounds. The science of analytical chemistry involves the application of physical chemistry in a very sophisticated way. Many of the newer instruments are so simple to operate that almost anyone can be trained to use them. However, a thorough understanding of what actually goes on inside the "black box" that encloses many such instruments is available only to those having a comprehensive knowledge of theoretical physical chemistry, and often of sophisticated electronics.

Test Your Memory

1. Name some acidic and basic gases.
2. What kinds of solid adsorbents could be used to remove each from a gas mixture?
3. What is *fractional distillation?*
4. How is it possible to separate *gases* by fractional distillation?
5. a) What is meant by a *permanent gas?*
   b) Why can liquid oxygen not be maintained at ordinary temperatures?
6. How might a pure gaseous compound be identified?
7. a) What is meant by *vacuum distillation?*
   b) What is the principal feature of a molecular still?
8. What is *solvent extraction?*
9. Why is sodium chloride less soluble in HCl or NaOH solutions than in water?

10. Why are solid and liquid substances normally omitted from dissolution equilibrium constant expressions?
11. How are differences in solubility used in the separation and identification of individual components of a mixture?
12. Which chlorides are least soluble?
13. a) Why does silver chloride dissolve in an ammonia solution?
    b) How could ammonia be removed from a solution?
14. Distinguish between qualitative and quantitative analysis.
15. What is meant by *combustion analysis?*
16. a) What is *emission spectroscopy?*
    b) What is a *spectrometer?*

Test Your Understanding

1. a) How might one separate ammonia from hydrogen? b) Oxygen from nitrogen?
2. Fractional distillation of petroleum under ordinary conditions leads to separation of the most volatile components, but beyond a certain temperature, decomposition begins. How might this decomposition be avoided?
3. In rock analysis, how might one separate silicon?
4. a) If the solubility of salt AB is 10^{-6} mole per liter, what is its solubility product?
    b) If the solubility of salt AB_2 is 10^{-6} mole per liter, what is its solubility product?
5. In a quantitative analysis for sulfate, 0.6538 g $BaSO_4$ is weighed, from 1.6543 g of unknown substance. What is the weight percentage of $SO_4^=$?
6. What molarity of silver ion was in solution if the AgCl precipitate from 100 ml weighed 0.6666 g?

32

HOW METALS ARE SEPARATED FROM THEIR ORES

THE NATURE OF ORES

Hundreds of compounds of metals occur in nature. Some of these natural sources are called **ores** and some are not. An ore is a *practical* source of the free metal. Whether a given chemical combination is a practical source of a metal or not depends on how the cost of releasing the metal compares with the price it will bring. Only a trace of a metal may be present in a rock from which extraction may be extremely difficult, but if when obtained the metal can be sold at a profit, the source is called an ore. On the other hand, a mineral containing large percentages of a certain metal without being a good economic source is not called an ore.

Some metals are sufficiently unreactive that they remain uncombined despite millions of years of exposure to moisture, air, carbon dioxide, traces of hydrogen sulfide, and other corrosive agents of the atmosphere. Examples are the precious metals—platinum, silver, and gold—which are therefore called **native** metals. The problem of separating metals from ores in which they occur as native metals is merely that of isolating them from the extraneous materials which usually surround them. Sometimes it is easier to dissolve them chemically and extract their compounds from the other material than it would be to find some physical means of separation.

But in the course of time, most metals have combined with nonmetals such as oxygen. Such metals occur in nature only combined with other elements which have withdrawn electrons from the metals to leave them in positive oxidation states. The problem of separating metals from ores in which they occur as chemical compounds is always that of returning the electrons which have been removed. In other words, the metal compounds must be reduced. Two methods are available: electrolysis and chemical reduction.

Electrolytic methods are always possible, but chemical reducing agents are usually cheaper. The disadvantage of chemical reducing agents is that they often tend to contaminate the metal which they liberate. Such contamination may make purification difficult. In such cases, a chemical reduction may be followed by an electrolytic purification. Examples of various processes are given in the following sections.

IRON AND STEEL

Iron

Iron occurs very widely distributed throughout the rocks and minerals of the earth's crust. Its principal practical sources are the ores **hematite,** consisting largely of the oxide Fe_2O_3, and **magnetite,** composed of Fe_3O_4. These ores are so rich in iron that it is not necessary to concentrate the iron compounds in them before reduction. Reduction of iron ore is carried out in huge, brick-lined towers 90 to 100 feet tall, called **blast furnaces.** Iron ore, coke, and limestone are charged to the top of the furnace continuously, while molten iron and melted silicates (**slag**) are drawn off at the bottom. Carbon dioxide escapes at the top.

Figure 32.1.   Diagram of a Blast Furnace for Iron.

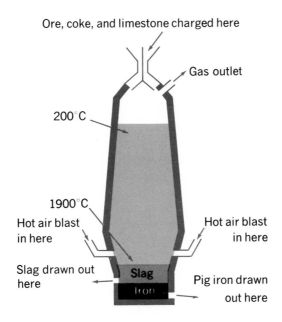

Ore, coke, and limestone charged here

Gas outlet

200°C

1900°C

Hot air blast in here

Hot air blast in here

Slag drawn out here

Slag

Iron

Pig iron drawn out here

The purpose of the coke is to supply carbon, as the chemical reducing agent, and carbon monoxide, also a reducing agent. The calcium carbonate, or limestone, is added to provide a means of getting rid of the extraneous silicate material that accompanies the iron oxide in the ore. Silicates of various metals vary widely in melting point. Some, like magnesium silicates, are very *refractory,* i.e., they have very high melting temperatures. Others, like those of calcium, melt relatively easily. Limestone supplies calcium to transform all the silicates to low-melting calcium silicate. The limestone decomposes at high temperature:

$$CaCO_3 \rightleftharpoons CO_2 + CaO$$

and the CaO reacts with the sand and other silicate materials:

$$CaO + SiO_2 \rightarrow CaSiO_3$$

You will recognize this reaction as a typical metal oxide reaction with non-metal oxide, the CaO being basic and the SiO_2 acidic. Sand also reacts directly with limestone at high temperatures:

$$CaCO_3 + SiO_2 \rightarrow CO_2 + CaSiO_3$$

This is the displacement of a volatile oxide, CO_2, by a nonvolatile oxide, SiO_2.

In the operation of the blast furnace, a blast of very hot air is admitted near the bottom, where it ignites the coke and forms a mixture of carbon dioxide and carbon monoxide. The carbon monoxide itself is a good reducing agent. As it rises through the heated mixture of ore, limestone, and coke, a number of chemical reactions occur, as illustrated by the following equations:

$$CO_2 + C \rightarrow 2\,CO$$

$$Fe_2O_3 + 3\,C \rightarrow 2\,Fe + 3\,CO$$

$$Fe_2O_3 + 3\,CO \rightarrow 2\,Fe + 3\,CO_2$$

$$Fe_3O_4 + 4\,C \rightarrow 3\,Fe + 4\,CO$$

$$Fe_3O_4 + 4\,CO \rightarrow 3\,Fe + 4\,CO_2$$

As the molten iron and molten silicates form, they trickle down through the mass of solids to the bottom. The denser iron forms a layer underneath a layer of less dense silicates, or slag. The iron is drawn off and cast in a form that, for some reason unrelated to its appearance, is called a **pig.** Pigs are separate chunks of crude iron, called **pig iron,** that is then the raw material for making iron and steel products. The slag is also drawn off and allowed to solidify. It may be used as gravel or fill. Or because of its calcium silicate composition, it may be ground up and mixed with other materials and heated to form **portland cement.** A single blast furnace may be operated continuously for months without interruption, producing 1000 tons of iron per day.

Very pure iron is relatively soft, easily corroded, and in general not a very useful material. But as with most metals, very small amounts of impurities produce very significant changes in physical properties. Also, like many metals, the physical, and especially the mechanical, properties depend very much on the crystal structure of the metal. This in turn, depends on the mechanical and thermal treatment it has undergone. The production of useful materials from crude pig iron, therefore, depends on: (1) controlling the concentrations and identities of impurities within rather narrow limits, and (2) applying the appropriate treatments to produce the desired crystalline characteristics.

Steel

Carbon is the chief impurity in pig iron. It is one of the most desirable impurities, provided its distribution and concentration throughout the iron are carefully controlled. It tends to impart much better mechanical strength. Steel, though not well defined, is made of iron usually containing a concentration of carbon between 0.5 and 2 per cent. Small concentrations of other metals are also used to give desired properties for special purposes. To prepare steel and other iron products, the crude iron must be remelted and treated to remove impurities, such as carbon, sulfur, and phosphorus. The most important process to accomplish this is called the **open hearth** process. Huge, relatively shallow trays of molten iron are heated in air or oxygen to oxidize the impurities. These then either volatilize or are absorbed by the material lining the hearth. Following this burning of the impurities comes the deliberate addition of carbon and whatever other ingredients are needed, in carefully measured quantities.

Innumerable special alloy steels have been prepared and are widely used. Chromium and nickel, in concentrations of a few per cent, increase the resistance of steel to corrosion. In concentrations of 10 to 30 per cent, they make up the class of substances known as **stainless steels.** Tungsten toughens the steel and permits cutting edges to withstand corrosion and dulling at the high temperatures produced by the friction of machining tools. Silicon gives iron resistance to corrosion by acids. Vanadium and manganese help toughen the steel for use in knives and axes. Many other alloying metals have useful effects, usually in concentrations not greater than a few per cent.

ALUMINUM

Aluminum is very widely dispersed through the rocks and minerals of the earth and is an important component of the clay and soil. Usually it is so securely tied up with silica, in the form of complex silicates, that it cannot easily be reduced to metallic aluminum. There is a mineral ore called **bauxite,** however, in which aluminum is combined chiefly with oxygen, in a hydrated form of aluminum oxide. Even here the reduction is not simple, because aluminum to oxygen bonds are extremely strong and chemical reducing agents tend to contaminate the aluminum. This problem was solved electrolytically by two men independently, one a Frenchman named Heroult, and the other a young man in Ohio named Charles Hall. Aluminum oxide was found to be soluble in the molten mineral **cryolite** (Na_3AlF_6). In this melt it can be electrolyzed, with aluminum metal forming at the cathode and oxygen at the anode. Side reactions cause some consumption of the cryolite also. Aluminum is difficult to purify once prepared impure, so it is important that the aluminum oxide be purified first. This is done by taking advantage of the amphoteric properties of aluminum oxide, which is therefore soluble in hot sodium hydroxide solution, although iron oxide impurities remain insoluble and can be filtered out. When the filtrate is cooled, the silicates remain in solution but the pure aluminum hydroxide separates and can be filtered off for drying and electrolysis.

COPPER

Copper occurs in ores usually containing less than 2 per cent of copper. It would be uneconomical to treat the 98 per cent or more of extraneous materials with any reagents needed, unless they were very cheap. Usually, therefore, it is desirable to concentrate the copper compounds by isolating them from the others. Copper ores commonly contain copper as the sulfide: for example, **covellite** (CuS) and **chalcocite** (Cu_2S). The ore is ground and mixed with water to which wetting agents have been added. The silica-containing materials are preferentially wetted by the water, and sink as **gangue.** The sulfide resists wetting and can be removed from the top as froth. This process is called **flotation.**

The concentrated sulfides are then **roasted and smelted** by heating in air. This converts the sulfur to sulfur dioxide, and oxidizes some of the impurities, and melts the metal. The metallic copper is left in a fairly pure form, but needs further purification. This is done best by electrolysis. The crude copper is made the anode, and copper deposits on the cathode in a very pure state while simultaneously dissolving from the anode. The impurities usually fall away from the anode as it dissolves, forming a sludge at the bottom. Traces of silver and gold are often associated with copper ores. The recovery of these metals from the anode sludge frequently pays for the electrolytic purification process.

ZINC

Zinc also occurs chiefly as the sulfide, in two different crystalline forms called **sphalerite** (or **zinc blende**), and **wurtzite.** Roasting the ore in air oxidizes the sulfur to sulfur dioxide and the zinc to ZnO, which can be reduced by heating with carbon:

$$2 \, ZnS + 3 \, O_2 \rightarrow 2 \, ZnO + 2 \, SO_2$$

$$ZnO + C \rightarrow Zn + CO$$

It is also possible to roast the ore more carefully. Then, instead of burning off the sulfur completely, the sulfide is oxidized to sulfate:

$$ZnS + 2 \, O_2 \rightarrow ZnSO_4$$

Unlike the sulfide, $ZnSO_4$ is water soluble. Zinc is well above hydrogen in the activity series. Nevertheless, it is possible to deposit zinc from aqueous solutions electrolytically, in preference to hydrogen, if conditions are adjusted properly.

Zinc is widely used to **galvanize** (coat) iron, protecting it from rusting. Zinc-copper alloys are known as **brass.**

TIN

The relative abundance of tin is very small. Fortunately, it occurs in a few deposits of high concentrations, largely as the mineral known as **cassiterite,** in which the tin compound is SnO_2. This oxide is readily reduced by heating with carbon. Tin is widely used for the plating of sheet iron cans known as "tin cans." It protects them from rusting, but only so long as it covers the iron completely. A hole in the coating permits the iron to rust faster than ordinarily because of the electrolytic effect of tin, which is less easily oxidized than the iron. Tin is alloyed with lead to form low-melting solder. Tin-copper alloys are known as **bronzes.**

LEAD

Galena (PbS) is the principal source of lead. It can be roasted completely to the oxide and sulfur dioxide:

$$PbS + 3 \, O_2 \rightarrow 2 \, PbO + 2 \, SO_2$$

The PbO is easily reduced to metallic lead by heating with carbon. Alternatively, the sulfide may be only partly oxidized and then heated:

$$PbSO_4 + PbS \rightarrow 2 \, Pb + 2 \, SO_2$$

MAGNESIUM

Oyster shells are nearly pure calcium carbonate. They make a convenient source of alkali at the ocean shore. Pools of ocean water can be treated with calcium hydroxide made from oyster shells, to precipitate the very insoluble magnesium hydroxide from the magnesium ions in the sea water. The hydroxide is then converted to magnesium chloride by treatment with hydrochloric acid, and electrolyzed in the molten state to liberate magnesium. Chemical reducing agents, notably an alloy of iron and silicon called **ferrosilicon,** are also used in producing magnesium from its oxide.

OTHER METALS

Special methods have been devised for the special problems associated with other individual metal ores, but in general the basic principles remain similar. The separation of metals from their compounds constitutes one of the most important modern industrial procedures. Although plastics and similar polymers may replace metals for some purposes, it is unlikely that anything can take their place completely.

Test Your Memory

1. a) What is an *ore?*
   b) What is meant by *native* as applied to ores?
2. Why is reduction important in isolating metals from their compounds?
3. Name and give the formulas for two iron ores.
4. Describe the operation of a *blast furnace,* including the appropriate chemical equations.
5. What are *steel, stainless steel, brass,* and *bronze?*
6. What is the *open hearth process?*
7. Identify: bauxite, cryolite, covellite, chalcocite, sphalerite, wurtzite, cassiterite.
8. What is *flotation?*
9. What is meant by *galvanized?*
10. What is the *Hall process?*
11. How can copper be purified by electrolysis?
12. How can zinc be obtained from its sulfide?
13. What metal is obtained from *galena,* and how?
14. How are oyster shells useful in obtaining which metal?
15. What is *ferrosilicon?*

Test Your Understanding

1. Why might CO be more effective than coke in the reduction of iron ore?
2. Suggest two methods to obtain nickel from NiO.
3. Explain why and how a tin-plated can rusts rapidly when the iron is exposed.
4. What advantages do hydrogen and carbon have over other possible reducing agents?

33

INTRODUCTION TO HYDROCARBONS

ALKANES

The simplest hydrocarbon is methane (CH_4). It is the chief component of natural gas, which occurs in enormous underground accumulations. Since carbon and hydrogen are so close together in electronegativity, the bonds in methane are not very polar. In fact, they are nearly nonpolar, with the carbon only slightly negative and the hydrogen just slightly positive. One carbon-hydrogen bond thus, has little effect on the other carbon bonds. This fact is in contrast to what would be expected if hydrogen either supplied the carbon with a considerable negative charge or removed much charge from it. Carbon joined to hydrogen can also join either to another carbon or to hydrogen, by each of its other bonding orbitals. **There is no theoretical limit to the number of carbon atoms that can join together.** In diamond, only carbon atoms are joined together. The bonding extends to the very limits of the crystal. Substitution of any carbon to carbon bond by a hydrogen to carbon bond is, in principle, possible. Therefore, enormous numbers of different carbon-hydrogen compounds are possible; many of these are known.

Suppose each carbon atom is represented as $-\overset{|}{\underset{|}{C}}-$ and each of the four indicated bonds can connect to a hydrogen atom or to another $-\overset{|}{\underset{|}{C}}-$.

Then any interconnected structure that can be drawn, filling all bonds that are not joined to another carbon with hydrogen, is a possible hydrocarbon. If one hydrogen atom is removed from a molecule of methane, the remaining group is called a **methyl radical,** CH_3-. The next simplest hydrocarbon results when two methyl radicals combine to form **ethane** (C_2H_6). This could also be written as CH_3CH_3. Ethane is also a gas but not quite as volatile as methane because it offers slightly greater opportunities for van der Waals interactions. If two hydrogen atoms are removed from one methane molecule and two methyl groups are substituted for them, the hydrocarbon **propane**

Table 33.1.   Homologous Series of Normal Alkanes, n-C_nH_{2n+2}

CH_4	methane	H—C—H with H above and below
C_2H_6	ethane	H—C—C—H with H above and below each C
C_3H_8	propane	H—C—C—C—H with H above and below each C
C_4H_{10}	butane	H—C—C—C—C—H with H above and below each C
C_5H_{12}	pentane	H—C—C—C—C—C—H with H above and below each C
C_6H_{14}	hexane	H—C—C—C—C—C—C—H with H above and below each C

($CH_3CH_2CH_3$) results. If another $-CH_2-$, called a **methylene** group, is inserted in the carbon chain, **butane** ($CH_3CH_2CH_2CH_3$) results. A third methylene group inserted forms $CH_3CH_2CH_2CH_2CH_3$, called **pentane.** There is no theoretical limit to the number of carbon atoms that can be linked together in such hydrocarbon chains.

Notice that these compounds differ from one another only in the number of methylene groups or their equivalent: methane has none; add one methylene, in effect, to methane and get ethane; propane has one methylene, butane two, pentane three. A comparison of these formulas shows that a "type formula" can be assigned to cover them all: C_nH_{2n+2}. When $n = 1$, the formula is CH_4. When $n = 2$, it is C_2H_6. When $n = 3$, it is C_3H_8. When $n = 10$, it is $C_{10}H_{22}$. A series of compounds differing only in the number of CH_2 groups, or their equivalent, is called a **homologous series.** This particular homologous series is called the **paraffin hydrocarbons,** or **alkanes.**

Isomers

All the hydrocarbons just described consist of consecutive carbon atoms in single chains. They are often referred to as "straight chain" hydrocarbons. Literally this is incorrect, for since carbon bonds are directed toward the corners of a regular tetrahedron with bond angles of $109°28'$, the chains must be zigzag instead of truly straight. By *straight* is actually meant *continuous* or *unbranched*. Branching is also possible. The change from ethane to propane could go only one way. In propane ($CH_3CH_2CH_3$), two different kinds of location for hydrogen can be recognized. It may be on either a methyl carbon or a methylene carbon. The six hydrogens situated on the two methyl groups are all in exactly equivalent positions. It does not matter which of these six we might replace by another methyl group. The result would be exactly the same: $CH_3CH_2CH_2CH_3$. However, the two hydrogens on the methylene carbon are differently located. If a methyl group were to be substituted for one of these (both are alike so it makes no difference which of the two), the result would be $CH_3CH(CH_3)_2$. Or we might think of it as trimethylmethane, with three methyl groups attached to the same carbon atom. The empirical formula of this compound is C_4H_{10}. The empirical formula of the straight chain compound is also C_4H_{10}.

These are not only empirical but also molecular formulas. When the molecular formulas are exactly alike but the molecules differ in the arrangement of the atoms, the compounds are called **isomers.** The "straight chain" compounds are called **normal alkanes** and are designated by the prefix *n-*. The first of the pair discussed here would be called ***n*-butane.** The branched chain compounds are called **isoparaffins** or **isoalkanes,** and are designated by *i-*. The second of the pair would be called **isobutane** or written as *i*-butane.

Isomeric hydrocarbons may be closely similar or quite different in their physical and chemical properties, but they are never exactly alike in any detail except formula and molecular weight. They are distinct and separate compounds. We have seen that for one, two, or three carbons, only one structure is possible, but for four carbons, two isomers exist. When the alkane contains five carbon atoms per molecule, **n-pentane** and a branched **isopentane**, $CH_3CH(CH_3)CH_2CH_3$, are possible, but there is also a third possibility, tetramethylmethane, $(CH_3)_4C$, called **neopentane.** The six-carbon alkanes, called **hexanes,** exist as five different isomers; the seven-carbon alkanes, called **heptanes,** exist as nine different isomers. There are eighteen different C_8 alkanes. As the number of carbon atoms per molecule increases, the number of possible structures increases very rapidly. By the time $C_{20}H_{42}$ is reached, the number of possible isomers has grown to 366,319. If you find this difficult to believe, sit down with paper and pencil and try drawing out all the possibilities yourself. And if we ran out of good names for the isomers when C_5 was reached, think what a predicament we are in for the hydrocarbons with a greater number of carbons.

Naming

Clearly some systematic naming procedure is absolutely essential. By international agreement such procedures have been developed. We will not go into all the details of naming all organic compounds. They follow the general procedure which can be easily outlined for the alkanes. One simply examines the structural formula of the hydrocarbon to determine which is the longest continuous chain in the molecule from any direction. The compound is named as a **derivative** of this chain. For example, if the longest chain has six carbon atoms, we call the compound a hexane. Then we number the carbon atoms of that six-membered chain, starting with 1 at the carbon nearest the first branch. These numbers serve to locate the branches, which are named according to the number of carbon atoms in each: methyl, ethyl, and so on. For example, instead of the name *isobutane,* we would observe that the longest continuous chain in its molecule has only three carbon atoms, from which we would name the compound a *propane.* It is a propane with a methyl group. In this example it does not matter where we begin the numbering, for the methyl group is on carbon atom number 2 in any case. We, therefore, name the compound, **2-methylpropane.** This is the **systematic name.** It tells any chemist in the world exactly what structure we are talking about.

The fuel hydrocarbon which has the octane number 100 and is used as a standard in measuring octane ratings is called *isooctane.* The name means only that it is one of seventeen different branched octanes. Nobody would know which one. The systematic name is **2,2,4-trimethylpentane.** This name indicates to anyone that the longest chain in the molecule has five carbon atoms, that two methyl groups are substituted for hydrogen on the second carbon atom in the chain, and a third methyl group is substituted for hydrogen on the fourth carbon atom of the chain. Figure 33.1 gives a number of illustrative structures and systematic names for alkane hydrocarbons.

Figure 33.1.   Some Representative Alkanes.

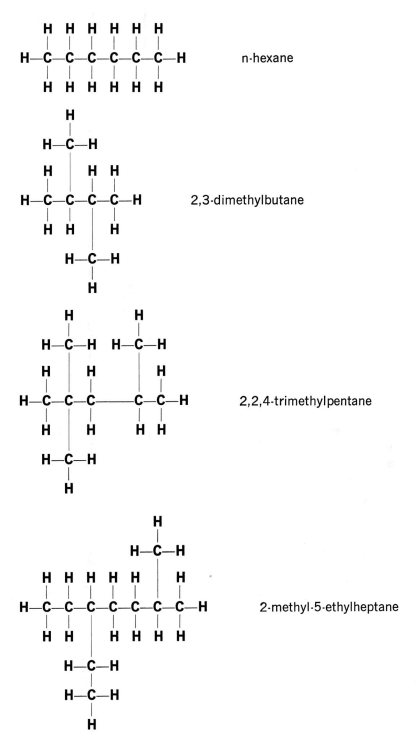

n-hexane

2,3-dimethylbutane

2,2,4-trimethylpentane

2-methyl-5-ethylheptane

Alkanes **377**

Figure 33.2 2-Methyl-3-bromo-4-hydroxy-5-nitrooctane.

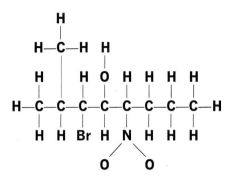

We will not discuss here in detail the naming of more complex compounds derived from hydrocarbons. You will recognize when you see such names that they are really very systematic and meaningful. For instance, if you should see the name *2-methyl-3-bromo-4-hydroxy-5-nitrooctane,* a compound which very possibly nobody has ever bothered to make, you would know its structure to consist of eight carbon atoms in a continuous chain, with a methyl group attached to the second, a bromine atom to the third, a hydroxyl group to the fourth, and a nitro (NO_2^-) group to the fifth. All the other carbon bonds are to hydrogen or a carbon in the chain.

OTHER TYPES OF HYDROCARBONS

If, instead of ending all chains with methyl groups, hydrocarbons could form rings, two fewer hydrogen atoms would be needed per molecule. Closure of the ring would use a bonding orbital of each of two carbon atoms that would otherwise be occupied with attachment to a hydrogen atom. Such hydrocarbons do exist; they are called **cycloalkanes** or **naphthenes.** The smallest possible ring is three-membered cyclopropane (C_3H_6). Although all larger sizes of rings are possible, by far the most common are the cyclopentane and cyclohexane rings. Hydrocarbons consisting of various alkyl groups attached to cycloalkane rings are called **naphthenic hydrocarbons.**

There exists an especially stable ring molecule, **benzene** (C_6H_6), in which each carbon is attached to one less hydrogen atom than in cyclohexane. Here the bonds make use of more than one orbital from each carbon atom and more than one electron pair per bond. This makes the carbon-carbon bonds in the six-membered ring shorter and more stable. Such rings are called **aromatic.** They have a special stability, tending to undergo chemical reactions without disrupting the ring structure. A benzene group with one hydrogen

Figure 33.3. Some Cycloalkanes or Cycloparaffins.

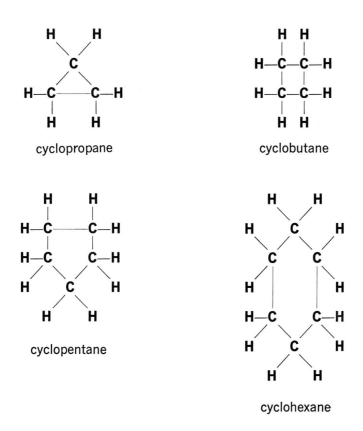

cyclopropane

cyclobutane

cyclopentane

cyclohexane

atom removed is called a **phenyl** group (C_6H_5-). Any organic compounds containing one or more phenyl groups are called *aromatic compounds*. There can also be aromatic compounds having what are termed *condensed rings,* which contain at least two rings having two carbon atoms in common. The simplest example is **naphthalene** ($C_{10}H_8$).

Carbon may also be joined to another carbon atom by double or triple as well as single bonds. Hydrocarbons having double bonds are called **olefins** or **alkenes.** The simplest example is **ethylene** or **ethene,** $CH_2{=}CH_2$. Alkenes are especially vulnerable to chemical attack of the double bond. They can also add molecule to molecule by means of this bond to form polymers. **Poly-ethylene** is a good example. (See the discussion of polymerization in Chapter 34.) If a hydrocarbon contains a triple bond, it is called an **alkyne.** The simplest example is **acetylene,** $HC{\equiv}CH$. This is a gas commonly used in oxyacetylene torches for welding. It is extremely reactive as a result of the triple bond and can be used in a great variety of syntheses of other organic compounds.

Figure 33.4.   Molecules of Benzene and Naphthalene (Aromatic Hydrocarbons).

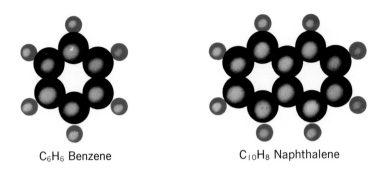

C$_6$H$_6$ Benzene   C$_{10}$H$_8$ Naphthalene

Imagine the different possibilities for forming hydrocarbon molecules by combining the alkane structures with double or triple bonds, in a variety of locations, together with aromatic groups and naphthenic groups. Clearly, millions of compounds consisting only of hydrogen and carbon are possible. Then imagine replacing different hydrogen atoms by halogen, oxygen, nitrogen, sulfur, or other atoms; you will appreciate why the scope of organic chemistry is practically limitless.

Figure 33.5.   C$_2$ Alkane, Alkene, and Alkyne.

Ethane (C$_2$H$_6$)
Each C is tetrahedral.

Ethylene (C$_2$H$_4$)
(ethene) Planar molecule

Acetylene (C$_2$H$_2$)
(ethyne) Linear

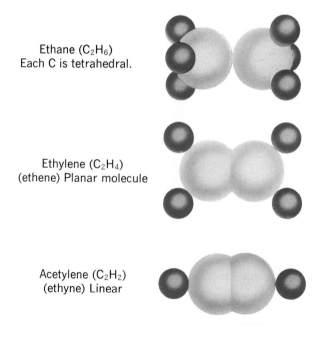

SOURCES OF HYDROCARBONS

Natural Gas

Methane has already been mentioned as an extremely abundant hydrocarbon found in natural gas. It is also a common product of the anaerobic (without oxygen) decomposition of organic matter by microorganisms.

Petroleum

The chief source of the higher molecular weight hydrocarbons, above methane and ethane, is petroleum. The term *petroleum* means oil from the rocks. It is usually found underground in reservoirs where it seems to have accumulated because some geological structure prevented its migration or escape. Its origin is not yet known, except that there is evidence of both animal and vegetable material being involved in its formation. Its composition and physical state vary widely. Petroleum may range from hard, tarry deposits to free-flowing liquids. In all forms it appears to be a mixture of hundreds, if not thousands, of different hydrocarbons, ranging from low to very high molecular weight. In its crude condition petroleum has relatively little practical use.

The principal treatment of petroleum, once it has been brought to the surface, is distillation. In huge stills, crude petroleums are separated into fractions of different volatility ranges. Although each is still a complex mixture, these fractions have useful properties and are often satisfactory for direct application. The lightest fraction consists of condensable gases, propane and butane primarily, which find wide application as "bottled gas" for fuel. The next most volatile fraction, ranging from C_5 to C_{10}, is the **natural gasoline** fraction which is blended with other components for automobile and aircraft gasoline. The range up to about C_{20} includes kerosene, diesel fuels, jet fuels, gas oil, and similar waxes, and asphalt. The higher boiling fractions cannot usually be distilled because of thermal decomposition. They must be separated by solvent extraction procedures.

To some extent the general composition of petroleum varies with the location of the reservoirs from which it is drawn. Petroleum from the Pennsylvania region has a relatively high proportion of long, chain alkanes. These have certain advantages for use as lubricating oils. Such petroleum is called **paraffin-base crude.** Midcontinent petroleums, such as those found in Louisiana, Oklahoma, and Texas, tend to have a higher proportion of cyclic groups. Such petroleums are called **naphthene base crudes.** California petroleums tend to contain greater amounts of aromatic hydrocarbons, and these are called **aromatic base** crudes. These are only rough categories. Many petroleums are called **mixed base crudes** because they do not clearly qualify for a more definite classification.

Petroleum chemists usually find it uneconomical if not impossible to isolate pure hydrocarbons from petroleum for special purposes. A great variety of methods have been developed for altering the composition and structure of naturally occurring fractions of hydrocarbons. One of the most important is called **cracking,** the deliberate decomposition of heavier hydrocarbons by heat, with or without the aid of catalysts to produce lower molecular weight substances of greater usefulness. It would be very difficult, for example, to supply the world's needs for gasoline directly from natural petroleum. Natural gasoline fractions are generally poor in quality and too small in quantity. Fortunately, much of the higher molecular weight material that might find relatively little application for other purposes can be cracked to provide hydrocarbons in the gasoline volatility range. Cracking tends to leave loose ends of the hydrocarbon fragments which become double bonds. These are susceptible to oxidation, forming undesirable gummy substances. Double bonds can be eliminated by subjecting the cracked material to the action of hydrogen under appropriate conditions with the help of catalysts. **Hydrogenation** replaces all the double bonds with bonds to hydrogen, making the hydrocarbons **saturated** (containing only single bonds). The lighter olefins formed by cracking can be caused to add to one another through their double bonds, forming higher molecular weight hydrocarbons. This process, **addition polymerization,** is discussed more fully in Chapter 34.

In the presence of catalysts, such as sulfuric acid or aluminum chloride, lighter olefins can also be caused to add alkanes to their double bonds. This very valuable process called **alkylation,** is used for preparing highly branched hydrocarbons of gasoline range. Such compounds are much in demand because they burn more slowly and evenly without knocking. There are many other processes, by which the naphthene rings are broken open, aromatic rings are created, and so on. Some of the tall towers connected to a maze of pipelines that you see in an oil refinery are distillation columns for the separation of petroleum fractions. Most of them, however, are equipment for carrying out these many other operations that are essential before natural petroleum can provide for man's needs.

The conventional uses of petroleum products do not require the separation of complex fractions into pure compounds. Petroleum can also be the source of pure organic compounds in general, containing oxygen, sulfur, nitrogen, and other elements in addition to the carbon and hydrogen. Any organic compounds synthesized from hydrocarbons of petroleum are called **petrochemicals.** The manufacture of petrochemicals is a huge industry, closely related to the petroleum industry and often an integral part of it, which has developed in recent years.

Oil Shale

Enormous quantities of rock containing organic matter, from which hydrocarbons and related products can be obtained, occur as **oil shale.** Parts of Colorado, Wyoming, and Utah contain whole mountains of it. The name is misleading, for there is no oil in oil shale. Examined closely, it can be seen to have a multilayered structure. Thin layers of yellowish brown material, called **kerogen,** are sandwiched in between much thicker layers of rock. Kerogen is a very complex material, organic in origin and of varying composition. When heated to cause thermal decomposition, its products are largely hydrocarbons. Although the impurities are much more abundant than in petroleum, proper treatment can produce about one barrel of useful hydrocarbon products from a ton of oil shale. But the producer must then dispose of the nearly one ton of waste rock which remains. This problem complicates the utilization of oil shale, for transportation is too costly and the disposal of the waste is difficult. The potential hydrocarbon reserves represented by the known deposits of oil shale are ample to take care of our needs for many years to come. Thus far, however, it has not proven very economical to exploit oil shale in competition with petroleum. Until petroleum reserves have been very badly depleted, oil shale will probably not be widely used.

The apparent availability of petroleum fluctuates in a cyclic manner. As the known reservoirs of petroleum are used up, the incentives for finding more are increased, so *more* people look *harder.* Looking for petroleum is a very expensive business because up to a million dollars can be wasted drilling in one poor location. But as any Texas oil millionaire can tell you, finding petroleum can be a very profitable business, too. When the incentives for searching increase, activity in prospecting increases. Up to now this has invariably led to additional discovery. When new petroleum reservoirs are discovered, the pressure for finding some substitute for petroleum decreases, not to increase again until the newer petroleum fields begin to be depleted. The development of our oil shale resources has therefore had a succession of ups and downs: ups, as fear of running out of petroleum developed, and downs, as new discoveries of petroleum abated these fears.

Coal

Our greatest reserve of carbon is in coal which occurs in vast, widely distributed deposits. It contains chiefly carbon, with a large mineral fraction that becomes ash when it is burned. Coal contains a little hydrogen, some oxygen, some sulfur, some phosphorus, and other elements. By appropriate treatment with hydrogen under heat and pressure, it is possible to cause some of the carbon-carbon bonds to break in favor of forming carbon-hydrogen bonds. The hydrogenation of coal promises to provide an abundant source of hydrocarbons when the need becomes acute enough to justify its greater expense.

Synthetic Sources

One "inorganic" approach to the synthesis of organic compounds is through the manufacture of acetylene. This is really a use of coal, for the process involves heating limestone with coke. **Coke** is coal from which the volatile products of thermal decomposition (coal tar) have been removed. At a very high temperature, the reaction between limestone and coke forms the compound called *calcium carbide:*

$$CaCO_3 + 4\,C \rightarrow 3\,CO + CaC_2$$

Acetylene (HC≡CH) is very weakly acidic. Calcium carbide can be regarded as the salt of acetylene, in which both hydrogen atoms have been displaced by one calcium atom: calcium acetylide. Hydrolysis of the salt of a very weak acid will furnish the free acid:

$$CaC_2 + 2\,H_2O \rightarrow Ca(OH)_2 + C_2H_2$$

Before the days of electrical systems in automobiles, their headlights were frequently *carbide lamps,* in which solid calcium carbide and water were the fuel. Water was dripped onto the calcium carbide at a suitable rate and the acetylene gas evolved was burned to produce a light. The light may not have been very adequate help for the driver, but it certainly allowed the innocent pedestrian to locate the oncoming auto and leap out of its way. As mentioned earlier, acetylene can be used to make a vast variety of organic compounds. It is, therefore, a potential substitute for petroleum.

Another and presently more important process of synthesizing hydrocarbons and their oxygen derivatives is to pass a mixture of hydrogen and carbon monoxide over appropriate catalysts at high temperature and pressure. The basic process was developed by Fischer and Tropsch, for whom the process is named. In addition to hydrocarbons, the process can also be varied to produce a great number of oxygen derivatives of hydrocarbons which are valuable in the organic chemical industry.

Test Your Memory

1. What is meant by a *straight chain?*
2. What is an *isomer?*
3. What is an *alkane?*
4. a) What is a *cycloparaffin?*
   b) What is a *naphthene?*
5. To what class of hydrocarbons does benzene belong?
6. How are alkenes and alkynes related to alkanes?
7. a) What is *petroleum?*
   b) What is meant by a *mixed base crude?*
8. Why is *oil shale* so called? Where is it found?
9. How can organic compounds be derived from coal and limestone?
10. What kind of a compound is *acetylene?*
11. What is involved in the *Fischer-Tropsch process?*
12. List the natural and the synthetic sources of hydrocarbons.
13. What are *petrochemicals?*

Test Your Understanding

1. Draw structural formulas for all possible isomers of C_8H_{18}. (Don't overlook the possibility of branches other than methyl.)
2. Name, in a systematic manner, each of the isomers you have drawn.

34

SOME HIGHLIGHTS OF ORGANIC SYNTHESIS

NATURAL AND SYNTHETIC

Perhaps the greatest achievement of chemistry has been the liberation of man from the limitation of using only naturally occurring materials. It is sometimes implied that *synthetic* substances are inferior to *natural* substances, but of course this depends on their application. In fact, most natural products in nature do not serve the same functions as those to which man wishes to put them. It is doubtful, for example, whether a silkworm would be better off in a nylon cocoon, whether petroleum was created with automobiles in mind, or whether vitamin A is stored in a shark's liver for the convenience of man. On the other hand, when a synthetic product proves superior to a natural one, this does not establish man's superiority over nature. Probably the product is being used for something other than its purpose in nature.

Often it is easier for the chemist, working under the conveniently controllable conditions of the laboratory, to produce a substance in pure form than it is for him to isolate the same substance from the complex mixture in which it occurs in nature. This is one reason for synthesizing a compound in the laboratory. Another reason is to make useful compounds not found in nature. The study of natural products and the synthesis of new products are both important occupations of the modern organic chemist. The subject is immense. We cannot do more here than try to survey what organic compounds are, and some of the ways they are synthesized and used.

Hydrocarbons, as a class, are relatively unreactive. The absence of low-energy vacant orbitals and of outer-shell lone pairs of electrons from both combined hydrogen and carbon leaves no easily vulnerable point of attack for outside reagents. Hydrocarbons can, however, be oxidized, not only by oxygen but also by halogens. Chlorine, for example, can react with a hydrocarbon by forming hydrogen chloride, substituting a chlorine atom where the hydrogen was. The reaction conditions must be carefully controlled to obtain good yields of desired products. Under the right conditions, methane can be chlorinated as follows:

$$CH_4 + Cl_2 \rightarrow CH_3Cl + HCl$$

$$CH_3Cl + Cl_2 \rightarrow CH_2Cl_2 + HCl$$

$$CH_2Cl_2 + Cl_2 \rightarrow CHCl_3 + HCl$$

$$CHCl_3 + Cl_2 \rightarrow CCl_4 + HCl$$

Chlorinated hydrocarbons are commonly used as solvents. For example, the last two steps of methane chlorination produce **chloroform** ($CHCl_3$) and **carbon tetrachloride** (CCl_4), both excellent solvents. Since such products are usually toxic, contact with the skin or inhalation of the vapors must be avoided. Carbon tetrachloride is commonly found in the home where it is used as spot remover and garment cleaner. It has a great advantage over gasoline in that it creates no fire hazard, but even a little vapor inhaled or liquid absorbed through the skin causes permanent damage to the liver. More extensive intake can be fatal.

Besides their utility as solvents, organic halides are very useful in chemical synthesis.

In recent years hundreds of compounds have been prepared in which the structures are just like those of hydrocarbons and their derivatives, but with fluorine substituted for every hydrogen atom that would be attached to carbon. These substances, the **fluorocarbons** and their derivatives, have potential scope which rivals that of carbon-hydrogen chemistry. The fluorine-substituted derivative of ethylene (C_2F_4) has been polymerized to form **teflon,** an extraordinarily stable and unreactive solid. One of its uses is as a coating for "nonstick" cooking pans. This relatively new and highly active field of chemical research will probably produce additional valuable developments in the years to come.

ALCOHOLS AND PHENOLS

If methyl chloride (CH_3Cl) is properly treated with sodium hydroxide, the chlorine can be replaced by hydroxyl (OH) to form **methyl alcohol** (CH_3OH). This is the first member of a homologous series of alcohols:

Figure 34.1. Stepwise Oxidation of Methane.

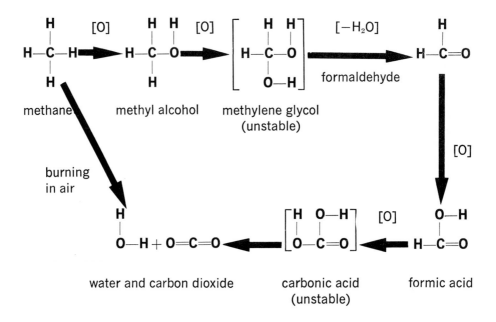

methane — methyl alcohol — methylene glycol (unstable) — formaldehyde

burning in air

water and carbon dioxide — carbonic acid (unstable) — formic acid

ethyl alcohol (CH_3CH_2OH), **propyl alcohol** ($CH_3CH_2CH_2OH$), **butyl alcohol** ($CH_3CH_2CH_2CH_2OH$), and so on. There are also many isomers, such as **isopropyl alcohol,** $CH_3CH(OH)CH_3$. All the alcohols of relatively low molecular weight are liquids held together, like water, by protonic bridges. The ability of an alcohol to form protonic bridges with water, as well as with its own molecules, may give it high solubility in water. The lower-weight alcohols are completely miscible. As the size of the hydrocarbon part of the molecule increases, however, the solubility in water decreases rapidly. The dissolution of a higher molecular weight alcohol in water would require the breaking of more protonic bridges in the water than would be replaced by protonic bridges to the alcohol hydroxyl group. On the other hand, as the hydrocarbon group becomes larger, miscibility with hydrocarbons and other organic compounds is increased.

Alcohols are valuable solvents and also very useful reagents in the synthesis of other organic compounds. The consumption of ethyl alcohol as an intoxicant is possible because it is the least poisonous of the family. Methyl alcohol can cause blindness and death, a fact discovered by unfortunate people who have thought "alcohol" was synonymous with ethyl alcohol.

When a hydroxyl group is attached to a benzene ring the resulting compound is called a **phenol.** Phenol itself, hydroxy benzene (C_6H_5OH), is quite different from alcohols derived from alkanes. It is much more acidic, corrosive to the skin, and more effective as a germicide; it is very poisonous. Phenol condenses with formaldehyde (see below) to form the synthetic resin called **Bakelite.** The "trivial" or common name for phenol is **carbolic acid.**

When a molecule contains two or more hydroxyl groups, it is called a *poly-hydric alcohol.* Two hydroxyl groups make it a **glycol.** The hydroxyl groups cannot be on the same carbon atom because such a compound generally decomposes to eliminate water. The simplest glycol is **ethylene glycol,** $CH_2(OH)CH_2(OH)$, the principal ingredient in the most common "perma-nent" radiator antifreeze. It is miscible with water through the formation of protonic bridges. It boils higher than alcohol because it has two hydroxyl groups per molecule. The water solutions freeze much lower than pure water.

If three hydroxyl groups—one on each of the three carbon atoms of propane—are substituted for hydrogen, the compound is **glycerine** or **glycerol.** This is a byproduct of the manufacture of soap from fats, as will be men-tioned later. Compounds with more than three hydroxyl groups constitute a class known as **carbohydrates,** which includes sugars, starches, and cellulose.

ETHERS

A rather common type of organic reaction is one in which a small molecule, such as water, is split out from two larger molecules, leaving them connected together. This is also the basis of **condensation polymerization** which is dis-cussed below. It can be accomplished with two molecules of ethyl alcohol by heating with concentrated sulfuric acid. This acid has a high affinity for water, which helps in its removal:

$$CH_3CH_2OH + HOCH_2CH_3 \xrightarrow{H_2SO_4} CH_3CH_2OCH_2CH_3 + H_2O$$

The product, a dialkyl oxide, is called **ether.** This particular one is called **diethylether,** but hundreds of different compounds can be called ethers. The simplest one is a gas, **dimethylether** (CH_3OCH_3). It can be an anesthetic, but is not as commonly used as diethylether, a very volatile liquid. Ethers, especially the very volatile ones, are highly inflammable. Great precautions must be taken in hospitals to avoid ignition of the anesthetic.

Ethers in general are excellent solvents. Because they are relatively un-reactive, they can serve as media for a variety of organic synthetic reactions. They do have the ability to act as electron donors, however, through the lone electron pairs on the oxygen. Thus, they assist the progress of some reactions by forming intermediate coordination complexes which then react further.

ALDEHYDES AND KETONES

The stepwise oxidation of hydrocarbons may be regarded as consisting of the successive replacement of hydrogen by hydroxyl. For example, the first oxida-tion product of methane would be methyl alcohol (CH_3OH). Substitution of

Figure 34.2. Some Types of Organic Oxygen Compounds.

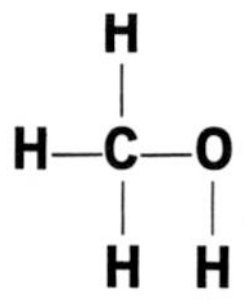

methyl *alcohol*

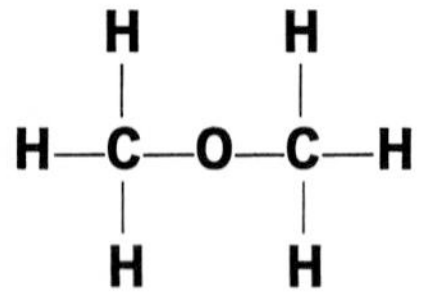

dimethyl *ether*

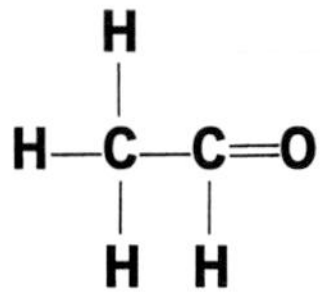

acet*aldehyde*

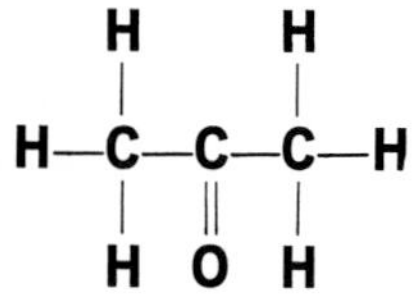

acetone
(a ketone)

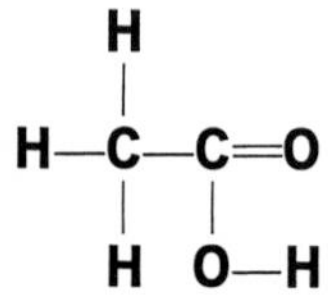

acetic *acid*
(a carboxylic acid)

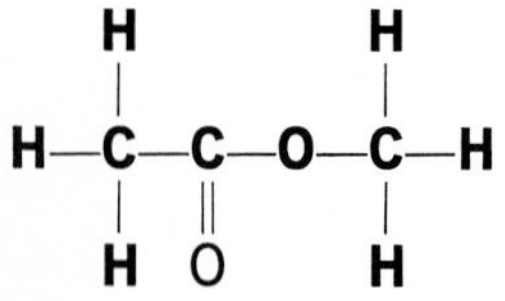

methyl acetate
(an ester)

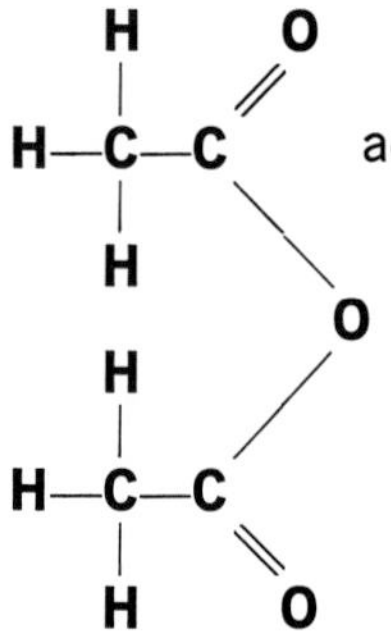

acetic *anhydride*

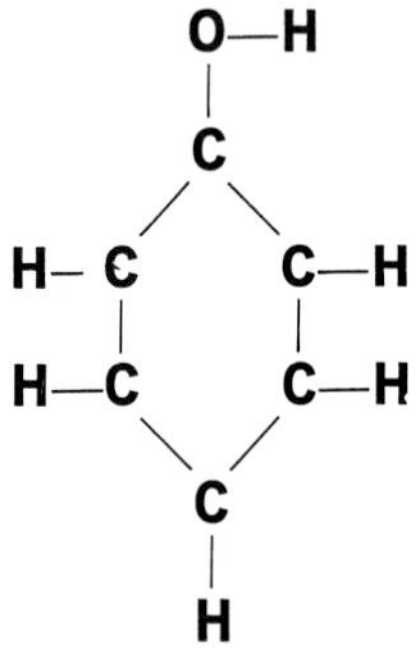

phenol

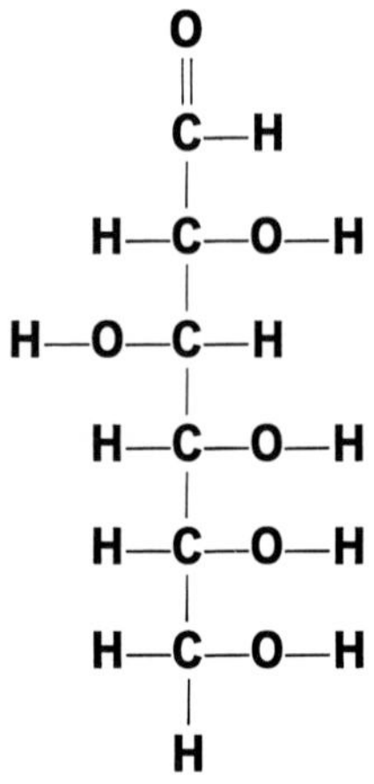

glucose
(a sugar)

a second hydrogen on the carbon would produce $CH_2(OH)_2$, but as pointed out earlier, such compounds so readily split out H_2O that they usually cannot be isolated, and this is no exception. The product after the loss of water is $H_2C=O$. This is **formaldehyde,** the first of a class of compounds characterized by the presence of the **aldehyde** group, –CHO. The formula is often written HCHO.

Oxidation of hydrocarbon with three or more carbons can take place at a methylene carbon, instead of at a methyl carbon. With propane, for example, the first product would be **isopropyl alcohol,** $CH_3CH(OH)CH_3$. Replacement of the second hydrogen on that carbon would give $CH_3C(OH)_2CH_3$, except that again water would be split out, and the product would be CH_3COCH_3. This is **acetone,** the first of a class of compounds, characterized by the presence of two alkyl groups on the **carbonyl** group (–C=O) and called **ketones.**

If a carbonyl carbon is attached to two alkyl groups, then the compound is a ketone. If the carbonyl carbon is attached to one hydrogen and one alkyl group, it is an aldehyde. This is the formal distinction between ketones and aldehydes. A study of their properties reveals that the presence of the hydrogen on the carbonyl carbon makes the compound much more vulnerable to oxidation than if there are two alkyl groups. Therefore, aldehydes are much more easily oxidized and, in general, more reactive, than ketones. Ketones can be used as solvents for the oxidation of other compounds because they resist oxidation. Acetone is a particularly valuable solvent, because it is miscible with water as well as with most organic solvents and compounds.

CARBOXYLIC ACIDS

Since a ketone has two alkyl groups on the carbonyl carbon, there are no additional hydrogen atoms to be replaced by hydroxyl. Thus, ketones resist further oxidation and break down in a more complex manner when strongly oxidized. Aldehydes have one more hydrogen on the carbonyl oxygen that can be replaced by hydroxyl. For example, formaldehyde could become **formic acid,** $HC(OH)=O$, so called because it can be obtained by the distillation of ants (Latin, *formica*). Aldehydes are usually named for the acid which they give on oxidation; hence the name *formaldehyde*. Formic acid is found in certain insect venoms. It is very corrosive to living tissues and is probably the chief source of the intense pain when a bee stings. Just being jabbed with that tiny needle would not be very painful; it is the shot of formic acid that hurts.

Formic acid is the first of a series of compounds characterized by the presence of at least one **carboxyl** group, customarily written –COOH, although its structure is

$$-\underset{\underset{\displaystyle OH}{|}}{C}=O.$$

These compounds are called **carboxylic acids.** They are much more acidic than alcohols because the presence of a second oxygen on the carboxyl carbon withdraws additional electrons, making the carbon-hydroxyl bond more polar and the hydroxyl hydrogen more acidic. The best known carboxylic acid is acetic acid. (CH_3COOH), which would result from successive oxidations of ethane through ethyl alcohol (CH_3CH_2OH) and acetaldehyde (CH_3CHO). The lower-weight acids are quite soluble in water, where they ionize only weakly. They are of unpleasant odor and often from unappetizing origins: sweat glands, rancid butter, male goats, and the like.

The acids of relatively high molecular weight, in which the carboxyl group is attached to a long hydrocarbon chain, are called **fatty acids,** because they can be isolated from natural fats. Metal salts of fatty acids are called soaps. Ordinary household soaps consist of sodium salts of such acids, while liquid soaps usually contain potassium salts. Lubricating greases are compounded from lubricating oil (usually hydrocarbons of high molecular weight) and soaps to give them a semisolid nature. Lithium soaps are used in greases for low-temperature applications and other special purposes. Calcium soaps, as well as soaps of various other metals, are widely used in greases.

ESTERS

It is possible to condense a carboxylic acid with an alcohol in much the same way that two alcohol molecules can condense, by heating them with sulfuric acid or some other dehydrating catalyst. With ethyl alcohol and acetic acid, for example, the reaction would be as follows:

$$CH_3CH_2OH + CH_3COOH \rightarrow CH_3COOCH_2CH_3 + H_2O$$

The condensation product is called an **ester.** This particular ester is known as **ethyl acetate.** Sometimes this reaction, called **esterification,** is regarded as analogous to the inorganic neutralization of an acid with a base to form a salt plus water. However, the analogy here is only formal, since an ester bears no resemblance to a salt, and the mechanism of esterification does not resemble that of neutralization.

Esters of lower molecular weight usually have very pleasant odors. They are found in the fragrances of flowers and the flavoring of ripe fruits and are synthesized to serve as artificial perfumes and flavorings.

The trihydroxyalcohol, **glycerol,** has three hydroxyl groups available for esterification. Natural fats consist of glyceryl triesters of long-chain fatty acids. An ester, in general, can be reconverted to its alcohol and a salt of its acid by treatment with a base. When natural fats are treated with sodium hydroxide, the products are the sodium salt of the fatty acids, which is a soap, and free glycerol. Since the process produces soap, it is called **saponification.** In pioneer days, soap was homemade by treating natural greases and fats with *lye,* usually a water extract of wood ashes which contained considerable potassium carbonate (K_2CO_3). Through hydrolysis of the carbonate ion, this solution is alkaline and saponifies the fats to make soap.

MERCAPTANS AND THIOETHERS

The substitution of sulfur for oxygen in alcohols and ethers produces the **thio** analogs; *thio* means "containing sulfur." The analogs of the alcohols are called **mercaptans** or **thiols.** They are much more volatile than alcohols as a result of the inability of sulfur to form protonic bridges as oxygen does. **Methyl mercaptan** (CH_3SH) is a gas, and the higher-weight mercaptans, though liquid, are also quite volatile. The mercaptans of relatively low molecular weight (up through eight or nine carbon atoms) are notorious for their foul odor, to which the human nose is extremely sensitive. **Ethyl mercaptan** (CH_3CH_2SH) is deliberately introduced into artificial gas (containing CO and H_2) so that leaks can easily be detected before anyone can be poisoned by the odorless carbon monoxide or blown up by a gas explosion. Traces of mercaptans are probably liberated in the cooking of certain vegetables, such as cabbage. One of the principal ingredients of the skunk's effective defense weapon is **butyl mercaptan** (C_4H_9SH). Anyone who has disturbed a skunk at close range will appreciate how persevering and tenacious the odor of this compound can be. No simple chemical antidote suitable for application to the skin seems to be known, but for some unknown reason, tomato juice, rubbed on the contaminated areas of skin and clothing, helps somewhat.

The sulfur analog of an ether is called a **thioether,** or simply a **sulfide.** Thus **dimethylsulfide** and **dimethylthioether** are both names for CH_3SCH_3.

AMINES

Alcohols and ethers may be regarded as derived from water by substituting first one, then two alkyl groups (designated as R) for the hydrogens. Similarly, substitution for the hydrogen atoms of ammonia leads to nitrogen compounds called **amines.** When only one hydrogen of the ammonia is replaced (RNH_2), the compound is called a **primary amine.** If two hydrogens are replaced, as in R_2NH, the compound is a **secondary amine.** If three hydrogens are replaced (R_3N), the compound is called a **tertiary amine.** The amines of lower molecular weight are gases since they form weaker protonic bridges than do water and alcohols. They have a fishy odor and are physiologically active. They can act as electron donors through the lone electron pair on the nitrogen, and can form salts such as **tetramethylammonium chloride,** $(CH_3)_4NCl$.

AMIDES

In a reaction analogous to their condensation with alcohols to form esters, carboxylic acids can react with ammonia, and with primary and secondary

Figure 34.3.   Structural Formulas of Miscellaneous Organic Compounds.

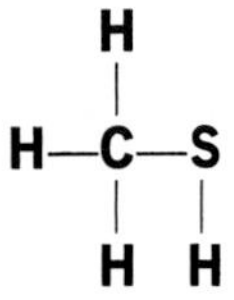

methyl *mercaptan*

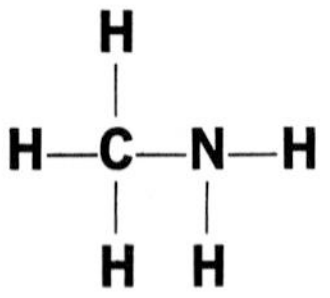

methyl *amine*

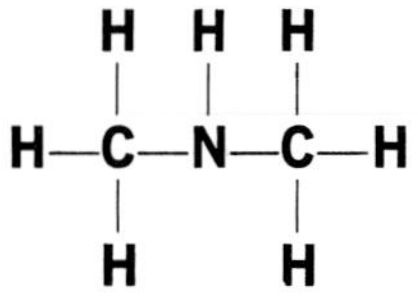

dimethyl *amine*

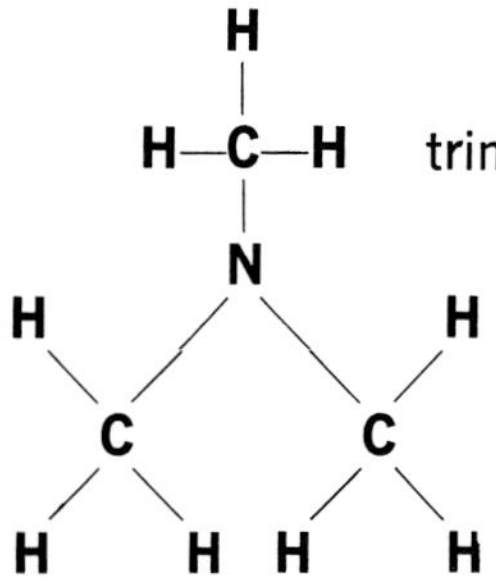

trimethyl*amine*

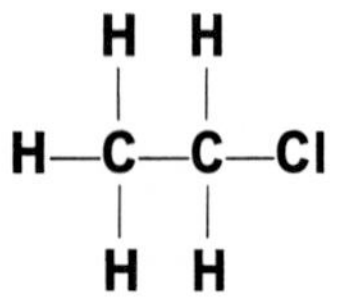

ethyl chloride

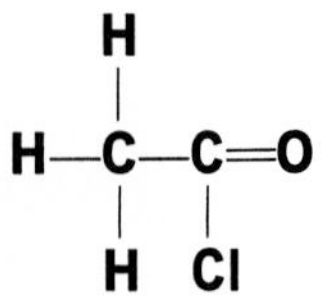

acetyl chloride
(an acid chloride)

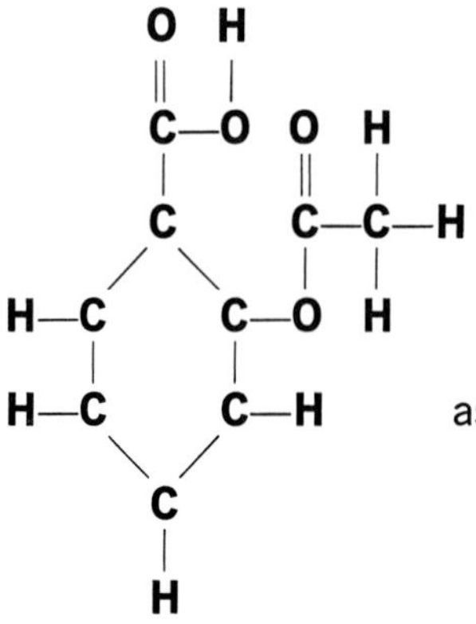

aspirin

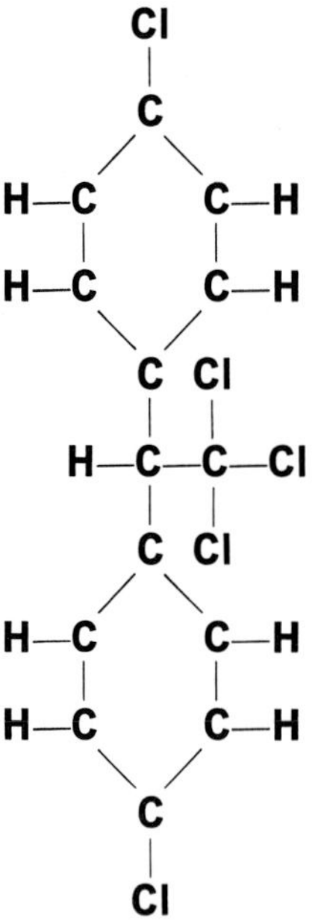

"DDT"

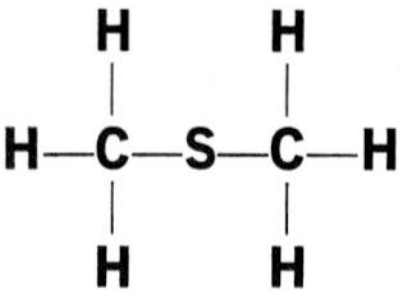

dimethyl *thioether*
(dimethyl sulfide)

amines. The products, formed by the splitting out of water, are called **amides.**
Some sample reactions of acetic acid, in the presence of an acid or base
catalyst, are as follows:

With *ammonia:*

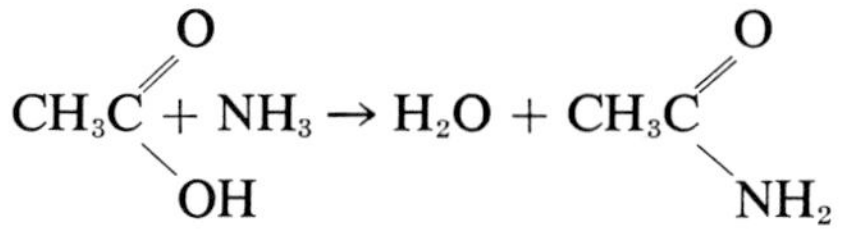

$$CH_3\overset{\displaystyle O}{\underset{\displaystyle OH}{C}} + NH_3 \rightarrow H_2O + CH_3\overset{\displaystyle O}{\underset{\displaystyle NH_2}{C}} \qquad \text{(primary amide)}$$

With *methylamine:*

$$CH_3COOH + CH_3NH_2 \rightarrow H_2O + CH_3CONHCH_3 \quad \text{(secondary amide)}$$

With *dimethylamine:*

$$CH_3COOH + (CH_3)_2NH \rightarrow H_2O + CH_3CON(CH_3)_2 \quad \text{(tertiary amide)}$$

With *trimethylamine:*

$$CH_3COOH + (CH_3)_3N \rightarrow [(CH_3)_3NH^+](CH_3COO^-)$$
$$\text{(ammonium salt)}$$

Note that tertiary amines *cannot* form amides.

Proteins are polymers based on the following linkage which characterizes amides (see Chapter 36):

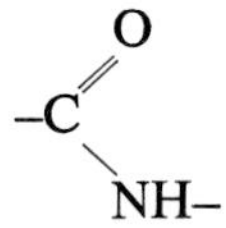

$$-\overset{\displaystyle O}{\underset{\displaystyle NH-}{C}}$$

Nylon (discussed below) is also a polyamide molecule. The now-infamous
hallucinogenic drug, LSD (lysergic acid diethylamide), is a tertiary amide.

POLYMERS

Polymers are long-chain organic molecules formed by the joining of many
small units of monomers. Two principal types of polymerization are recognized. One involves simply the sequential addition of each successive monomer
molecule to form, ultimately, a very large polymer molecule. This is **addition**

Figure 34.4. Addition Polymerization.

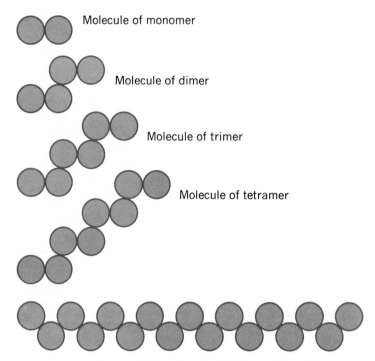

Molecule of monomer

Molecule of dimer

Molecule of trimer

Molecule of tetramer

Fragment of molecule of "higher polymer"

polymerization. The familiar material **polyethylene,** is derived from the **ethylene** monomer (C_2H_4). These C_2H_4 molecules join together to form extremely long chains, which can be represented by the formula $(C_2H_4)_x$, where x represents a large but unknown number. Although ethylene is a very reactive gas, its polymer is a very unreactive, nonvolatile solid.

The second principal type, **condensation polymerization,** involves the joining together of small molecules through the splitting out of smaller molecules, most commonly water. The splitting out of water has been observed as crucial to the formation of ethers, esters, and amides. In general, we can represent this process as the reaction of two molecules, ROH and $R'XH$, in which X might be oxygen or the NH of an amine. Splitting out water leaves RXR', a general representation of an ether, ester, or amide. Condensation polymerization requires that water, or some other small molecule, be split out from *both* ends of the larger molecule rather than just one. This allows the chain to grow. We can therefore represent the polymerization as the reaction of $HOROH$ with $HXR'XH$ to form a long-chain polymer product, $HORXR'$ $XRXR'$ $XRX \ldots R'$ XH.

What formula would you write to represent a polymer formed by condensing HO-CH$_2$-CH$_2$-OH by water-splitting?

An example of a condensation polymer is nylon. It is formed from adipic acid, HOOC(CH$_2$)$_4$COOH(HOROH), where R=OC(CH$_2$)$_4$CO and hexamethylenediamine H$_2$N(CH$_2$)$_6$NH$_2$H$XR'X$H, where X=NH, R=(CH$_2$)$_6$. Loss of hydrogen from each end of the diamine and hydroxyl from both ends of the acid molecules forms water. The residues of these molecules join together in long chains as nylon.

Figure 34.5. Condensation Polymerization.

Three molecules of a monomer condense by splitting out two smaller molecules such as H$_2$O and forming one

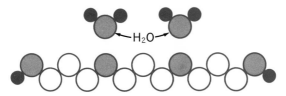

molecule of trimmer.

Each end of this trimer is still capable of condensing with another molecule of monomer (or dimer or trimer or any polymeric species) to form a still larger molecule of **condensation polymer.**

Test Your Memory

1. What is an *alkyl halide?*
2. What are the *fluorocarbons?*
3. From what is *teflon* made?
4. What is an *alcohol?* How does it differ from a *phenol?*
5. What is a *glycol?*
6. What is the structural formula of glycerol?
7. What is the chief component of common permanent antifreeze?
8. What is a *carbohydrate?*
9. Name six different types of organic compounds of oxygen, and distinguish among them.

10. How did the pioneers make soap?
11. What are *mercaptans* and *thioethers?*
12. What are *amines* and how may they vary?
13. a) What is *addition polymerization?* b) *Condensation polymerization?*

Test Your Understanding

1. Identify the class of each of the following: (a) CH_3CHO, (b) CH_3Br, (c) $CH_3CH(OH)CH_3$, (d) $CH_3CH_2OCH_3$, (e) CH_3CH_2SH, (f) $CH_3CH=CH_2$, (g) CH_3COOCH_3, (h) $CH_3CH_2COCH_3$, (i) CH_3COOH, (j) $CH_3NHCH_2CH_3$, (k) $CH_3CH_2CH_2CH_2SCH_2CH_3$.
2. From your knowledge of inorganic oxides, predict the relative acidities of CH_3OH and $HCOOH$.
3. Why do you think diethylether is more volatile than water?
4. What kinds of organic compounds might be associated through protonic bridging?

35

HOW INORGANIC CHEMICALS ARE MADE

HEAVY CHEMICALS

This chapter will illustrate how a number of chemical principles are applied in the manufacture of industrial inorganic chemicals. This should give you some idea of how such materials are obtained and how they are useful directly or indirectly in your daily living. Most of the substances to be discussed here are classified as **heavy chemicals,** referring not to their density but to their large-scale production. Sulfuric acid, for example, is less than twice as dense as water, but it is one of the most important chemicals of industry. Enough of it is manufactured in the United States to provide every man, woman, and child with at least a good glassful every day of the year. Most of us, however, willingly relinquish our share to the chemical industry where it is better appreciated. Throughout the world, the per capita consumption of sulfuric acid provides a reasonably accurate index of the relative standard of living, since it is so thoroughly tied in with economic prosperity through manufacturing. Like other heavy chemicals, its production is essential and basic, not merely to other chemical industry, but to our whole economy.

LIME PRODUCTS

The great natural source of lime products is limestone, or calcium carbonate ($CaCO_3$). Calcium carbonate itself would be expected to be alkaline through hydrolysis of the carbonate ion, but it is very insoluble. Therefore, its ions are not readily available for hydrolysis. It may be termed a complex oxide, since it is the product of combination of a basic oxide (CaO) and an acidic oxide (CO_2). When heated, all such oxides tend to decompose to their component oxides, or sometimes to other products. Limestone is fairly stable, but at temperatures above 500°C the rate of decomposition is sufficient to produce a measurable equilibrium pressure of carbon dioxide:

$$CaCO_3 \rightleftharpoons CaO + CO_2$$

Since the other two components of this system are solids of unchanging concentration, the equilibrium constant is measured solely by the pressure of carbon dioxide: $K = P_{CO_2}$.

Le Chatelier's principle tells us that raising the pressure here would cause carbon dioxide to unite with calcium oxide to reform calcium carbonate. Reducing the pressure, on the other hand, should upset the equilibrium by slowing the reverse reaction and favoring decomposition. If the decomposition of calcium carbonate is carried out at a pressure lower than the equilibrium pressure for that temperature, equilibrium cannot be attained, and the calcium carbonate will continue to decompose until it is all gone. So we could carry the decomposition to completion at 500° if we needed it. At this temperature, however, the decomposition is slow, even if all the carbon dioxide is removed as it forms. What effect on the equilibrium will changing the temperature have? Le Chatelier's principle tells us that an endothermic reaction is favored by elevating the temperature while an exothermic reaction is favored by lowering the temperature. Since the decomposition of calcium carbonate is endothermic, it will be favored by raising the temperature. The equilibrium constant is constant only at a constant temperature. Raising the temperature will increase the value of the equilibrium constant. In other words, it will raise the pressure of carbon dioxide. At a temperature of 900°, the equilibrium pressure equals one atmosphere. Above that temperature, the decomposition will proceed rapidly if the system is not enclosed but the carbon dioxide is allowed to escape.

The carbon dioxide released is not necessarily discarded, but may be used, as in *dry ice* for refrigerating purposes. The calcium oxide, however, is the important product, while the carbon dioxide is a **byproduct.** Byproducts are usually those which are not the primary purpose of the reaction. In many chemical processes, however, economical operation depends on proper ingenuity in making full use of all byproducts. In effect, this cuts down costs by increasing profits.

Calcium oxide, as mentioned earlier, is strongly basic. The reaction of calcium oxide with water is a reaction of a strongly basic oxide with an amphoteric oxide, and generates considerable heat. In fact, if the hydration occurs within a small space where heat is not easily dissipated, enough heat to ignite wooden storage bins can be evolved. Calcium oxide is commonly called **quicklime.** Its hydration is called **slaking.** Slaked lime is calcium hydroxide, $Ca(OH)_2$. Both forms are often called merely "lime," but this is unsafe practice because the hydroxide is much easier to handle than the oxide. Football players have been burned, for instance, when their noses ploughed a furrow across a newly limed yard line, because the lines were marked with quicklime instead of slaked lime, which looks just like it. It is much better to mark such lines with powdered calcium carbonate.

The greatest single use of calcium hydroxide is for neutralizing the acidity created by the decomposition of organic matter in the soil. Most vegetables grow best in a soil that is slightly alkaline, and relatively few plants do well in soil that is very acidic. Large amounts of lime are also used in the building industry in wall plaster and in special mortar. The finishing plaster in buildings is usually a mixture of calcium hydroxide and magnesium hydroxide, the latter giving somewhat better smoothness of application. The plaster hardens initially by forming crystalline hydrates of calcium and magnesium hydroxides. As time goes on, carbon dioxide from the atmosphere slowly combines with the hydroxide in the wall, forming calcium carbonate. Before the days of portland cement, mortar for holding building stones together was made by mixing sand with calcium hydroxide. It has been found that the conversion to carbonate occurs so slowly that even after several centuries, carbon dioxide has not penetrated appreciably beyond the first few inches, in a rock wall several feet thick.

Calcium hydroxide is only slightly soluble in water, but a slurry of the solid in water serves very well as the cheapest industrial source of hydroxide ions, with a wide variety of chemical process applications.

Limestone or lime can be used in the manufacture of portland cement. This extremely useful material is largely a mixture of calcium silicates and calcium aluminum silicates. It is manufactured by heating a mixture of finely ground lime-like substances, such as limestone, with clay-like substances, such as natural clays or other complex silicates. The temperature is elevated to the point where melting of the silicates just barely begins and the powdered materials start to sinter together into lumps. These are then cooled and ground to the fine powder known as portland cement. **Concrete,** which is commonly but erroneously called *cement,* is an aggregate of sand, gravel, and portland cement, held together by the latter. The "glue" is provided by the addition of water, which reacts to form hydrated crystalline silicates that give the aggregate some strength within a few hours. The setting of concrete continues for more than a year, as very complex hydration and other reactions slowly proceed within it.

SILICATE PRODUCTS

Glass

Portland cement is, of course, both a silicate product and a lime product. Other useful materials, such as glass, also involve silicates and lime. Glass is a term applicable to a wide range of compositions having in common the fact that once melted, they cool without crystallizing. Because of the giant molecule structure of sand itself, and the complex structures of some silicates, it is very difficult for them to form neatly symmetrical crystals from the melt except over a long period of time, even if the compound is "pure." Introduction of appreciable concentrations of impurities, such as other metal oxides or silicates, makes crystallization even more difficult. As the liquid melt cools, it becomes more and more viscous. At ordinary temperatures it is still liquid, in principle, but so viscous that it appears to be solid. Many crystalline salts are white because of the reflection of light from many crystal faces within them. Such faces are absent from these supercooled liquids, which are, therefore, translucent and called **glasses.** They usually consist of a mixture of silicates, although to some extent they can include boric oxide and almost any combination of metal oxides.

Perhaps the best-known forms of glass are combinations of sodium and calcium silicates, called **soft glass.** The raw materials are sand and any source of sodium and calcium oxides. Remember that silica is acidic and that any acidic oxide can displace another more volatile acidic oxide from its complex salt, regardless of how they compare in acidity. Because silica is so low in volatility, it can displace sulfur trioxide from sulfates, carbon dioxide from carbonates, or phosphoric oxide from phosphates when heated with them. It is unnecessary, therefore, to provide the sand with sodium oxide or calcium oxide directly: the source of sodium or calcium oxide may be the carbonate or the sulfate as well. For manufacturing ordinary glass, sodium carbonate, limestone, and sand are commonly heated until they melt together. The nonmetal oxides, here carbon dioxide, are displaced by the silica, which forms a mixture of silicates that cools to a glass. Cooling is kept very slow, to avoid introducing thermal strains. Such slow cooling is called **annealing.**

One important disadvantage of soft glass is that all silicate materials have poor thermal conduction. Soft glass combines this with significant thermal expansion, which makes it very difficult to heat soft glass uniformly. Almost inevitably, part of it will expand before the rest, creating strains that often result in shattering. Not much can be done to improve the thermal conductivity of glass. In fact, its insulating qualities are often very advantageous. The thermal expansion coefficient, however, can be varied by changing the composition. Adding boric oxide to the silicates and changing the metal oxide concentrations can produce glass (e.g., Pyrex) that has a very low coefficient of thermal expansion and is therefore much more resistant to thermal shock.

A great variety of glasses can be made for special purposes by varying their composition over a wide range.

Ceramics

The manufacture of building bricks out of clay is also a process that makes use of silicate materials. Clay is chiefly a complex mixture of silicates. Heating it first drives out the moisture and oxidizes any organic matter. The temperature is then raised until the lowest melting components of the silicates begin to melt. The rest remains solid and holds the shape of the object being baked. The mass is then allowed to cool, extremely slowly so as not to introduce thermal strains. When the brick has been thoroughly annealed and cooled, it has far greater strength than the original dried clay could have had. The component particles that did not melt are held firmly cemented together by the glass that formed from the lowest melting components.

This same principle is applied to many other ceramic products, such as chinaware and porcelain. In the making of china or porcelain, the starting materials are much purer, and the melting process is carried out to a greater degree, increasing the "glassiness" of the final product. This makes it smooth, firm, hard, and strong, if properly annealed.

OTHER BASIC SUBSTANCES

Sodium Carbonate

Sodium carbonate ($NaCO_3$) is a very valuable chemical with many useful industrial applications, some of which involve its basicity through hydrolysis. It is commonly called **soda ash.** If a solution of sodium carbonate is mixed with a solution of calcium chloride, the insoluble calcium carbonate precipitates out, leaving a solution of sodium chloride. An ingenious engineer named Ernest Solvay (1838–1922) worked out a method for reversing this process to make carbonate from salt and limestone. In the **Solvay process,** saturated brine ($NaCl$ solution) is treated with carbon dioxide and ammonia. The carbon dioxide reacts with water to form an acidic solution:

$$CO_2 + H_2O \rightleftharpoons H^+ + HCO_3^-$$

> It is known that only a small fraction of dissolved CO_2 is in the form of carbonic acid (H_2CO_3) and its ions. Can you account for the dissolution of the remaining CO_2?

The ammonia reacts with water to form a basic solution:

$$NH_3 + H_2O \rightleftharpoons NH_4^+ + OH^-$$

But there cannot be a solution that is both acidic and basic, to an appreciable extent, at the same time. The hydrogen ion formed by the dissolution of carbon dioxide reacts with the hydroxide ion that is formed by the dissolution of the ammonia, producing water. This leaves the bicarbonate ion, HCO_3^-, and the ammonium ion, NH_4^+, together in the solution with the sodium and the chloride ions. Whenever a collection of dissolved ions is brought together, a precipitate will form if any combination of those ions exceeds the solubility product of their salt. Here the least soluble combination possible, and one for which the solubility product is exceeded under these conditions, is that of sodium ion and bicarbonate ion. They form $NaHCO_3$ which precipitates and is filtered off. The filtrate is a solution of ammonium chloride.

Any acid salt, such as sodium bicarbonate, tends to disproportionate when heated, forming the free acid and the neutral salt. The sodium bicarbonate is heated to produce the following reaction:

$$2\,NaHCO_3 \rightarrow Na_2CO_3 + CO_2 + H_2O$$

This yields sodium carbonate, the product initially sought. The carbon dioxide is available to be directed into more brine, for further reaction.

The most expensive material for this reaction is the ammonia. The process would never be economical if the ammonia were just used once and then thrown away. It is important, therefore, to recover it from the ammonium chloride solution. The reason that ammonium ion forms is that an ammonia molecule has a lone pair of electrons on the nitrogen that can attract a hydrogen ion. Ammonia in water is only a weak base, however, because it can acquire protons from the water only to a small extent. The hydroxide ions that are created are much stronger bases than water molecules. Given a chance, they will recombine with their proton in much the same way that hydroxide ions will reclaim their protons from hydronium ions. If the ammonium ions encounter hydroxide ions, they will lose their extra protons, forming water and free ammonia. To recover the ammonia from the ammonium chloride solution, hydroxide ions are added and the solution is warmed to drive out the ammonia:

$$NH_4^+ + OH^- \rightleftharpoons NH_3 + H_2O$$

The cheapest source of hydroxide ions is limestone, the original source of the carbon dioxide. For every mole of carbon dioxide produced, a mole of calcium oxide is left behind. This, hydrated to the hydroxide, becomes a ready source of hydroxide ions for the recovery of the ammonia, which, like the extra carbon dioxide, is recycled to precipitate more sodium bicarbonate.

The only thing left is the solution from which the ammonia was recovered, now a solution of calcium chloride ($CaCl_2$), the byproduct of the Solvay process. Summarizing, the Solvay process succeeds in converting calcium carbonate and sodium chloride to sodium carbonate and calcium chloride. A roundabout way is necessary since the products overall are less stable than the reactants.

Sodium Hydroxide

When a high concentration of hydroxide ions in solution is needed, sodium hydroxide is the best base to use since it is extremely soluble. Although it is much more expensive than calcium hydroxide, it has important applications. One way of making sodium hydroxide is by adding calcium hydroxide to a solution of sodium carbonate. Calcium carbonate precipitates at once, leaving a solution of sodium hydroxide. More commonly, however, sodium hydroxide is a product of the electrolysis of brine. Sometimes this process is operated primarily to obtain chlorine; in this case hydrogen and sodium hydroxide are byproducts. At other times, chlorine is too abundant to bring a good price; sodium hydroxide is then the most sought-after of the products. Evaporation of the solution, after electrolysis has discharged all the chloride ions, leaves the solid sodium hydroxide. The solid is very **hygroscopic** (absorbs moisture readily from the air), becoming wet with solution very quickly in ordinary air; hence it is not usually handled in this form. Instead, it is dissolved in water to form the usual laboratory reagent solution of sodium hydroxide. Since silica and silicate materials are acidic as a result of the silicon dioxide, they are attacked by strong alkali. Glass bottles are slowly attacked by sodium hydroxide solutions. This is not too serious a matter, but glass stoppers must be avoided because the action of hydroxide solution between the glass surfaces causes the stopper to become "frozen" in place. This is why rubber stoppers are usually placed in bottles of sodium hydroxide solution.

Ammonia

Ammonia represents by far the greatest source of **fixed nitrogen.** Only a few plants are able to make use of the nitrogen from the atmosphere directly, and only then with the help of certain soil bacteria. The rest simply use up the nitrogen that is in combined form in the soil. When it is gone, plant growth is no longer possible. **Fixation** of nitrogen means combining it with other elements so that it may become available to plants. It is absolutely essential to good agricultural processes to be able to supply fixed nitrogen to the soil when needed.

Nitrogen molecules are surpassed only by carbon monoxide molecules in the strength of their bonds. Hydrogen molecules are themselves held together by strong bonds, but the triple bonds of N_2 are more than twice as strong. Before nitrogen and hydrogen can unite to form ammonia, these bonds must be broken. Despite this, the reaction between N_2 and H_2 is exothermic, which in theory should produce good yields of ammonia, but the difficulty is in getting the reaction to go. The fact that fixed nitrogen is needed not only for agriculture but also for explosives stimulated the development during World War I, by the German chemist Fritz Haber, of the famous **Haber process** for the synthesis of ammonia:

$$N_2 + 3 H_2 \rightleftharpoons 2 NH_3$$

Since the number of moles of gas decreases from four to two from left to right, using Le Chatelier's principle we predict that this equilibrium would produce higher concentrations of ammonia at higher pressures. Since the reaction is exothermic, the temperature should be kept as low as is feasible. At high temperatures, the reverse reaction, decomposition, is favored. Haber's chief contribution was the development of an iron-containing catalyst which speeds up the attainment of equilibrium. Although elevated, temperatures then need not be too high to give good yields of ammonia. The need for a catalyst obviously stems from the necessity of splitting the very stable nitrogen molecule into atoms before reaction can proceed.

An appreciable amount of the nitrogen that is combined in coal is released as ammonia when coal is converted to coke by heating to drive off the volatile matter. This process is called **destructive distillation.** The ammonia is usually absorbed in sulfuric acid to form ammonium sulfate which is used as fertilizer.

SOME INDUSTRIAL ACIDS

Sulfuric Acid

Sulfuric acid was first described about A.D. 1300 by an unknown Spaniard who wrote under the name of Geber, an Arabian alchemist who had lived six centuries earlier. It was one of the early manufactures in the newly formed United States, and has become one of the most important industrial chemicals.

The roasting of sulfide ores produces much sulfur dioxide which today is usually converted to sulfuric acid. In older times it was released, and sometimes still is, into the atmosphere, destroying all the vegetation for miles around. This is a source of serious atmospheric pollution. Most of the sulfur for sulfuric acid, however, is found in deposits of the element that lie anywhere from several hundred to several thousand feet below the surface of the earth, principally in Louisiana and Texas. An engineer named Herman **Frasch** developed a very useful process for bringing this sulfur to the surface without going down after it with conventional mining equipment. Recognizing that sulfur melts at about 116°C, only a little higher than the boiling point of water, he reasoned that it could be melted with *superheated* water, i.e., water heated under pressure. In the **Frasch process,** a hole is drilled to the sulfur bed and a system of three concentric pipes is inserted. Superheated water is pumped down through the outside pipe to melt the sulfur and to keep it melted on its way up through the middle pipe. Compressed air is forced down the central pipe where it forms a froth with the melted sulfur and water. This mixture rises through the middle pipe, to be poured into huge outdoor bins where the sulfur solidifies into a hard mass. This mass is dynamited to break it up into chunks or powder, which is then transported to the sulfuric acid plants. Most of the sulfur produced in this way is used for manufacturing sulfuric acid.

Sulfur burns in air chiefly to form sulfur dioxide (SO_2). Although bond energies indicate that sulfur trioxide is more stable than a mixture of sulfur dioxide and oxygen, the burning goes no further without special encouragement. As in the Haber process and others, a product which should be formed

Figure 35.1.   Frasch Process for Recovering Sulfur from Beneath Surface.

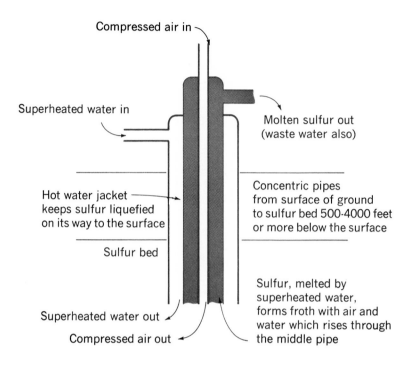

is in fact not formed because of the high activation energy required. A catalyst is needed to speed the desired reaction. The sulfur is extraordinarily pure as it comes from the underground beds, but contains a little arsenic that is highly undesirable. The burning of the sulfur to sulfur dioxide also burns the arsenic to form a smoke of arsenious oxide (As_4O_6). This must be removed before the sulfur dioxide can be successfully converted to the trioxide, or else it will contaminate the sulfuric acid. (A mass poisoning of British beer drinkers was traced to the production of beer cans from metal that had been treated with sulfuric acid containing a little arsenic, so the hazard is not to be disregarded.) An electrostatic precipitator collects the arsenious oxide smoke by discharging the particles and allowing them to come together. The sulfur dioxide is then mixed with air and passed over a heated *contact catalyst*. Finely divided platinum works as a catalyst, but it is relatively easily poisoned (its function is destroyed) by very tiny traces of residual arsenic. A catalyst not so easily poisoned, and considerably cheaper, contains **vanadium pentoxide,** more correctly **vanadium (V) oxide** (V_2O_5). The SO_2 becomes SO_3:

$$2\ SO_2 + O_2 \xrightarrow{V_2O_5} 2\ SO_3$$

From its use of a contact catalyst, this process is known as the **contact process.**

Sulfur trioxide at slightly elevated temperatures is a gas, although it easily condenses to liquid or solid forms through polymerization. In ordinary air it fumes heavily, giving a very dense white smoke. A trace of sulfur *di*oxide in the air can be tasted, giving an unpleasant sensation in the throat. A trace of sulfur *tri*oxide in the air causes an almost irresistible tendency to cough.

Sulfur trioxide and water are miscible in all proportions by a chemical reaction that cannot be completely reversed. They combine with the evolution of much heat. Thus, one would expect that the formation of sulfuric acid from sulfur trioxide and water would be one of the simplest reactions to accomplish:

$$SO_3 + H_2O \rightarrow H_2SO_4$$

You will recognize this as the interaction of a strongly acidic oxide, SO_3, and an amphoteric oxide, water, forming an acid, as the oxygen of the water contributes an electron pair to the highly positive sulfur atom. In fact, however, as soon as sulfur trioxide encounters water vapor, it forms a very stable fog of sulfuric acid. This fog does not coagulate and is not readily absorbed by water. In the industrial manufacture of sulfuric acid, therefore, the sulfur trioxide is absorbed in dilute sulfuric acid instead of water. Here the absorption appears to occur much more readily.

Figure 35.2.   Molecules of Sodium Trioxide and Sulfuric Acid.

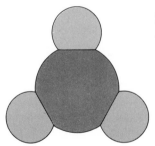

A molecule of SO_3 has a planar triangular shape, with short sulfur-to-oxygen bonds indicating greater than single-bond character.

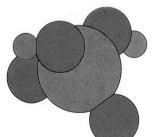

By addition of water, SO_3 forms sulfuric acid (H_2SO_4). Its molecules are tetrahedral, with SO bonds shorter than the S-OH bonds. The positive H and negative O cause sulfuric acid to be a liquid associated through protonic bridging.

Concentrated sulfuric acid contains about 98 per cent H_2SO_4. If SO_3 is added to unite with the remaining 2 per cent of water to bring the composition up to 100 per cent H_2SO_4, it is found that this extra SO_3 is not so firmly held. Complicated interactions in concentrated sulfuric acid produce a number of different species, so that "100 per cent sulfuric acid" does not actually contain only H_2SO_4 molecules. It contains also $H_3SO_4^+$, $H_2S_2O_7$, H_3O^+, HSO_4^-, and other species.

Additional SO_3 may easily be dissolved in concentrated sulfuric acid, to any extent desired. The solution formed contains SO_3 attached to H_2SO_4, in the form of unstable **pyrosulfuric acid** ($H_2S_2O_7$) and other species. Fumes appear when this solution is exposed to the air, so it is known as **fuming sulfuric acid** or **oleum.** Industrial products are known as 10 per cent oleum, 20 per cent oleum, 65 per cent oleum, and others, representing the percentage of excess sulfur trioxide present.

Concentrated sulfuric acid, and especially the oleums, have a very high affinity for water. Consequently, they are useful in assisting chemical reactions in which water is split out. Mixtures of nitric acid and concentrated sulfuric acid are very effective **nitrating mixtures.** One of the large-scale uses of sulfuric acid is to assist in the formation of explosives containing **nitro** ($-NO_2$) groups.

Hydrochloric Acid

Much of the hydrochloric acid needed in industry and the laboratory comes as a byproduct of the chlorination of hydrocarbons. Remember that chlorine attacks a C-H bond by forming C-Cl and HCl. This HCl can be dissolved in water up to concentrations of about 35 per cent by weight. This solution is called *concentrated hydrochloric acid*. Not all of the hydrogen chloride in this solution is in the form of ions. Molecular hydrogen chloride escapes easily, which accounts for the fumes when you remove the stopper from a bottle of hydrochloric acid. There is little evidence that hydrogen chloride molecules can form protonic bridges among themselves. Presumably this is because the chlorine atoms are too large, allowing the electron pairs to spread out too thinly to attract the protonic hydrogen of another molecule. However, the hydrogen of HCl is quite positive. It can be attracted strongly to lone pairs on the oxygen of water, forming protonic bridges in this way, thus explaining the very high solubility of molecular hydrogen chloride in water.

Hydrochloric acid is very corrosive to many common metals, especially iron. Even gaseous hydrogen chloride, probably with at least a trace of moisture present, corrodes iron pipe rapidly. In the manufacture of hydrochloric acid by any process, the hydrogen chloride and the acid must be kept out of contact with iron. Otherwise they will corrode and dissolve it and the acid will contain it. Commercial acid containing some iron has a yellowish brown color and is called **muriatic acid.** If it had been made in glass or noncorrodible plastic, it would be colorless, like the laboratory reagent.

When a special need for hydrochloric acid arises that cannot be satisfied by a byproduct acid, it can be made in the old-fashioned way by the action of concentrated sulfuric acid on sodium chloride. This is an example of a volatile acid being displaced from its salt by a relatively nonvolatile acid:

$$NaCl + H_2SO_4 \rightarrow HCl + NaHSO_4$$

$$NaCl + NaHSO_4 \rightarrow HCl + Na_2SO_4$$

In this stepwise reaction, the first step goes at ordinary temperatures and the second requires heating. **Sodium bisulfate** ($NaHSO_4$), also called **sodium acid sulfate,** is a solid that dissolves readily in water to give an acidic solution. It has applications wherever a solid acid is useful. The final byproduct, crude sodium sulfate, is called **salt cake.** It can be used to produce pure sodium sulfate, or as a source of sodium oxide in the manufacture of cheap glass. It can also undergo reduction by coke under severe conditions:

$$Na_2SO_4 + 4\,C \rightarrow Na_2S + 4\,CO$$

Sodium sulfide is an easily hydrolyzed solid, solutions of which can be used for softening the hairs on hides in the leather industry, or for various chemical purposes.

The sulfuric acid-salt process for making hydrogen chloride and hydrochloric acid is one of the oldest of industrial processes. It was discovered by a German chemist, Johann Rudolf Glauber (1604–1668). The residue, sodium sulfate, became known as *Glauber's salt,* and in the form of a hydrate is known as that today. Glauber discovered that his salt was an effective laxative, whereupon he labelled it *sal mirabile,* which means "marvelous salt." This discovery launched him into a successful business of manufacturing and selling this and other compounds for medicinal purposes. No doubt if he were alive today we would know him through television commercials.

Nitric Acid

Nitric acid (HNO_3), a strong acid in aqueous solution, has a variety of properties that make it especially useful. In dilute solutions it acts as a source of hydrogen ions, forming nitrates such as sodium nitrate and ammonium nitrate that are excellent sources of nitrogen for plant food. In concentrated solutions, which contain about 70 per cent of HNO_3 in water, it is a strong oxidizing agent through the nitrate, which is reduced to NO or NO_2, depending on conditions. Most metals that resist oxidation by hydronium ions, such as copper, may be readily dissolved by nitric acid, since electrons are removed even from resistant sources by strongly oxidizing reagents. In such reactions, hydrogen is not displaced but rather forms water:

$$8\,HNO_3 + 3\,Cu \rightarrow 3\,Cu(NO_3)_2 + 2\,NO + 4\,H_2O$$

HNO_3 is a powerful oxidizing agent in very concentrated solutions, or in the pure state in which it is a volatile, somewhat unstable liquid. **Fuming nitric acid,** a reddish-brown liquid containing excess NO_2 dissolved in it, can set fire to wood. When mixed with concentrated sulfuric acid or oleum, nitric acid acts as a powerful nitrating reagent. For example, methylbenzene, called **toluene,** can be nitrated to give the product **trinitrotoluene,** or **TNT,** a well-known and very powerful explosive:

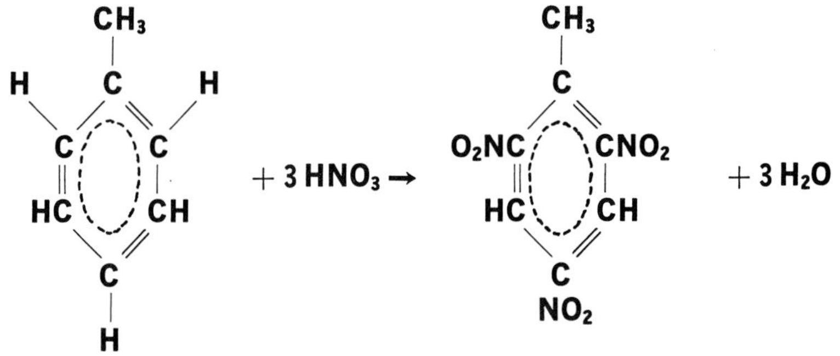

Large deposits of sodium and potassium nitrates are found in a desert area of Chile, in **saltpeter** beds. Nitric acid can be made from this material by treatment with concentrated sulfuric acid:

$$NaNO_3 + H_2SO_4 \rightarrow NaHSO_4 + HNO_3$$

The second hydrogen of the sulfuric acid cannot be utilized here as in HCl production, because at the higher temperature required, nitric acid is unstable. Therefore, sodium bisulfate is the byproduct, in a form called **nitre cake.**

By far the most important method of nitric acid manufacture begins with ammonia. If introduced into a gas flame, this gas will burn partially to form water and nitrogen. With pure oxygen and a catalyst, however, it is possible to burn both the hydrogen and the nitrogen of the ammonia:

$$4\,NH_3 + 5\,O_2 \rightarrow 4\,NO + 6\,H_2O$$

Nitric oxide (NO) or nitrogen (II) oxide is an unstable, poisonous compound that will take on additional oxygen readily at lower temperatures to form **nitrogen dioxide** (NO_2) or nitrogen (IV) oxide, a red-brown, poisonous gas. NO_2 dissolves in water by reacting with it:

$$3\,NO_2 + H_2O \rightarrow 2\,HNO_3 + NO$$

The byproduct, nitric oxide, is oxidized by air to NO_2 and recycled. Thus, whether ammonia is used directly or converted to nitric acid, the Haber process is essential for the fixation of nitrogen.

FERTILIZERS

Ammonium salts, free ammonia introduced directly into the soil, and nitrates all provide excellent, water-soluble nitrogen sources for plant growth. Organic sources of nitrogen, such as dried blood, are also very valuable as plant foods.

Nitrogen is not the only mineral element required for plant growth. Of the many we might mention here, only two are considered almost as important: potassium and phosphorus.

Potassium is usually calculated as **potash** (K_2O) when the percentage composition of fertilizers is determined. Present in practically all soils, potassium occurs combined in complex silicates that make up clays. As such, it is not available to plants. Potassium chloride is usually the form in which potassium is supplied in fertilizers.

Phosphorus is usually supplied to the soil as phosphates. Ordinary phosphate rock, consisting largely of $Ca_3(PO_4)_2$, is too insoluble to be useful to plants. Acid salts are always more soluble than neutral salts, and the introduction of some hydrogen into calcium phosphates makes them valuable as fertilizer components. The cheapest treatment of calcium phosphate rock is by the addition of concentrated sulfuric acid, giving a mixture of calcium acid phosphate and calcium sulfate. This mixture can be used as it is because the calcium sulfate is inert in the soil. It is not very efficient, however, to transport all this useless extra material. By making phosphoric acid first, then using this to treat phosphate rock, the product contains only **superphosphate,** $CaHPO_4$ and $Ca(H_2PO_4)_2$, all of which is readily soluble in water and an excellent source of phosphorus for plants.

The composition of fertilizers is often described by three numbers, such as "5-10-5." This means 5 per cent potassium as K_2O (i.e., the equivalent of 5 per cent K_2O), 10 per cent "available" nitrogen, and 5 per cent of phosphorus calculated as P_2O_5 (i.e., the equivalent of 5 per cent P_4O_{10}).

Many other elements are also essential to plant health, but usually only in trace quantities.

Test Your Memory

1. What is meant by the *heavy chemical* industry?
2. a) What is the formula for limestone?
   b) Write an equation for the thermal decomposition of limestone.
3. What is the chemical composition for dry ice?
4. a) Identify *quicklime* and *slaked lime*.
   b) How is lime used?
5. What is the meaning of *byproduct?*
6. What is *portland cement?* How does it differ from concrete?
7. a) What is *glass?*
   b) How is *soft glass* made?
8. What is *annealing* and why is it necessary?
9. Describe the *Solvay process,* using chemical equations where possible, and identifying the major product and byproduct.

10. How can NH_3 be recovered from ammonium salts?
11. How is NaOH obtained?
12. What is meant by the *fixation* of nitrogen and how is it accomplished?
13. Write a chemical equation for the Haber process.
14. Describe the *Frasch process*.
15. Describe the *contact process*.
16. What is *oleum?*
17. What is *muriatic acid* and how can it be manufactured?
18. What is *TNT?*
19. What is *saltpeter?*
20. What are the chief components of fertilizers?
21. What is meant by *6-12-6* fertilizer?

Test Your Understanding

1. What effect on the decomposition pressure of limestone would be exerted by the addition of calcium oxide? Why?
2. Why is silica able to displace more strongly acidic oxides from their salts?
3. How much Na_2O could be provided to a glass melt by one ton of Na_2CO_3?
4. What volume of CO_2 could be obtained from a ton of limestone and how much would it weigh?
5. What quantity of ammonia, in volume at STP, would be recovered from ten tons of a ten weight per cent solution of NH_4Cl? What weight of $Ca(OH)_2$ would be needed?
6. What weight of sulfur would be needed to produce 6,000 tons of sulfuric acid, assuming only 99 per cent conversion?
7. As a source of H^+ ions, which would be cheaper, hydrochloric acid (35 per cent by weight) at $20 per ton, or sulfuric acid (98 per cent by weight) at $14 per ton?
8. If "stomach acid" is 1 per cent HCl, what strength of H_2SO_4 would produce the same *p*H?

36

THE CHEMISTRY OF LIFE

BIOCHEMISTRY

The chemistry of those predominantly organic compounds that are involved in life processes is called **biochemistry.** Biochemistry has recently become an indispensable part of biology. As more and more biochemical discoveries are made, we can expect to be able to understand better how living organisms grow, function, and reproduce. In this sense we shall all be able to know more about life. What this knowledge may lead to, no one can tell. Perhaps we shall triumph over pain and physical suffering. Perhaps we shall learn to stay young, or at least, to age more slowly and more gracefully. Perhaps we shall be able to influence heredity or to counteract adverse environment. Perhaps we shall learn how to nourish our bodies more scientifically or to make more effective use of our brains. All these—and more—seem possible as our knowledge of the chemistry of living systems continues to increase.

Within the scope of this book we can only suggest a few areas of special biochemical interest. Of these, perhaps the greatest current interest is in the field of proteins.

Proteins

Proteins are exceedingly complex substances of highest importance to life processes. They can be broken down into **amino acids** by hydrolysis, organic compounds in which a carboxyl group and an amine group are attached to the same carbon atom:

$$R—CH—COOH$$
$$|$$
$$NH_2$$

Some typical amino acids are shown with their structures in Figure 36.1. Amino acids, in turn, can be dehydrated to form amide condensation products called **polypeptides.** The first step can be represented by:

$$R-\underset{\underset{\displaystyle NH_2}{|}}{CH}-COOH + H_2N\underset{\underset{\displaystyle R}{|}}{CH}-COOH \rightarrow R-\underset{\underset{\displaystyle NH_2}{|}}{CH}-CO-NH-\underset{\underset{\displaystyle R}{|}}{CH}-COOH + H_2O$$

Proteins are believed to be high molecular weight polypeptides, characterized by the repeating amides linkage

$$-\underset{\underset{\displaystyle O}{\parallel}}{C}-\underset{\underset{\displaystyle H}{|}}{N}-$$

When different amino acids condense together, as they must to form proteins, the variety of possible polypeptides or proteins that can be formed is enormous. Suppose only four different amino acid units—*A*, *B*, *C*, and *D*—are each used only once, building a "tetrapeptide." Twelve different arrangements are possible: *ABCD, ACBD, ABDC, ADBC, ACDB, ADCB, BADC, BDAC, BACD, BCAD, CABD, CBAD.* As the number of amino acid units and the number of amino acids increases, the number of possible arrangements increases to astronomical proportions. With only one each of seven different amino acids, there are 5,040 different arrangements. Natural proteins are many times larger.

Insulin is a hormone protein having a molecular weight of about 48,000. It took ten years of very difficult research to find out the sequence of the seventeen different amino acids that are involved in the 51 amino acid segments that make up this protein, and this is a relatively simple protein. Tobacco plants suffer a virus disease called *tobacco mosaic.* The virus causing this is also a protein, with molecular weight of about 40,000,000. And the virus causing influenza has molecules five to eight times larger yet.

Most proteins are similar in approximate elemental composition. They consist of about 50-55 per cent carbon, 5-7 per cent hydrogen, 15-18 per cent nitrogen, 20-25 per cent oxygen, and 0.4-2.5 per cent or less of sulfur. Some contain small amounts of other elements too, such as phosphorus, or a metal such as copper or iron. **Hemoglobin** of the blood, for instance, is a protein containing about 0.33 per cent iron. One of the simpler proteins of milk is **B-lactoglobulin,** which has a molecular weight close to 42,000. Its molecular formula is believed to be close to $C_{1864}H_{3012}O_{576}N_{468}S_{21}$. Many proteins have formulas a thousand times, or more, larger.

Proteins often occur in attachment to other types of compounds. These combinations are called *conjugated proteins.* Some of the most interesting are the **nucleoproteins,** in which simple proteins are attached to **nucleic acids.** Nucleic acids are very complex substances in which sugar and phosphoric acid are condensed with compounds of carbon, hydrogen, or nitrogen in which nitrogen is joined in rings with carbon atoms. The sugars involved are either **D-ribose,** of formula $C_5H_{10}O_5$, or **D-2-deoxyribose,** $C_5H_{10}O_4$. These two sugars lead to two types of nucleic acid, called **ribonucleic acid (RNA)** and **deoxyri-**

Figure 36.1.   Some Amino Acid Structures.

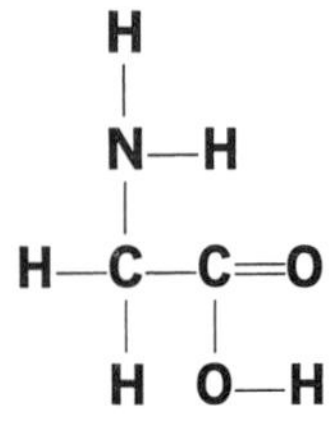

glycine

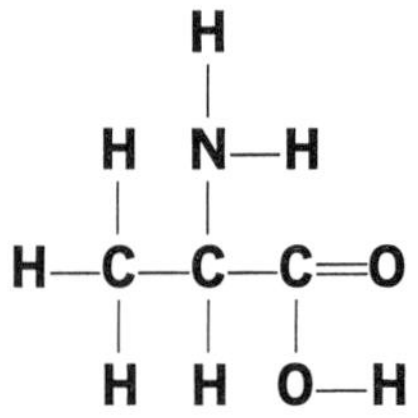

alanine

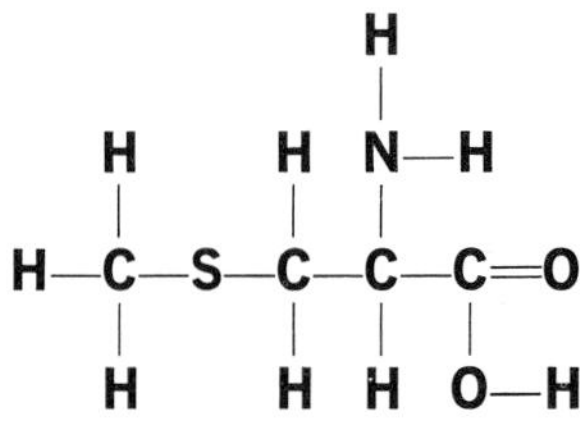

methionine

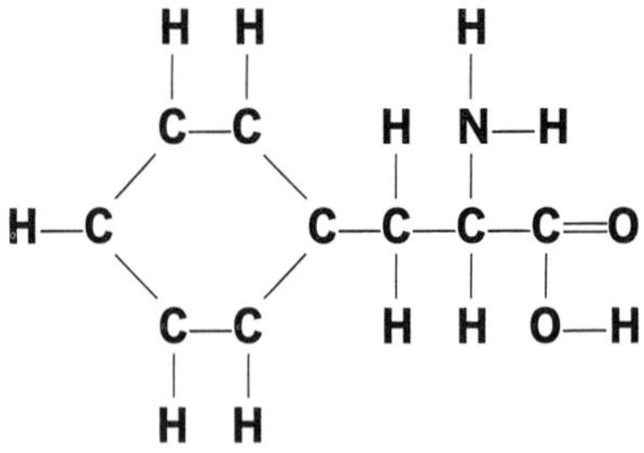

phenylalanine

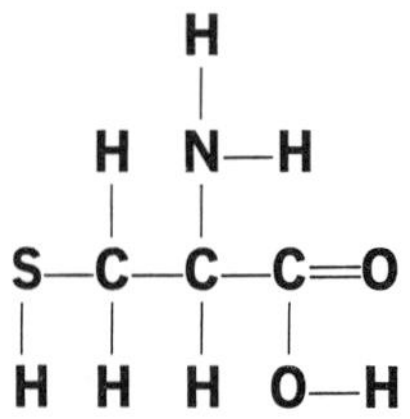

cysteine

bonucleic acid (DNA). These complex substances probably contain millions of atoms per molecule.

DNA occurs in the nucleus of animal and plant cells. It is thought to be the material which contains the genetic code for the synthesis of specific proteins. The proper sequence of amino acids in these proteins is built in by DNA, acting through a messenger substance, RNA. The RNA is believed to act as a sort of template or pattern assuring the correct sequence of amino acids in the synthesis of new protein materials for the proliferation of cells. Here, therefore, must lie the key to heredity and to the proper growth and development of all living organisms. This is why the study of these substances is fundamental to an understanding of life itself.

Enzymes

In the chemical laboratory, many reactions of organic chemistry require rather drastic conditions of temperature, pressure, acidity, or basicity to permit them to proceed. Yet very similar reactions, often the identical reactions, take place in living organisms under the much milder conditions required for healthy growth of the organism. This sometimes amazing difference appears to be associated with an extraordinary group of substances called **enzymes.** These proteins, or protein-containing compounds, have remarkable catalytic powers. About 500 different enzymes have now been purified and characterized.

Each enzyme appears to have a highly specific function. For example, one enzyme called **catalase** has the property of decomposing hydrogen peroxide (H_2O_2):

$$2 \ H_2O_2 \xrightarrow{\text{catalase}} 2 \ H_2O + O_2$$

This particular enzyme appears to have *absolute specificity,* since hundreds of other compounds have been tested with it, with no observable result; it only affects hydrogen peroxide.

Although relatively few enzymes are quite this specific, many possess group specificity. One, for instance, helps in the oxidation of several alcohols to aldehydes. Still others are specific in affecting only one of two very similar, "mirror-image" molecular structures.

Enzymes are extremely important in aiding the digestion of foods by hydrolyzing proteins, carbohydrates, and other substances to simpler molecules. They also assist growth and energy-producing processes.

In some instances the action of enzymes is greatly helped by relatively less complex organic compounds called **coenzymes.** A remarkable structural similarity has been noted between coenzymes and the compounds called vitamins, discussed below. At least several of the known vitamins are either coenzymes themselves or form part of a more complex coenzyme.

Figure 36.2. Structural Formulas of Some Vitamins.

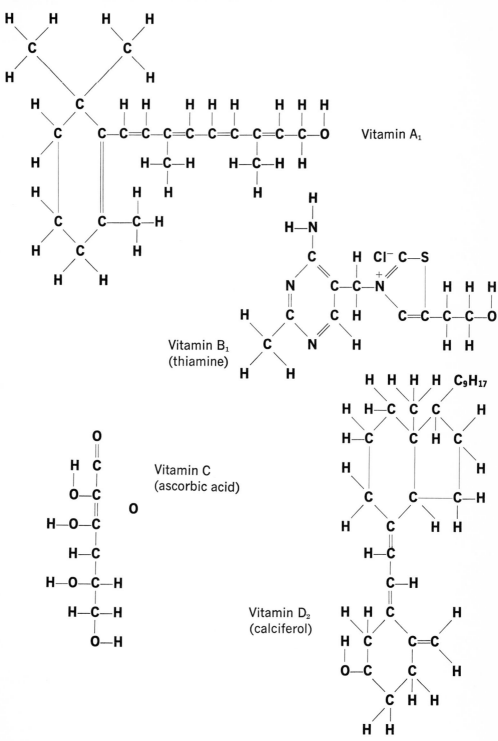

Vitamin A₁

Vitamin B₁
(thiamine)

Vitamin C
(ascorbic acid)

Vitamin D₂
(calciferol)

A **vitamin** is a naturally occurring substance that, in small traces, is essential to the diet. A number of such substances are now recognized. Structural formulas for some of these are given in Figure 36.2.

Vitamin A plays an important role in vision. It is found in yellow or orange vegetables, such as carrots, among other sources.

Vitamin B_1, **thiamin,** occurs in whole grains, nuts, yeast, and various meats. It is involved in the metabolism of carbohydrates. In its absence the deficiency disease called *beriberi* results. One of the early practical achievements of biochemistry was the discovery that this disease could be prevented by the simple dietary precaution of eating some unpolished rice along with polished rice. The active ingredient in rice hulls, thiamin, was then isolated, and later synthesized, by Robert R. Williams.

Vitamin B_2, **riboflavin,** occurs in many foods including milk, liver, fish, and eggs. It appears to participate in the metabolism of proteins, fatty acids, and carbohydrates.

Niacin, also called nicotinic acid, and its amide, niacinamide, are found in relatively large quantities in liver, fish, and eggs. Niacin is an oxidation product of nicotine which is contained in tobacco. Two important coenzymes include these structures.

Vitamin B_6, called **pyridoxine,** is thought to be essential in the metabolism of unsaturated acids.

Pantothenic acid occurs in liver, eggs, and vegetables. It seems to be involved with metabolism of proteins, carbohydrates, and fats, as part of a more complex coenzyme.

Vitamin C is called **ascorbic acid.** Its absence from the diet causes the deficiency disease known as *scurvy.* Early sailors were sometimes called "limeys" because it was known hundreds of years ago that scurvy could be prevented by including citrus fruit in the diet. Tomatoes are now known to be a good source, also. The function of Vitamin C in the body is not clearly understood, although it is believed to be part of a respiratory enzyme system. This vitamin is especially easily oxidized, requiring that fruit juices or vegetables containing it be protected from the air if their vitamin C content is to be maintained.

Vitamin D is necessary for the metabolism of calcium and phosphorus, for good development of bones and teeth to prevent the disease called *rickets.* Several compounds have these properties and are designated as D_1, D_2, D_3, etc. The common vitamin D of codliver oil is D_3.

Other groups of compounds are classified as Vitamin E, the "antisterility vitamin"; and Vitamin K, which is involved in the clotting of blood.

THE PRODUCTION OF ENERGY

Much work has been done in an attempt to determine how muscles do work: how food is converted to energy by the body. The processes are much too complex for this book. It will have to suffice to observe that many steps and many different enzyme systems appear to be involved. Glucose, for example, is oxidized in the absence of oxygen to **pyruvic acid** ($CH_3COCOOH$). This may be reduced in the muscle to lactic acid ($CH_3CHOHCOOH$), which, when accumulated, appears related to the feeling of fatigue. The pyruvic acid is then oxidized by oxygen to CO_2 and water, the end products:

$$CH_3COCOOH + 5\ (O) \rightarrow 3\ CO_2 + 2\ H_2O.$$

Such processes are called **catabolic.**

PHOTOSYNTHESIS

Equally important, and absolutely essential for the maintenance of life, is the production of carbohydrates from carbon dioxide and water with the aid of light. This **anabolic** process is called **photosynthesis.** It is made possible by complex compounds called **chlorophylls.** These contain magnesium, as well as carbon, hydrogen, oxygen, and nitrogen.

Light apparently catalyzes a reaction in which oxygen is produced from water, and hydrogen is added to complex substances. Then CO_2 is transformed, through enzyme-catalyzed reactions, to carbohydrates, with the help of the hydrogen-containing substances. Fatty acids, amino acids, and other compounds are also products of photosynthesis.

SUMMARY

Biochemistry is far too large and complex a subject to be summarized in so brief a treatment as has been provided here. Perhaps, however, this has made it possible for you to gain some idea of its scope, magnitude, and importance. If we take the human body as an example of a complex, living organism, we must marvel at the fantastic organization and synchronization of chemical processes which create it from the minerals, water, and air, and keep it functioning smoothly. Compared to the human body, the most intricate of man's constructions is ridiculously crude, and the most complex chemical manufacturing plant is indeed simple. One may confidently predict that the study of biochemistry will continue to engage some of man's finest talents for the duration of human existence.

Still, the compounds of all living matter contain the same kinds of atoms, with the same fundamental properties, as the simplest substances we know. Ultimately, a thorough knowledge of biochemistry must therefore depend on a thorough understanding of the structure and qualities of atoms. Fundamental chemistry lies at the heart of all knowledge of matter, both inanimate and living.

Test Your Memory

1. What is *biochemistry?*
2. What is a *protein?*
3. What is the characteristic linkage of polypeptides?
4. In what molecular weight range do proteins occur?
5. What do *DNA* and *RNA* stand for?
6. What is an *enzyme?*
7. What is a *vitamin?*
8. What is *photosynthesis?*
9. How are iron and magnesium especially important in biochemistry?

Test Your Understanding

1. If the molecular weight of a protein is 5.6×10^7, how many molecules of it would be present in 1 g?
2. What is the weight percentage composition of *B-lactoglobulin?*

INDEX

Einstein, 101
Eka-boron, 95
Eka-silicon, 95
Eka-aluminum, 95
Electrical charge, 61
Electricity, oxidation-reduction by, 291
Electrochemistry, 61
Electrodes, 292
Electrode potential, 305; significance of, 310; table, 307
Electrolysis, 293, 366
Electrolyte, 223, 292
Electron, 61, 64, 97; delocalized, 111; energy level of, 74; valence, 110; wave properties of, 72
Electron affinity, 164
Electron energy level, 80, 114
Electron spin, 77
Electronegativity, 150; equalization of, 154; schematic representation of, 152; principle of equalization of, 155, 156
Electronic configurations, 81, 83
Electronic theater, 78
Electrostatic precipitator, 407
Element, 7; chemical, 10, 20; concept of, 9; discovery of, chronology of, 11; history of, 9; inner transitional, 89; major group, 89; metallic, 109; metalloid, 109; nonmetallic, 109; occurrence of, 12; transitional, 89; transuranium, 101
Emission spectroscopy, 364
Emission spectrum, 70
Empedocles, 9
Empirical formulas, 23, 25; determination of, 43
Endothermic, 55, 187
Energy, 53; activation, 229; bond, 117; hydration, 310; kinetic, 179; molecular, distribution of, 184; nuclear, 101; potential, 183; production of, 419
Enthalpy, 55
Entropy, 214
Enzyme, 417
Equation, chemical, 49
Equilibrium, chemical, 231; effect of changing concentration on, 233; effect of temperature on, 235; physical, 181; thermal, 54
Equilibrium constant, 232
Equivalent, electrochemical, 297
Equivalent weight, 218
Ester, 392
Esterification, 392
Ethane, 374; oxidation of, 392
Ethene, 379
Ethers, 389
Ethyl acetate, 392
Ethyl alcohol, 388, 392
Ethyl mercaptan, 393
Ethylene, 379
Ethylene dibromide, 318

Ethylene glycol, 389
Exothermic, 55, 187

F

f orbital, 75
Face-centered cubic, 113
Fahrenheit, 39
Fallout, 103
Faraday, 61, 97, 291, 297
Fats, 16
Fatty acid, 392
Fermi, 102
Ferrosilicon, 372
Fertilizer, 412
Fischer-Tropsch process, 384
Fission, 101
Fissionable, 199
Flotation, 370
Fluorescence, 98
Fluorine, chemical properties of, 317; Physical properties of, 316; production of, 314
Fluorite structure, 171
Fluorocarbons, 387
Forces, cohesive, 179
Formaldehyde, 391
Formic acid, 391
Formula, chemical, 21; electronic, 144; empirical, 23, 25; molecular, 25; structural, 143
Formula weight, 33
Fractions, 355
Fractional crystallization, 356
Fractionating column, 355
Fractional distillation, 355
Frasch process, 406
Free radical, 236
Fusion, 181
Fusion, heat of, 183; nuclear, 104

G

Galena, 371
Galvanizing, 371
Gangue, 370
Gas, critical temperature of, 355; natural, 381; ideal, laws for, 204; molecular weight of, 207; nonideal, 204
Gas analysis, 354
Gas constant, 205
Gas laws, combined, 205
Gas molecule, path of, 197
Gas oil, 381
Gases, 189, 196; kinetic molecular theory of, 196
Gaseous state, 179
Gasoline, natural, 381
Geber, 406
Geiger counter, 106
Glass, 401, 26

Iron oxide, reduction of, 368
Iron sulfide, solubility product of, 359
Isoalkanes, 375
Isobutane, 375
Isomer, 145, 375
Isooctane, 376
Isopentane, 376
Isopropyl alcohol, 388, 391
Isotopes, 29, 65

J

Jet fuels, 381
Joliot-Curie, 100

K

Kelp, 316
Kelvin, 202
Kerogen, 383
Kerosene, 381
Ketone, 391
Kilocalorie, 54
Kilogram, 39
Kinetic energy, 179
Kinetic molecular theory, 196
Kinetics, 236
Kossel, 159
Krypton, atmospheric, 196

L

Lactic acid, 420
Lactoglobulin, 415
Langmuir, 116
Lavoisier, 243
Law of octaves, 94
Lead, analysis of, 360; production of, 371
Lead carbonate, solubility product of, 359
Lead chloride, solubility product of, 359
Lead chromate, solubility product of, 359
Lead iodide, solubility product of, 359
Lead storage battery, 308
Lead sulfate, solubility product of, 359
Lead sulfide, solubility product of, 359
Lead tetraethyl, 318
Lead, tetramethyl, 318
Le Chatelier, 234
Le Chatelier's principle, 234, 405
Length, units of, 38
Lewis, 116, 159
Ligand, 132
Lime, 254
Lime products, 399
Limestone, 367, 368; decomposition of, 399
Limey, 419
Liquid state, 181
Liquid, 190; analysis of, 356; representative inorganic, 191
Liter, 38
Lithium aluminum hydride, 341

Lithium chloride, 323; properties of, 332
Lithium hydride, 343; properties of, 350
Lithium hydroxide, 266
Lithium oxide, 265; properties of, 275
Lithosphere, 12
Litmus, 288
Logarithms, 285
Lomonosov, 243
Lysergic acid diethylamide (LSD), 395

M

M8 elements, special stability of, 160
Magnesium, action of water on, 337; occurrence of, 13; production of, 371
Magnesium chloride, 328; bond energy in, 167; properties of, 332
Magnesium hydride, 347; properties of, 350
Magnesium hydroxide, 271; solubility product of, 359
Magnesium oxide, 271; bond energy of, 167; melting and boiling point of, 191; properties of, 275
Magnetite, 367
Major group element, 89; electronic configuration of, 88; valence structure of, 126
Malleability, 114
Man, composition of, 17
Manganese dioxide, 315
Manganese fluoride, bond energy in, 167
Manometer, 199
Mass, 30; unit of, 39
Matter, classification of, 1
Matter-waves, 72
McMillan, 101
Mean free path, 198
Mechanical strength, 194
Meitner, 101
Melting, 180
Melting point, 181, 192; mixed, 181
Mendeleev, 95
Mercaptan, 393
Mercuric oxide, decomposition of, 51, 244
Mercury, analysis of, 360
Mercury sulfide, solubility product of, 359
Metal, native, 366; reaction with water, 301, 336
Metallic properties, explanation of, 113
Metalloid, 108
Metals, bonding in, 108, 110; electron energy in, 114
Metal oxides, 253; acid-base properties of, 254
Metathesis, 52
Meter, 38
Methane, 345, 373; atmospheric, 196; heat of combustion of, 56; melting and boiling point of, 190; origin of, 381; oxidation of, 389; properties of, 350
Methyl alcohol, 387
Methyl chloride, 387